Put a roc[...] ith CGP!

GCSE Ph[...] it mildly.
Luckily, we've squeez[...] this CGP book —
plus exam pr[...]e to the test.

How to access your free Online Edition

This book includes a free Online Edition to read on your PC, Mac or tablet.
To access it, just go to **cgpbooks.co.uk/extras** and enter this code...

0230 9712 1258 3320

By the way, this code only works for one person. If somebody else has used this book before you, they might have already claimed the Online Edition.

CGP — still the best! ☺

Our sole aim here at CGP is to produce the highest quality books — carefully written, immaculately presented and dangerously close to being funny.

Then we work our socks off to get them out to you — at the cheapest possible prices.

Contents

Topic P6 — Radioactivity

Topic P7 — Energy

Topic P8 — Global Challenges

Topic P9 — Practical Skills

Published by CGP
From original material by Richard Parsons.

Contributors: Paddy Gannon.
Editors: Jane Ellingham, Emily Garrett, Rachael Marshall, Sam Pilgrim.

ISBN: 978 1 78294 568 0

With thanks to Peter Rich and Sarah Williams for the proofreading.
With thanks to Ana Pungartnik for the copyright research.

Printed by Elanders Ltd, Newcastle upon Tyne.
Clipart from Corel®

The Scientific Method

This section isn't about how to 'do' science — but it does show you the way most scientists work.

Scientists Come Up With Hypotheses — Then Test Them

1) Scientists try to explain things. They start by observing something they don't understand.
2) They then come up with a hypothesis — a possible explanation for what they've observed.
3) The next step is to test whether the hypothesis might be right or not. This involves making a prediction based on the hypothesis and testing it by gathering evidence (i.e. data) from investigations. If evidence from experiments backs up a prediction, you're a step closer to figuring out if the hypothesis is true.

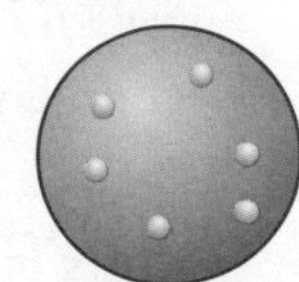

About 100 years ago, scientists hypothesised that atoms looked like this.

Several Scientists Will Test a Hypothesis

1) Normally, scientists share their findings in peer-reviewed journals, or at conferences.
2) Peer-review is where other scientists check results and scientific explanations to make sure they're 'scientific' (e.g. that experiments have been done in a sensible way) before they're published. It helps to detect false claims, but it doesn't mean that findings are correct — just that they're not wrong in any obvious way.
3) Once other scientists have found out about a hypothesis, they'll start basing their own predictions on it and carry out their own experiments. They'll also try to reproduce the original experiments to check the results — and if all the experiments in the world back up the hypothesis, then scientists start to think the hypothesis is true.
4) However, if a scientist does an experiment that doesn't fit with the hypothesis (and other scientists can reproduce the results) then the hypothesis may need to be modified or scrapped altogether.

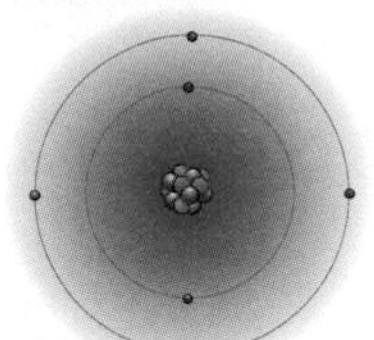

After more evidence was gathered, scientists changed their hypothesis to this.

If All the Evidence Supports a Hypothesis, It's Accepted — For Now

1) Accepted hypotheses are often referred to as theories. Our currently accepted theories are the ones that have survived this 'trial by evidence' — they've been tested many times over the years and survived.
2) However, theories never become totally indisputable fact. If new evidence comes along that can't be explained using the existing theory, then the hypothesising and testing is likely to start all over again.

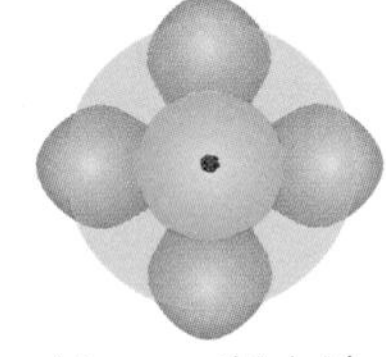

Now we think it's more like this.

Theories Can Involve Different Types of Models

1) A representational model is a simplified description or picture of what's going on in real life. Like all models, it can be used to explain observations and make predictions. E.g. the Bohr model of an atom is a simplified way of showing the arrangement of electrons in an atom (see p.12). It can be used to explain electron excitations in atoms.
2) Computational models use computers to make simulations of complex real-life processes, such as climate change. They're used when there are a lot of different variables (factors that change) to consider, and because you can easily change their design to take into account new data.
3) All models have limitations on what they can explain or predict. E.g. the Big Bang model (a model used to describe the beginning of the Universe) can be used to explain why everything in the Universe is moving away from us. One of its limitations is that it doesn't explain the moments before the Big Bang.

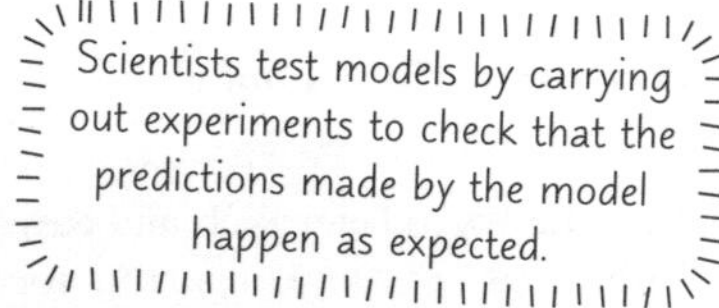

Scientists test models by carrying out experiments to check that the predictions made by the model happen as expected.

I'm off to the zoo to test my hippo-thesis...

The scientific method has developed over time, and many people have helped to develop it. From Aristotle to modern day scientists, lots of people have contributed. And many more are likely to contribute in the future.

Communication & Issues Created by Science

Scientific developments can be great, but they can sometimes raise more questions than they answer...

It's Important to Communicate Scientific Discoveries to the General Public

Some scientific discoveries show that people should change their habits, or they might provide ideas that could be developed into new technology. So scientists need to tell the world about their discoveries.

Radioactive materials are used widely in medicine for imaging and treatment (see p.79). Information about these materials needs to be communicated to doctors so they can make use of them, and to patients, so they can make informed decisions about their treatment.

Scientific Evidence can be Presented in a Biased Way

1) Reports about scientific discoveries in the media (e.g. newspapers or television) aren't peer-reviewed.
2) This means that, even though news stories are often based on data that has been peer-reviewed, the data might be presented in a way that is over-simplified or inaccurate, making it open to misinterpretation.
3) People who want to make a point can sometimes present data in a biased way. (Sometimes without knowing they're doing it.) For example, a scientist might overemphasise a relationship in the data, or a newspaper article might describe details of data supporting an idea without giving any evidence against it.

Scientific Developments are Great, but they can Raise Issues

Scientific knowledge is increased by doing experiments. And this knowledge leads to scientific developments, e.g. new technologies or new advice. These developments can create issues though. For example:

Economic issues: Society can't always afford to do things scientists recommend (e.g. investing in alternative energy sources) without cutting back elsewhere.

Personal issues: Some decisions will affect individuals. For example, someone might support alternative energy, but object if a wind farm is built next to their house.

Social issues: Decisions based on scientific evidence affect people — e.g. should fossil fuels be taxed more highly? Would the effect on people's lifestyles be acceptable...

Environmental issues: Human activity often affects the natural environment. For example, building a dam to produce electricity will change the local habitat so some species might be displaced. But it will also reduce our need for fossil fuels, so will help to reduce climate change.

Science Can't Answer Every Question — Especially Ethical Ones

1) We don't understand everything. We're always finding out more, but we'll never know all the answers.
2) In order to answer scientific questions, scientists need data to provide evidence for their hypotheses.
3) Some questions can't be answered yet because the data can't currently be collected, or because there's not enough data to support a theory.
4) Eventually, as we get more evidence, we'll answer some of the questions that currently can't be answered, e.g. what the impact of global warming on sea levels will be. But there will always be the "Should we be doing this at all?"-type questions that experiments can't help us to answer...

Think about new drugs which can be taken to boost your 'brain power'.

- Some people think they're good as they could improve concentration or memory. New drugs could let people think in ways beyond the powers of normal brains.
- Other people say they're bad — they could give you an unfair advantage in exams. And people might be pressured into taking them so that they could work more effectively, and for longer hours.

THE GAZETTE
BRAIN-BOOSTING DRUGS MAKE A MOCKERY OF EXAMS

THE POST
GENIUS PILLS TO BECOME THE NEW COFFEE

Tea to milk or milk to tea? — Totally unanswerable by science...

Science can't tell you whether or not you should do something. That's for you and society to decide. But there are tons of questions science might be able to answer, like where life came from and where my superhero socks are.

Risk

By reading this page you are agreeing to the risk of a paper cut or severe drowsiness...

Nothing is Completely Risk-Free

1) A hazard is something that could potentially cause harm.
2) All hazards have a risk attached to them — this is the chance that the hazard will cause harm.
3) The risks of some things seem pretty obvious, or we've known about them for a while, like the risk of causing acid rain by polluting the atmosphere, or of having a car accident when you're travelling in a car.
4) New technology arising from scientific advances can bring new risks, e.g. scientists are unsure whether nanoparticles that are being used in cosmetics and suncream might be harming the cells in our bodies. These risks need to be considered alongside the benefits of the technology, e.g. improved sun protection.
5) You can estimate the size of a risk based on how many times something happens in a big sample (e.g. 100 000 people) over a given period (e.g. a year). For example, you could assess the risk of a driver crashing by recording how many people in a group of 100 000 drivers crashed their cars over a year.
6) To make decisions about activities that involve hazards, we need to take into account the chance of the hazard causing harm and how serious the consequences would be if it did. So if an activity involves a hazard that's very likely to cause harm, with serious consequences if it does, it's considered high risk.

People Make Their Own Decisions About Risk

1) Not all risks have the same consequences, e.g. if you chop veg with a sharp knife you risk cutting your finger, but if you go scuba-diving you risk death. You're much more likely to cut your finger during half an hour of chopping than to die during half an hour of scuba-diving. But most people are happier to accept a higher probability of an accident if the consequences are short-lived and fairly minor.
2) People tend to be more willing to accept a risk if they choose to do something (e.g. go scuba diving), compared to having the risk imposed on them (e.g. having a nuclear power station built next door).
3) People's perception of risk (how risky they think something is) isn't always accurate. They tend to view familiar activities as low-risk and unfamiliar activities as high-risk — even if that's not the case. For example, cycling on roads is often high-risk, but many people are happy to do it because it's a familiar activity. Air travel is actually pretty safe, but a lot of people perceive it as high-risk.
4) People may over-estimate the risk of things with long-term or invisible effects, e.g. ionising radiation.

Investigations Can be Hazardous

1) Hazards from science experiments might include:
   - Lasers, e.g. if a laser is directed into the eye, this can cause blindness.
   - Gamma radiation, e.g. gamma-emitting radioactive sources can cause cancer.
   - Fire, e.g. an unattended Bunsen burner is a fire hazard.
   - Electricity, e.g. faulty electrical equipment could give you a shock.

2) Part of planning an investigation is making sure that it's safe.
3) You should always make sure that you identify all the hazards that you might encounter. Then you should think of ways of reducing the risks from the hazards you've identified. For example:
   - If you're working with springs, always wear safety goggles. This will reduce the risk of the spring hitting your eye if the spring snaps.
   - If you're using a Bunsen burner, stand it on a heat proof mat. This will reduce the risk of starting a fire.

You can find out about potential hazards by looking in textbooks, doing some internet research, or asking your teacher.

Not revising — an unacceptable exam hazard...

The world's a dangerous place, but if you can recognise hazards, decide how to reduce their risks, and be happy to accept some risks, you can still have fun. Just maybe don't go skydiving with a great white shark on Friday 13th.

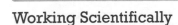

Designing Investigations

Dig out your lab coat and dust down your badly-scratched safety goggles... it's investigation time.

Investigations Produce Evidence to Support or Disprove a Hypothesis

1) Scientists observe things and come up with hypotheses to explain them (see page 2). You need to be able to do the same. For example:

   Observation: People have big feet and spots. Hypothesis: Having big feet causes spots.

2) To determine whether or not a hypothesis is right, you need to do an investigation to gather evidence. To do this, you need to use your hypothesis to make a prediction — something you think will happen that you can test. E.g. people who have bigger feet will have more spots.
3) Investigations are used to see if there are patterns or relationships between two variables, e.g. to see if there's a pattern or relationship between the variables 'number of spots' and 'size of feet'.

Evidence Needs to be Repeatable, Reproducible and Valid

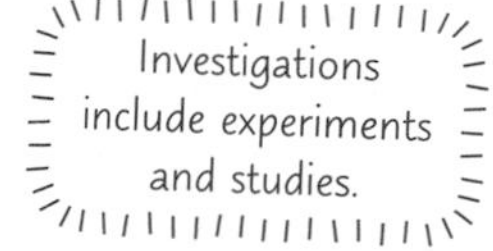
Investigations
include experiments
and studies.

1) Repeatable means that if the same person does an experiment again using the same methods and equipment, they'll get similar results.
2) Reproducible means that if someone else does the experiment, or a different method or piece of equipment is used, the results will still be similar.
3) If data is repeatable and reproducible, it's reliable and scientists are more likely to have confidence in it.
4) Valid results are both repeatable and reproducible AND they answer the original question. They come from experiments that were designed to be a FAIR TEST...

To Make an Investigation a Fair Test You Have to Control the Variables

1) In a lab experiment you usually change one variable and measure how it affects another variable.
2) To make it a fair test, everything else that could affect the results should stay the same — otherwise you can't tell if the thing you're changing is causing the results or not.
3) The variable you CHANGE is called the INDEPENDENT variable.
4) The variable you MEASURE when you change the independent variable is the DEPENDENT variable.
5) The variables that you KEEP THE SAME are called CONTROL variables.

   You could find how current through a circuit component affects the potential difference (p.d.) across the component by measuring the p.d. at different currents. The independent variable is the current. The dependent variable is the potential difference. Control variables include the temperature of the component, the p.d. of the power supply, etc.

6) Because you can't always control all the variables, you often need to use a control experiment. This is an experiment that's kept under the same conditions as the rest of the investigation, but doesn't have anything done to it. This is so that you can see what happens when you don't change anything at all.

The Bigger the Sample Size the Better

1) Data based on small samples isn't as good as data based on large samples. A sample should represent the whole population (i.e. it should share as many of the characteristics in the population as possible) — a small sample can't do that as well. It's also harder to spot anomalies if your sample size is too small.
2) The bigger the sample size the better, but scientists have to be realistic when choosing how big. For example, if you were studying the effects of living near a nuclear power plant, it'd be great to study everyone who lived near a nuclear power plant (a huge sample), but it'd take ages and cost a bomb. It's more realistic to study a thousand people, with a mixture of ages, genders, and races.

This is no high street survey — it's a designer investigation...

Not only do you need to be able to plan your own investigations, you should also be able to look at someone else's plan and decide whether or not it needs improving. Those examiners aren't half demanding.

Collecting Data

You've designed the perfect investigation — now it's time to get your hands mucky and collect some data.

Your Data Should be Repeatable, Reproducible, Accurate and Precise

1) To check repeatability you need to repeat the readings and check that the results are similar. You need to repeat each reading at least three times.
2) To make sure your results are reproducible you can cross check them by taking a second set of readings with another instrument (or a different observer).
3) Your data also needs to be ACCURATE. Really accurate results are those that are really close to the true answer. The accuracy of your results usually depends on your method — you need to make sure you're measuring the right thing and that you don't miss anything that should be included in the measurements. E.g. estimating the volume of an irregularly shaped solid by measuring the sides isn't very accurate because this will not take into account any gaps in the object. It's more accurate to measure the volume using a eureka can (see page 13).
4) Your data also needs to be PRECISE. Precise results are ones where the data is all really close to the mean (average) of your repeated results (i.e. not spread out).

Brian's result was a curate.

Repeat	Data set 1	Data set 2
1	12	11
2	14	17
3	13	14
Mean	13	14

Data set 1 is more precise than data set 2.

Your Equipment has to be Right for the Job

1) The measuring equipment you use has to be sensitive enough to measure the changes you're looking for. For example, if you need to measure changes of 1 cm^3 you need to use a measuring cylinder or burette that can measure in 1 cm^3 steps — it'd be no good trying with one that only measures 10 cm^3 steps.
2) The smallest change a measuring instrument can detect is called its RESOLUTION. E.g. some mass balances have a resolution of 1 g, some have a resolution of 0.1 g, and some are even more sensitive.
3) Also, equipment needs to be calibrated by measuring a known value. If there's a difference between the measured and known value, you can use this to correct the inaccuracy of the equipment.

You Need to Look out for Errors and Anomalous Results

1) The results of your experiment will always vary a bit because of RANDOM ERRORS — unpredictable differences caused by things like human errors in measuring. The errors when you make a reading from a ruler are random. You have to estimate or round the distance when it's between two marks — so sometimes your figure will be a bit above the real one, and sometimes it will be a bit below.
2) You can reduce the effect of random errors by taking repeat readings and finding the mean. This will make your results more precise.
3) If a measurement is wrong by the same amount every time, it's called a SYSTEMATIC ERROR. For example, if you measured from the very end of your ruler instead of from the 0 cm mark every time, all your measurements would be a bit small. Repeating your experiment in the exact same way and calculating a mean won't correct a systematic error.
4) Just to make things more complicated, if a systematic error is caused by using equipment that isn't zeroed properly, it's called a ZERO ERROR. For example, if a mass balance always reads 1 gram before you put anything on it, all your measurements will be 1 gram too heavy.
5) You can compensate for some systematic errors if you know about them though, e.g. if your mass balance always reads 1 gram before you put anything on it you can subtract 1 gram from all your results.
6) Sometimes you get a result that doesn't fit in with the rest at all. This is called an ANOMALOUS RESULT. You should investigate it and try to work out what happened. If you can work out what happened (e.g. you measured something totally wrong) you can ignore it when processing your results.

If there's no systematic error, then doing repeats and calculating a mean can make your results more accurate.

Watch what you say to that mass balance — it's very sensitive...

Weirdly, data can be really precise but not very accurate. For example, a fancy piece of lab equipment might give results that are really precise, but if it's not been calibrated properly those results won't be accurate.

Processing and Presenting Data

Processing your data means doing some calculations with it to make it more useful. Once you've done that, you can present your results in a nice chart or graph to help you spot any patterns in your data.

Data Needs to be Organised

1) Tables are dead useful for organising data.
2) When you draw a table use a ruler and make sure each column has a heading (including the units).

You Might Have to Process Your Data

1) When you've done repeats of an experiment you should always calculate the mean (average). To do this add together all the data values and divide by the total number of values in the sample.
2) You can also find the mode of your results — this is the value that occurs the most in your set of results.
3) The median can be found by writing your results in numerical order — the median is the middle number.

Ignore anomalous results when calculating the mean, mode and median.

EXAMPLE:

The results of an experiment show the extension of two springs when a force is applied to both of them. Calculate the mean, mode and median of the extension for both springs.

Spring	Repeat (cm)					Mean (cm)	Mode (cm)	Median (cm)
	1	2	3	4	5			
A	18	26	22	26	28	(18 + 26 + 22 + 26 + 28) ÷ 5 = 24	26	26
B	11	14	20	15	20	(11 + 14 + 20 + 15 + 20) ÷ 5 = 16	20	15

Round to the Lowest Number of Significant Figures

The first significant figure of a number is the first digit that's not zero. The second and third significant figures come straight after (even if they're zeros). You should be aware of significant figures in calculations.

1) In any calculation, you should round the answer to the lowest number of significant figures (s.f.) given.
2) Remember to write down how many significant figures you've rounded to after your answer.
3) If your calculation has multiple steps, only round the final answer, or it won't be as accurate.

EXAMPLE: The mass of a solid is 0.24 g and its volume is 0.715 cm³. Calculate the density of the solid.

Density = 0.24 g ÷ 0.715 cm³ = 0.33566... = 0.34 g/cm³ (2 s.f.) — Final answer should be rounded to 2 s.f.

(0.24 g: 2 s.f.; 0.715 cm³: 3 s.f.)

If Your Data Comes in Categories, Present It in a Bar Chart

1) If the independent variable is categoric (comes in distinct categories, e.g. solid, liquid, gas) you should use a bar chart to display the data.
2) You also use them if the independent variable is discrete (the data can be counted in chunks, where there's no in-between value, e.g. number of protons is discrete because you can't have half a proton).
3) There are some golden rules you need to follow for drawing bar charts:

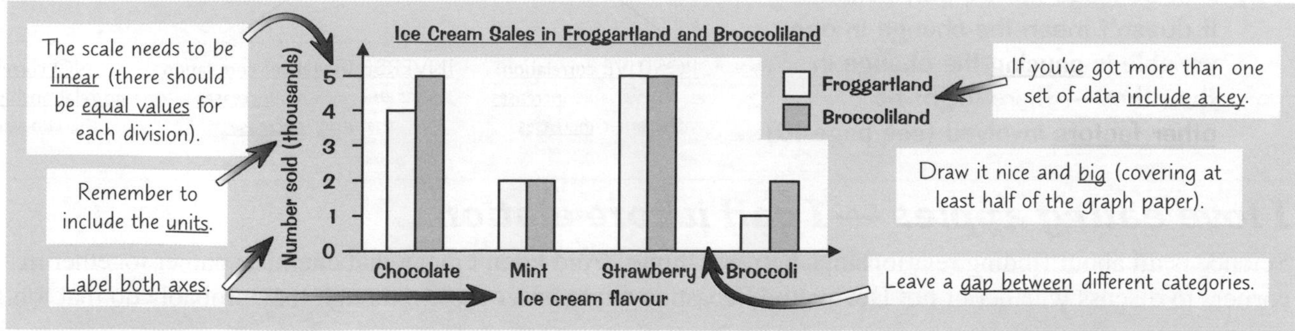
The scale needs to be linear (there should be equal values for each division).
Remember to include the units.
Label both axes.
Ice Cream Sales in Froggartland and Broccoliland
Number sold (thousands)
0
1
2
3
4
5
Chocolate
Mint
Strawberry
Broccoli
Ice cream flavour
Froggartland
Broccoliland
If you've got more than one set of data include a key.
Draw it nice and big (covering at least half of the graph paper).
Leave a gap between different categories.

If Your Data is Continuous, Plot a Graph

If both variables are continuous (numerical data that can have any value within a range, e.g. length, volume, temperature) you should use a graph to display the data.

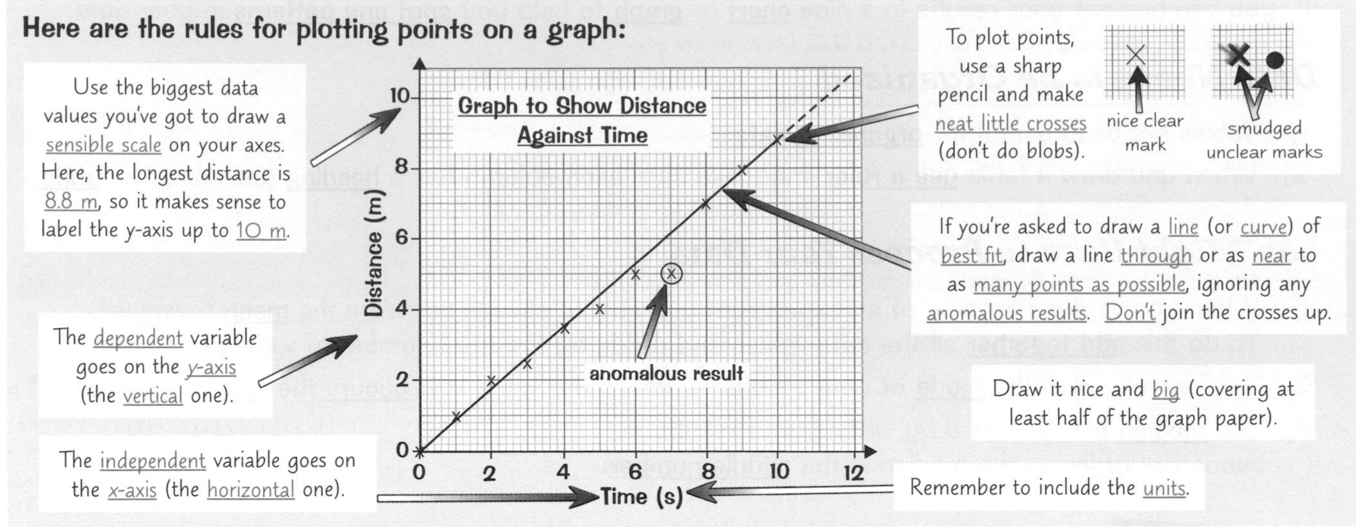

Here are the rules for plotting points on a graph:
Use the biggest data values you've got to draw a sensible scale on your axes. Here, the longest distance is 8.8 m, so it makes sense to label the y-axis up to 10 m.
The dependent variable goes on the y-axis (the vertical one).
The independent variable goes on the x-axis (the horizontal one).
Graph to Show Distance Against Time
Distance (m)
Time (s)
anomalous result
To plot points, use a sharp pencil and make neat little crosses (don't do blobs).
nice clear mark
smudged unclear marks
If you're asked to draw a line (or curve) of best fit, draw a line through or as near to as many points as possible, ignoring any anomalous results. Don't join the crosses up.
Draw it nice and big (covering at least half of the graph paper).
Remember to include the units.

Graphs Can Give You a Lot of Information About Your Data

1) The gradient (slope) of a graph tells you how quickly the dependent variable changes if you change the independent variable.

$$\text{gradient} = \frac{\text{change in } y}{\text{change in } x}$$

This graph shows the distance travelled by a vehicle against time. The graph is linear (it's a straight line graph), so you can simply calculate the gradient of the line to find out the speed of the vehicle.

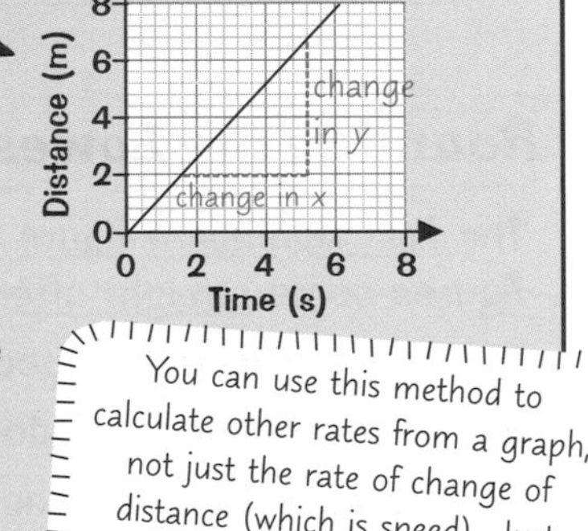

1) To calculate the gradient, pick two points on the line that are easy to read and a good distance apart.
2) Draw a line down from one of the points and a line across from the other to make a triangle. The line drawn down the side of the triangle is the change in y and the line across the bottom is the change in x.

Change in $y = 6.8 - 2.0 = 4.8$ m Change in $x = 5.2 - 1.6 = 3.6$ s

$$\text{Rate} = \text{gradient} = \frac{\text{change in } y}{\text{change in } x} = \frac{4.8 \text{ m}}{3.6 \text{ s}} = 1.3 \text{ m/s}$$

The units of the gradient are (units of y)/(units of x).

You can use this method to calculate other rates from a graph, not just the rate of change of distance (which is speed). Just remember that a rate is how much something changes over time, so x needs to be the time.

2) To find the gradient of a curve at a certain point, draw a tangent to the curve at that point and then find the gradient of the tangent. See page 24 for details on how to do this.
3) The intercept of a graph is where the line of best fit crosses one of the axes. The x-intercept is where the line of best fit crosses the x-axis and the y-intercept is where it crosses the y-axis.

Graphs Show the Relationship Between Two Variables

1) You can get three types of correlation (relationship) between variables:
2) Just because there's correlation, it doesn't mean the change in one variable is causing the change in the other — there might be other factors involved (see page 10).

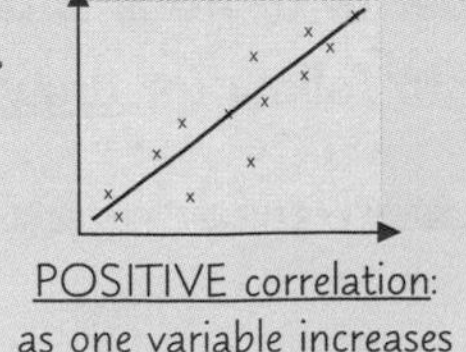
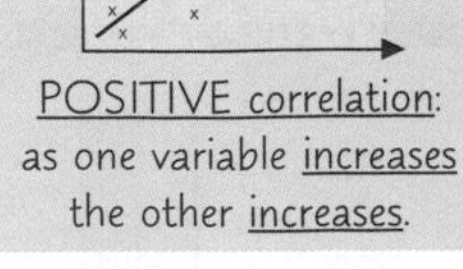
POSITIVE correlation: as one variable increases the other increases.

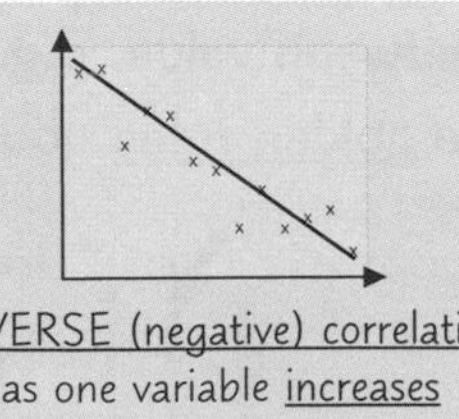
INVERSE (negative) correlation: as one variable increases the other decreases.

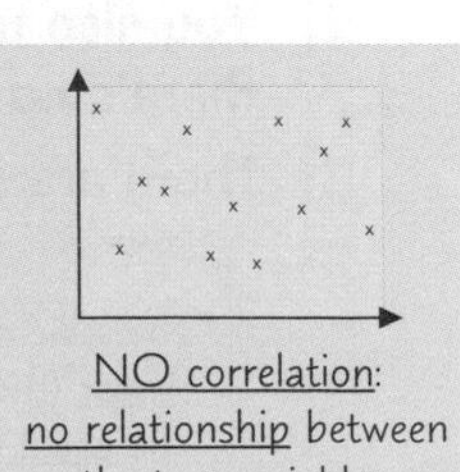
NO correlation: no relationship between the two variables.

I love eating apples — I call it core elation...

Science is all about finding relationships between things. And I don't mean that chemists gather together in corners to discuss whether or not Devini and Sebastian might be a couple... though they probably do that too.

Units and Equations

Graphs and maths skills are all very well, but the numbers don't mean much if you can't get the units right.

S.I. Units Are Used All Round the World

1) It wouldn't be all that useful if I defined volume in terms of bath tubs, you defined it in terms of egg-cups and my pal Sarwat defined it in terms of balloons — we'd never be able to compare our data.
2) To stop this happening, scientists have come up with a set of standard units, called S.I. units, that all scientists use to measure their data. Here are some S.I. units you'll see in physics:

Quantity	S.I. Base Unit
mass	kilogram, kg
length	metre, m
time	second, s
temperature	kelvin, K

Scaling Prefixes Can Be Used for Large and Small Quantities

1) Quantities come in a huge range of sizes. For example, the volume of a swimming pool might be around 2 000 000 000 cm^3, while the volume of a cup is around 25 cm^3.
2) To make the size of numbers more manageable, larger or smaller units are used. These are the S.I. base unit (e.g. metres) with a prefix in front:

prefix	tera (T)	giga (G)	mega (M)	kilo (k)	deci (d)	centi (c)	milli (m)	micro (μ)	nano (n)
multiple of unit	10^{12}	10^9	1 000 000 (10^6)	1000	0.1	0.01	0.001	0.000001 (10^{-6})	10^{-9}

3) These prefixes tell you how much bigger or smaller a unit is than the base unit. So one kilometre is one thousand metres.

The conversion factor is the number of times the smaller unit goes into the larger unit.

4) To swap from one unit to another, all you need to know is what number you have to divide or multiply by to get from the original unit to the new unit — this is called the conversion factor.
   - To go from a bigger unit (like m) to a smaller unit (like cm), you multiply by the conversion factor.
   - To go from a smaller unit (like g) to a bigger unit (like kg), you divide by the conversion factor.
5) Here are some conversions that'll be useful for GCSE physics:

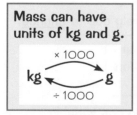

Mass can have units of kg and g.

kg → g: × 1000; g → kg: ÷ 1000

Energy can have units of J and kJ.

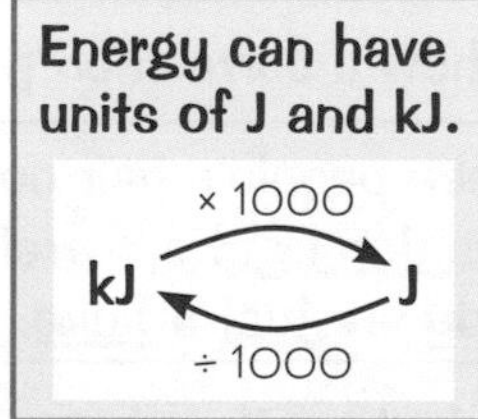

Volume can have units of m^3 and cm^3.

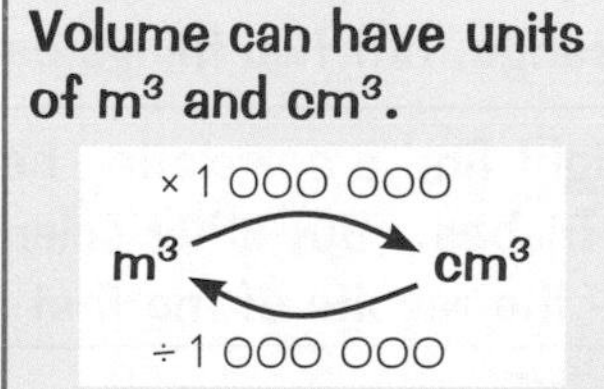

Density can have units of kg/m^3 and g/cm^3.

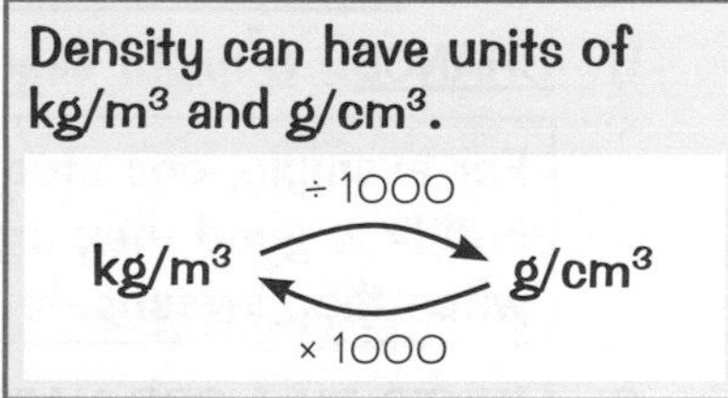

6) Numbers can also be written in standard form (see page 12), e.g. 1×10^2 m = 100 m. Make sure you know how to work with standard form on your calculator.

Always Check The Values in Equations and Formulas Have the Right Units

1) Equations show relationships between variables.
2) To rearrange an equation — whatever you do to one side of the equation also do to the other.

wave speed = frequency × wavelength. You can rearrange this equation to find the frequency by dividing each side by wavelength to give: frequency = wave speed ÷ wavelength.

3) To use a formula, you need to know the values of all but one of the variables. Substitute the values you do know into the formula, and do the calculation to work out the final variable.
4) Always make sure the values you put into an equation or formula have the right units. For example, you might have done an experiment to find the speed of a trolley. The distance the trolley travels will probably have been measured in cm, but the equation to find speed uses distance in m. So you'll have to convert your distance from cm to m before you put it into the equation.
5) To make sure your units are correct, it can help to write down the units on each line of your calculation.

I wasn't sure I liked units, but now I'm converted...

It's easy to get in a muddle when converting between units, but there's a handy way to check you've done it right. If you're moving from a smaller unit to a larger unit (e.g. g to kg) the number should get smaller, and vice versa.

Drawing Conclusions

Congratulations — you're nearly at the end of a gruelling investigation, time to draw conclusions.

You Can Only Conclude What the Data Shows and NO MORE

1) Drawing conclusions might seem pretty straightforward — you just look at your data and say what pattern or relationship you see between the dependent and independent variables.

The table on the right shows the potential difference across a light bulb for three different currents through the bulb:

Current (A)	Potential difference (V)
6	4
9	10
12	13

CONCLUSION: A higher current through the bulb gives a higher potential difference across the bulb.

2) But you've got to be really careful that your conclusion matches the data you've got and doesn't go any further.

You can't conclude that the potential difference across any circuit component will be higher for a larger current — the results might be completely different.

3) You also need to be able to use your results to justify your conclusion (i.e. back up your conclusion with some specific data).

The potential difference across the bulb was 9 V higher with a current of 12 A compared to a current of 6 A.

4) When writing a conclusion you need to refer back to the original hypothesis and say whether the data supports it or not:

The hypothesis for this experiment might have been that a higher current through the bulb would increase the potential difference across the bulb. If so, the data supports the hypothesis.

Correlation DOES NOT Mean Cause

If two things are correlated (i.e. there's a relationship between them) it doesn't necessarily mean a change in one variable is causing the change in the other — this is REALLY IMPORTANT — DON'T FORGET IT. There are three possible reasons for a correlation:

1) CHANCE: It might seem strange, but two things can show a correlation purely due to chance.

For example, one study might find a correlation between people's hair colour and how good they are at frisbee. But other scientists don't get a correlation when they investigate it — the results of the first study are just a fluke.

2) LINKED BY A 3RD VARIABLE: A lot of the time it may look as if a change in one variable is causing a change in the other, but it isn't — a third variable links the two things.

For example, there's a correlation between water temperature and shark attacks. This isn't because warmer water makes sharks crazy. Instead, they're linked by a third variable — the number of people swimming (more people swim when the water's hotter, and with more people in the water you get more shark attacks).

3) CAUSE: Sometimes a change in one variable does cause a change in the other. You can only conclude that a correlation is due to cause when you've controlled all the variables that could, just could, be affecting the result.

For example, there's a correlation between smoking and lung cancer. This is because chemicals in tobacco smoke cause lung cancer. This conclusion was only made once other variables (such as age and exposure to other things that cause cancer) had been controlled and shown not to affect people's risk of getting lung cancer.

I conclude that this page is a bit dull...

...although, just because I find it dull doesn't mean that I can conclude it's dull (you might think it's the most interesting thing since that kid got his head stuck in the railings near school). In the exams you could be given a conclusion and asked whether some data supports it — so make sure you understand how far conclusions can go.

Uncertainties and Evaluations

Hurrah! The end of another investigation. Well, now you have to work out all the things you did wrong.

Uncertainty is the Amount of Error Your Measurements Might Have

1) When you repeat a measurement, you often get a slightly different figure each time you do it due to random error. This means that each result has some uncertainty to it.
2) The measurements you make will also have some uncertainty in them due to limits in the resolution of the equipment you use (see page 6).
3) This all means that the mean of a set of results will also have some uncertainty to it. You can calculate the uncertainty of a mean result using the equation:
4) The larger the range, the less precise your results are and the more uncertainty there will be in your results. Uncertainties are shown using the '±' symbol.

The range is the largest value minus the smallest value.

$$\text{uncertainty} = \frac{\text{range}}{2}$$

The table below shows the results of a trolley experiment to determine the speed of the trolley as it moves along a horizontal surface. Calculate the uncertainty of the mean.

Repeat	1	2	3	mean
Speed (m/s)	2.06	2.02	2.04	2.04

1) First work out the range:
Range = 2.06 − 2.02
= 0.04 m/s

2) Use the range to find the uncertainty:
Uncertainty = range ÷ 2 = 0.04 ÷ 2 = 0.02 m/s

So, uncertainty of the mean = 2.04 ± 0.02 m/s

5) Measuring a greater amount of something helps to reduce uncertainty. For example, in a speed experiment, measuring the distance travelled over a longer period compared to a shorter period will reduce the percentage uncertainty in your results.

Evaluations — Describe How it Could be Improved

An evaluation is a critical analysis of the whole investigation.

1) You should comment on the method — was it valid?
Did you control all the other variables to make it a fair test?
2) Comment on the quality of the results — was there enough evidence to reach a valid conclusion? Were the results repeatable, reproducible, accurate and precise?
3) Were there any anomalous results? If there were none then say so. If there were any, try to explain them — were they caused by errors in measurement? Were there any other variables that could have affected the results? You should comment on the level of uncertainty in your results too.
4) All this analysis will allow you to say how confident you are that your conclusion is right.
5) Then you can suggest any changes to the method that would improve the quality of the results, so that you could have more confidence in your conclusion. For example, you might suggest changing the way you controlled a variable, or increasing the number of measurements you took. Taking more measurements at narrower intervals could give you a more accurate result. For example:

Springs have an elastic limit (a maximum extension before they stop springing back to their original size). Say you use several identical springs to do an experiment to find the elastic limit of the springs. If you apply forces of 1 N, 2 N, 3 N, 4 N and 5 N, and from the results see that the elastic limit is somewhere between 4 N and 5 N, you could then repeat the experiment with one of the other springs, taking more measurements between 4 N and 5 N to get a more accurate value for the elastic limit.

6) You could also make more predictions based on your conclusion. Then further experiments could be carried out to test them.

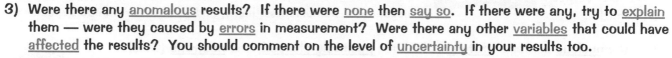

When suggesting improvements to the investigation, always make sure that you say why you think this would make the results better.

Evaluation — next time, I'll make sure I don't burn the lab down...

So there you have it — Working Scientifically. Make sure you know this stuff like the back of your hand. It's not just in the lab that you'll need to know how to work scientifically. You can be asked about it in the exams as well.

The History of the Atom and Atomic Structure

Atoms are the tiny particles of matter (stuff that has a mass) which make up everything. We used to think they were solid little spheres (like mini ball-bearings), then some clever clogs did some experiments...

The Theory of Atomic Structure Has Changed Over Time

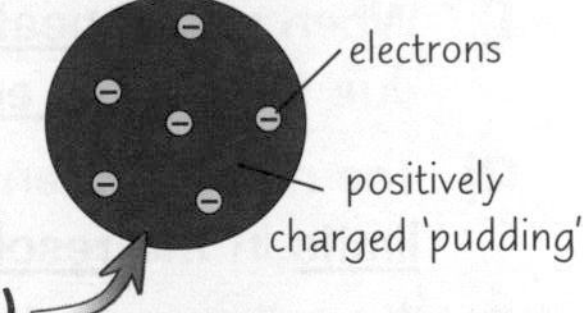
electrons
positively charged 'pudding'

1) In 1897 J J Thomson figured out that atoms weren't solid spheres. His measurements of charge and mass showed that an atom must contain smaller, negatively charged particles — electrons. From his results, he made a model of the atom known as the 'plum pudding model' (or the 'Thomson model') where negative electrons were spread through the positive 'pudding' that made up most of the atom.
2) In 1909 Ernest Rutherford, working with Hans Geiger and Ernest Marsden, conducted the famous gold foil experiment. They fired positively charged alpha particles at an extremely thin sheet of gold.
3) From the plum pudding model, they expected the particles to pass straight through the gold sheet, or only be slightly deflected. But although most of the particles did go straight through the sheet, some were deflected more than they had expected, and a few were deflected back the way they had come — something the plum-pudding model couldn't explain.
4) Rutherford came up with the theory of the nuclear atom to explain this new evidence. In his model, most of the mass of an atom is concentrated in a tiny, positively charged nucleus at the centre, surrounded by a 'cloud' of negative electrons — most of the atom is empty space.

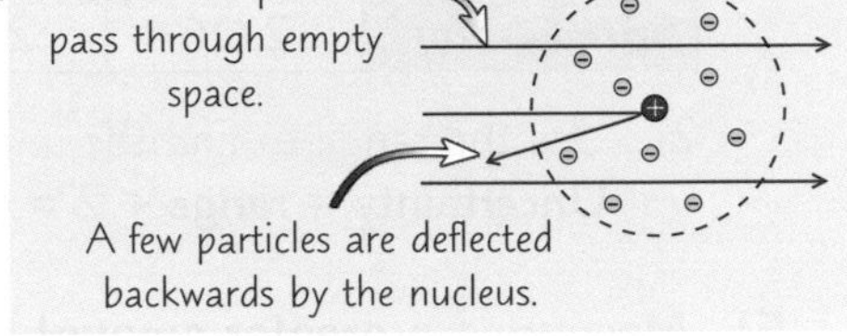
Most of the particles pass through empty space.
A few particles are deflected backwards by the nucleus.

5) Scientists realised that electrons in a 'cloud' around the nucleus of an atom like this would be attracted to the nucleus, causing the atom to collapse.
6) Niels Bohr got round this a few years later by proposing a new model where the electrons are in shells. He suggested that electrons can only exist in these shells (or fixed orbits), and not anywhere in-between. Each shell has a fixed energy. His theory was pretty close to the model of the atom shown below.

The Atom is Made Up of Protons, Neutrons and Electrons

Protons, neutrons and electrons are all subatomic particles — particles that are smaller than atoms.

The quantities to do with atoms are really tiny, so they're written in standard form:

$A \times 10^n$

A is always a number between 1 and 10.

n is the number of places the decimal point would move if you wrote the number out in decimal form. It's negative for numbers less than 1, and positive for numbers greater than 1.

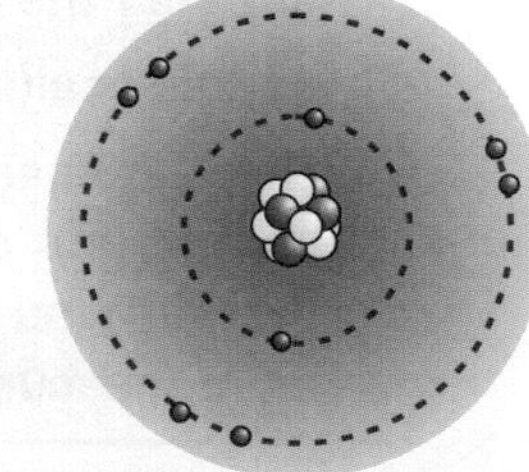

1) The nucleus contains protons (which are positively charged) and neutrons (which are neutral) — which gives it an overall positive charge. The nucleus is tiny — the nuclear radius is about 1×10^{-15} m. Almost the whole mass of the atom (about 1×10^{-23} g, depending on the element) is concentrated in the nucleus.
2) The rest of the atom is mostly empty space. The negative electrons whizz round outside the nucleus really quickly, in electron shells. They give the atom its overall size — the diameter of an atom is around 1×10^{-10} m — so the nuclear radius is around 10 000 times smaller than the atomic radius.
3) Atoms can join together to form molecules — e.g. molecules in oxygen gas are made up of two atoms of oxygen bonded together. Small molecules like this have a typical size of 10^{-10} m — they're roughly the same size as an atom.

Particle	Relative mass	Relative charge
Proton	1	+1
Neutron	1	0
Electron	0.0005	–1

I prefer the chocolate pudding model myself...

Scientists, eh? As soon as they've worked out one theory, they're off to find another. It's almost like they haven't thought about the people who have to revise them at all.

Q1 Describe the Thomson model of the atom. [1 mark]

Q2 Describe the current model of the structure of an atom. [3 marks]

Density

Time for some maths I'm afraid. But at least it comes with a fun experiment, so it's not all bad....

Density is Mass per Unit Volume

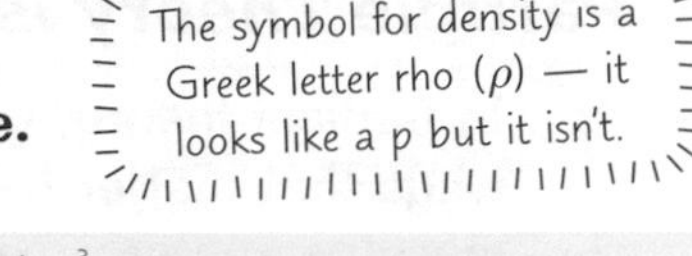
The symbol for density is a Greek letter rho (ρ) — it looks like a p but it isn't.

Density is a measure of the 'compactness' (for want of a better word) of a substance. It relates the mass of a substance to how much space it takes up.

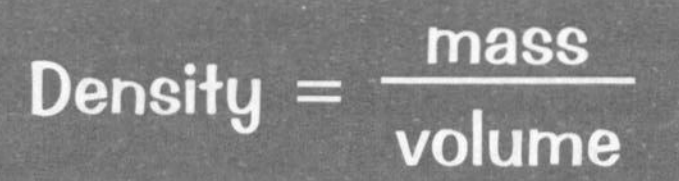
$\text{Density} = \frac{\text{mass}}{\text{volume}}$

$\frac{m}{\rho \times V}$

Pine $\rho = 0.5$ g/cm^3

Oil $\rho = 0.8$ g/cm^3

Water $\rho = 1$ g/cm^3

Iron $\rho = 7.9$ g/cm^3

The units of density are g/cm^3 or kg/m^3.

1) The density of an object depends on what it's made of. Density doesn't vary with size or shape.
2) The average density of an object determines whether it floats or sinks — a solid object will float on a fluid if it has a lower average density than the fluid.

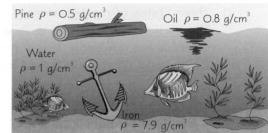

You Can Measure the Density of Solids and Liquids

1) To measure the density of a substance, measure the mass and volume of a sample of the substance and use the formula above.
2) You can measure the mass of a solid or liquid using a mass balance.
3) To measure the volume of a liquid, you can just pour it into a measuring cylinder.
4) 1 ml = 1 cm^3. If you need to convert a volume into other units, e.g. m^3, remember you need to cube the scaling factor for converting distance units to get the scaling factor for converting volume units. For example, to convert 50 cm^3 into m^3, you need to divide by $100^3 = 1\,000\,000$ (as there are 100 cm in 1 m). So 50 cm^3 = 50 ÷ 1 000 000 = 5×10^{-5} m^3.
5) If you want to measure the volume of a solid cuboid, measure its length, width, and height, then multiply them together. To find the volume of a solid cylinder, measure the diameter of one of the circles at the base, then halve this to give a radius. Then measure the cylinder's height, and use the formula volume = $\pi \times \text{radius}^2 \times \text{height}$.
6) An object submerged in water will displace a volume of water equal to its own volume. You can use this to find the volume of any object, for example using a eureka (Archimedes) can:

The volume of any prism is the area of its base multiplied by its height.

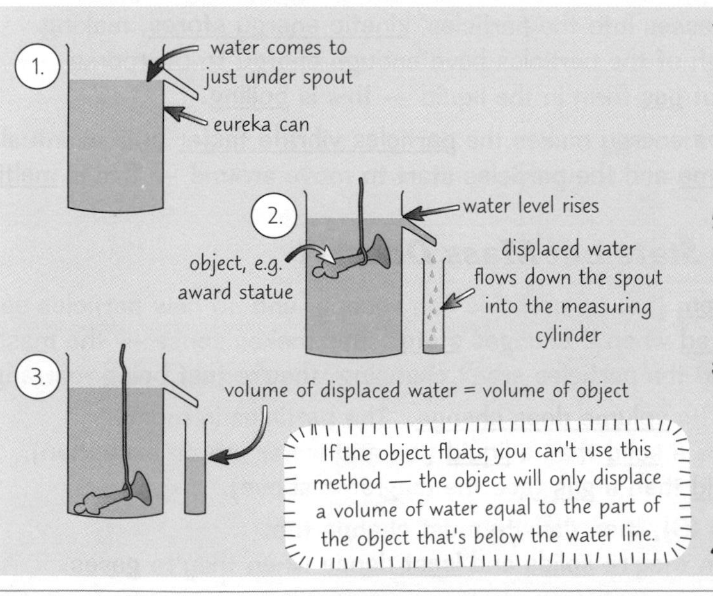
1.
water comes to just under spout
eureka can
2.
water level rises
object, e.g. award statue
displaced water flows down the spout into the measuring cylinder
3.
volume of displaced water = volume of object
If the object floats, you can't use this method — the object will only displace a volume of water equal to the part of the object that's below the water line.

PRACTICAL

1) You need the eureka can to be filled so that the water level is just under the spout. The best way to do this is to slightly over-fill the can then let the extra water drain away.
2) Place a measuring cylinder under the spout, then gently lower your object in the can, e.g. using a thin, strong thread. The displaced water will start to come out of the spout.
3) Wait for the spout to stop dripping, then measure the volume of water collected in the cylinder. This is the volume of water displaced by the object, which is equal to the volume of the object.
4) Repeat three times and calculate a mean.

I'm feeling a bit dense after that lot...

Converting between units with volumes catches people out all the time, so be careful.

Q1 Describe an experiment to calculate the density of an irregular solid object. [4 marks]

Q2 An object has a mass of 4.5×10^{-2} kg and a volume of 75 cm^3. Calculate its density in kg/m^3. [3 marks]

Particle Theory and States of Matter

According to particle theory, everything's made of tiny little balls. The table, this book, your Gran...

Particle Theory is a Way of Explaining Matter

1) In particle theory, you can think of the particles that make up matter as tiny balls. You can explain the ways that matter behaves in terms of how these tiny balls move, and the forces between them.
2) Three states of matter are solid (e.g. ice), liquid (e.g. water) and gas (e.g. water vapour). The particles of a substance in each state are the same — only the arrangement and energy of the particles are different. If you reverse a change of state, the particles go back to how they were before. So physical changes (e.g. melting or boiling) are different from chemical reactions.

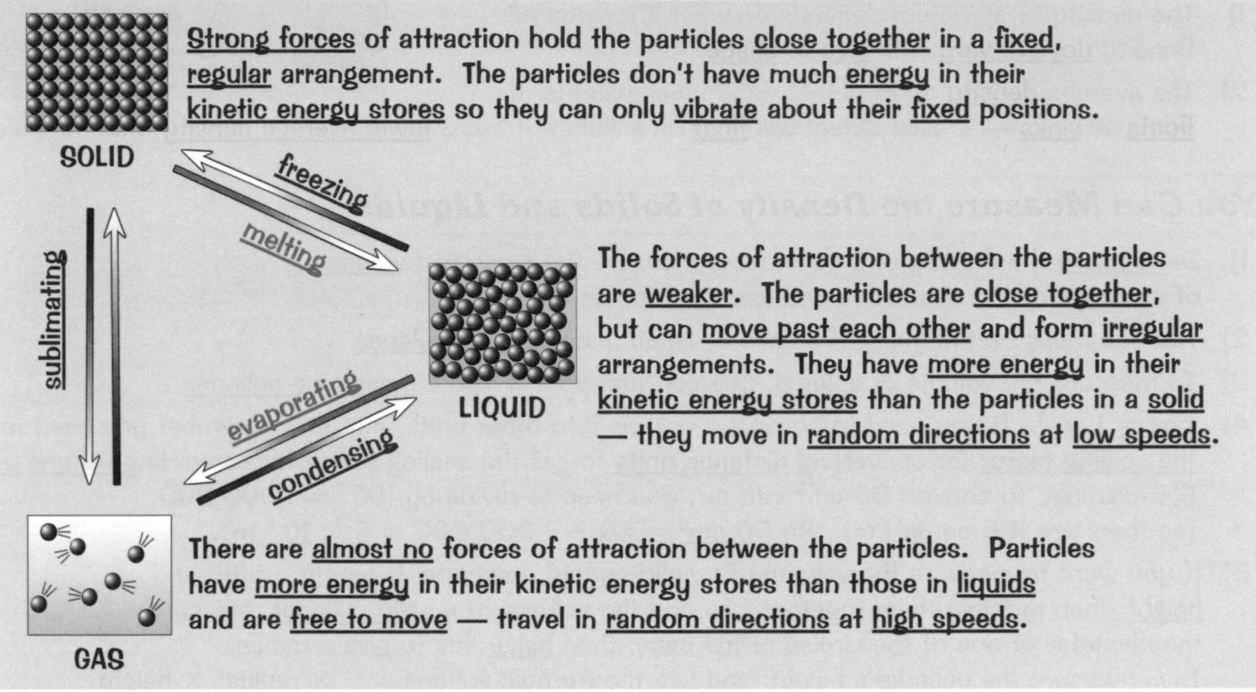

Strong forces of attraction hold the particles close together in a fixed, regular arrangement. The particles don't have much energy in their kinetic energy stores so they can only vibrate about their fixed positions.
SOLID
freezing
melting
sublimating
The forces of attraction between the particles are weaker. The particles are close together, but can move past each other and form irregular arrangements. They have more energy in their kinetic energy stores than the particles in a solid — they move in random directions at low speeds.
LIQUID
evaporating
condensing
There are almost no forces of attraction between the particles. Particles have more energy in their kinetic energy stores than those in liquids and are free to move — travel in random directions at high speeds.
GAS

3) The energy in a substance's thermal energy store is held by its particles in their kinetic energy stores — this is what the thermal energy store actually is.
4) When you heat a liquid, the extra energy passes into the particles' kinetic energy stores, making them move faster. Eventually, when enough of the particles have enough energy to overcome their attraction to each other, big bubbles of gas form in the liquid — this is boiling.
5) It's similar when you heat a solid. The extra energy makes the particles vibrate faster until eventually the forces between them are partly overcome and the particles start to move around — this is melting.

Density of a Substance Varies with State but Mass Doesn't

1) Provided you're working with a closed system (i.e. no particles can escape, and no new particles can get in) the mass of a substance isn't affected when it changes state. This makes sense — the mass of a substance is the mass of its particles, and the particles aren't changing, they're just being rearranged.
2) However, when a substance changes state its volume does change. The particles in most substances are closer together when they're a solid than a liquid (ice and water are an exception), and are closer together when they're a liquid than a gas (see the diagrams above).
3) Since density = mass ÷ volume (see page 13), then density must change too. Generally, substances are most dense when they're solids and least dense when they're gases.

Physics — it's really about state of mind...

Remember, the mass of a substance just comes from the particles, not the spaces between them. So as something expands or contracts, its volume changes but its mass stays the same.

Q1 Explain how the density of a typical substance changes as it changes from solid, to liquid to gas. [4 marks]

Specific Heat Capacity

The temperature of something isn't quite the same thing as the energy stored in the substance's thermal energy store. That's where specific heat capacity comes in...

Specific Heat Capacity Relates Temperature and Energy

1) Heating a substance increases the energy in its thermal energy store (or the kinetic energy stores of its particles, see page 14). You may sometimes see this referred to as the internal energy of a substance.
2) In kinetic theory, temperature is a way of measuring the average internal energy of a substance.
3) However, it takes more energy to increase the temperature of some materials than others. E.g. you need 4200 J to warm 1 kg of water by 1 °C, but only 139 J to warm 1 kg of mercury by 1 °C. Materials which need to gain lots of energy to warm up also release loads of energy when they cool down again. They store a lot of energy for a given change in temperature.
4) The change in the energy stored in a substance when you heat it is related to the change in its temperature by its specific heat capacity. The specific heat capacity of a substance is the change in energy in the substance's thermal store needed to raise the temperature of 1 kg of that substance by 1 °C. E.g. water has a specific heat capacity of 4200 J/kg°C (that's pretty high).
5) You need to know how to use the equation relating temperature, energy, mass and specific heat capacity:

Change in Thermal Energy (J) = Mass (kg) × Specific Heat Capacity (J/kg°C) × Change in Temperature (°C)

You can Find the Specific Heat Capacity of a Substance

PRACTICAL

You can use this experiment to find the specific heat capacity of a liquid, e.g. water, or a solid, e.g. a metal cylinder.

1) Use a mass balance to measure the mass of your substance.
2) Set up the experiment shown below. Make sure the joulemeter reads zero.

Add a conducting gel between the heater and the metal cylinder to improve conduction and make your results more accurate.

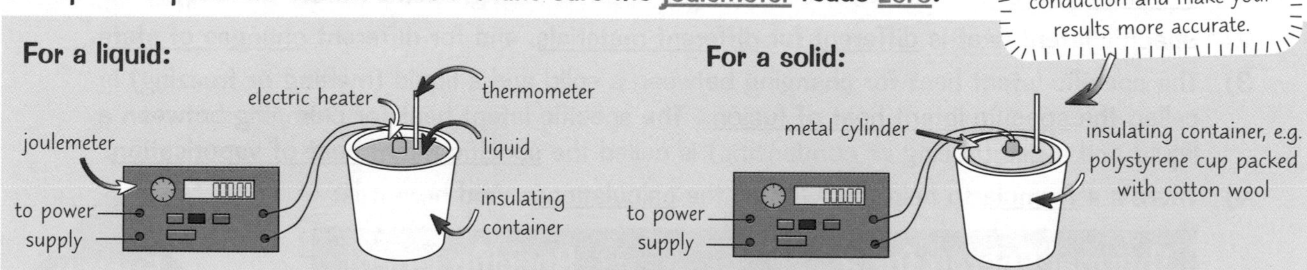

3) Measure the temperature of the substance you're investigating, then turn on the power.
4) Keep an eye on the thermometer. When the temperature has increased by e.g. ten degrees, stop the experiment and record the energy on the joulemeter, and the increase in temperature.
5) You can then calculate the specific heat capacity of your substance by rearranging the equation above and plugging in your measurements.
6) Repeat the whole experiment at least three times, then calculate the mean (see page 7) specific heat capacity of your substance.
7) You need to watch out for systematic errors due to energy escaping from your experiment. The insulating container helps by reducing the amount of energy that escapes from the sides and the bottom of the substance you're investigating. You could reduce these energy losses further by adding a lid to the container.

You could also use a voltmeter and ammeter instead of a joulemeter, time how long the heater was on for, then calculate the energy supplied (see p.44).

I wish I had a high specific fact capacity...

Make sure you learn that equation — it's a bit of a tricky one.

Q1 If a metal has a specific heat capacity of 420 J/kg°C, calculate how much the temperature of a 0.20 kg block of the metal will increase by if 1680 J of energy are supplied to it. [3 marks]

Specific Latent Heat

If you heat up a pan of water on the stove, the water never gets any hotter than 100 °C. You can carry on heating it up, but the temperature won't rise. How come, you say? It's all to do with latent heat...

You Need to Put In Energy to Break Intermolecular Bonds

1) Remember, when you heat a solid or liquid, you're transferring energy to the kinetic energy stores of the particles in the substance, making the particles vibrate or move faster.
2) When a substance is melting or boiling, you're still putting in energy, but the energy's used for breaking intermolecular bonds rather than raising the temperature — there are flat spots on the heating graph.

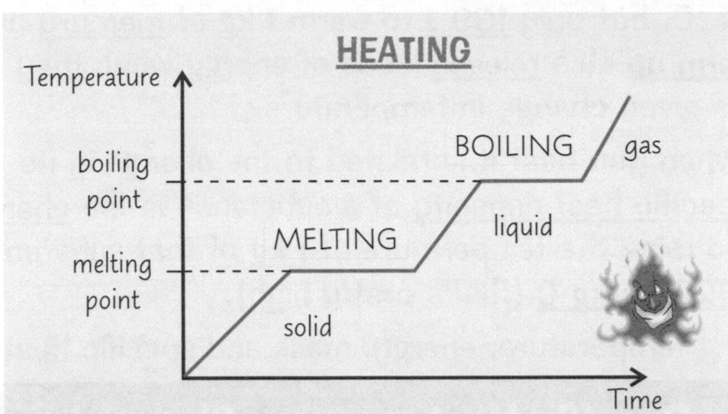

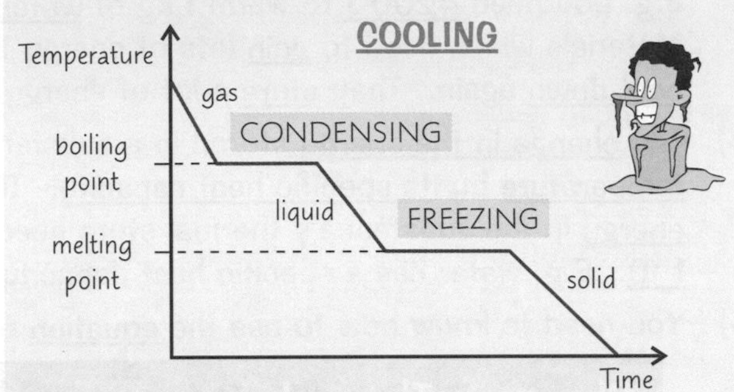

3) When a substance is condensing or freezing, bonds are forming between particles, which releases energy. This means the temperature doesn't go down until all the substance has turned into a liquid (condensing) or a solid (freezing).

Specific Latent Heat is the Energy Needed to Change State

1) The specific latent heat of a change of state for a substance is the change of energy in its thermal energy store when 1 kg of the substance changes state without changing its temperature (i.e. the substance has got to be at the right temperature already).
2) Specific latent heat is different for different materials, and for different changes of state.
3) The specific latent heat for changing between a solid and a liquid (melting or freezing) is called the specific latent heat of fusion. The specific latent heat for changing between a liquid and a gas (boiling or condensing) is called the specific latent heat of vaporisation.
4) There's a formula to help you with all the calculations. And here it is:

Thermal Energy for a Change in State (J) = Mass (kg) × Specific Latent Heat (J/kg)

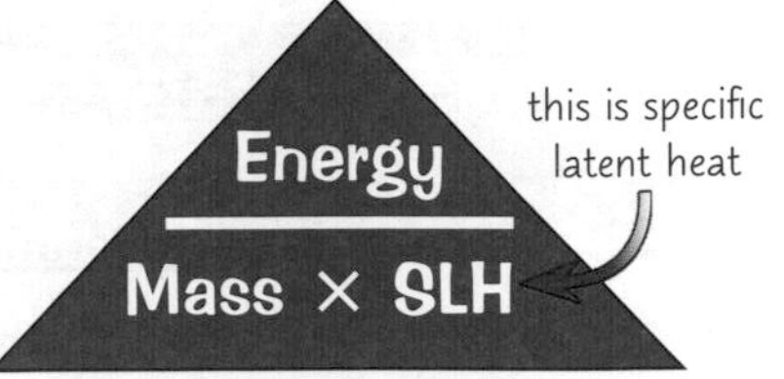

EXAMPLE:

The specific latent heat of vaporisation for water is 2.26×10^6 J/kg. 2.825×10^6 J of energy is used to boil dry a pan of water at 100 °C. What was the mass of water in the pan?

Thermal energy of change of state = mass × specific latent heat,
so mass = thermal energy of change of state ÷ specific latent heat
$= 2.825 \times 10^6 \div 2.26 \times 10^6 = 1.25$ kg

You came across standard form on page 12, e.g. $2.26 \times 10^6 = 2260000$.

Breaking Bonds — Blofeld never quite manages it...

Fun fact: this stuff explains how sweating cools you down — the energy that builds up in your body when you exercise is used to change liquid sweat into gas, rather than increasing your temperature. Nice...

Q1 Sketch a graph showing how the temperature of a sample of water will change over time as it's constantly heated from –5 °C to 105 °C. [3 marks]

Pressure of Gases

Gas particles fly around, bump into things and exert forces on them. This is happening to you right now — the air around you is exerting pressure on you (unless you're somehow reading this in space).

Colliding Gas Particles Create Pressure

1) According to particle theory, matter is made up of very small, constantly moving particles. The warmer something is, the more these particles are moving.
2) In a gas, these particles are free to move around in completely random directions.
3) As gas particles move about, they randomly bang into each other and whatever else gets in the way, like the walls of their container.
4) Gas particles are very small, but they still have a mass. When they collide with something, they exert a force on it.
5) All these collisions cause a net force on the inside surface of the container. The force acting per unit area is the pressure.
6) The more particles there are in a given volume, the more often they'll collide with the walls of the container, and with each other, so the higher the pressure will be.

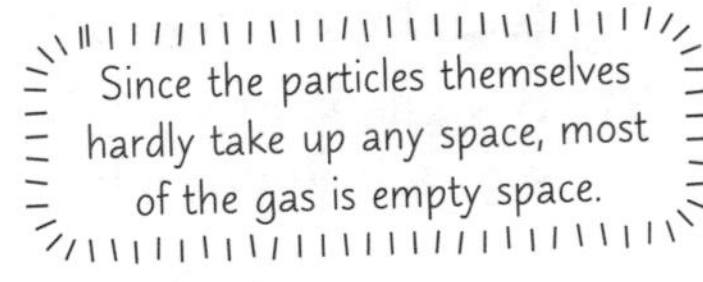

Since the particles themselves hardly take up any space, most of the gas is empty space.

Changing the Temperature Changes the Pressure

A sealed container is an example of a closed system — no matter can get in or out.

1) The pressure a gas exerts on its container also depends on how fast the particles are going and how often they hit the walls.
2) If you hold a gas in a sealed container with a fixed volume and heat it, energy is transferred to the kinetic energy stores of the gas particles and they move faster. This means the particles hit the container walls harder and more often, creating more pressure.
3) If the gas is cooled, the particles have less energy and move less quickly. The particles hit the walls with less force and less often, so the pressure is reduced.

At Constant Temperature "pV = Constant"

1) If you put the same amount of gas in a bigger container (i.e. increase the volume), the pressure will decrease, as there'll be fewer collisions between the gas particles and the container's walls.
2) If you reduce the volume, the particles get more squashed up and so they hit the walls more often, hence the pressure increases.
3) For a fixed amount of gas at a constant temperature, this leads to the equation:

$$\text{pressure (Pa)} \times \text{volume (m}^3\text{)} = \text{constant}$$

EXAMPLE:

A gas at a pressure of 25 000 Pa is compressed from a volume of 0.040 m^3 down to a volume of 0.020 m^3. The temperature of the gas does not change. Find the new pressure of the gas, in Pa.

Before the gas is compressed, pressure × volume = 25 000 × 0.040 = 1000

As pressure × volume = constant, after the gas is compressed, pressure × 0.020 = 1000

So pressure = 1000 ÷ 0.020 = 50 000 Pa

The volume's decreased, so you'd expect the pressure to increase.

Gas particles need to watch where they're going...

Remember, the more gas particles there are, and the faster they travel, the higher the pressure. Simple...

Q1 Explain how a gas exerts pressure on its container. [2 marks]

Q2 Explain what happens to the pressure of a gas in a sealed container when its temperature decreases. [4 marks]

More Pressure of Gases

Don't breathe out yet — there's still more about pressure that you need to know.

A Change in Pressure can Cause a Change in Volume

1) You know from page 17 that a gas exerts a force on its container due to collisions between the particles and the walls of the container. These collisions happen in random directions, but add together to produce a net force at right angles to the wall of the container:

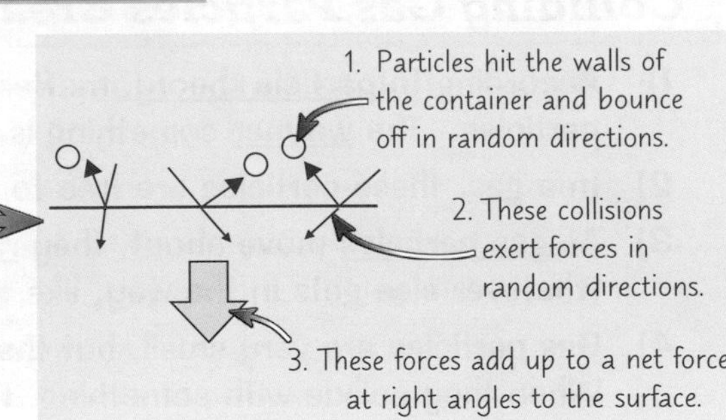

1. Particles hit the walls of the container and bounce off in random directions.
2. These collisions exert forces in random directions.
3. These forces add up to a net force at right angles to the surface.

2) If the pressure of a gas is increased (e.g. by heating it) this force increases. If the pressure of a gas is decreased (e.g. by cooling it) this force decreases.
3) If a gas is in a container that can change volume, e.g. a balloon, this can change the volume of the container, and so the gas.

This isn't just about balloons — it's true for any container that can change volume.

There's Pressure on the Outside of a Container Too

1) Unless it's in a vacuum, the outside of a gas container is also under pressure from whatever's around it — e.g. atmospheric pressure from the air (see p.19).
2) If a balloon isn't expanding or contracting, then the pressure (and force) of the gas inside the balloon pushing outwards is equal to the pressure (and force) of the air outside the balloon pushing inwards.
3) However, if you increase the pressure of the gas inside the balloon, then the force pushing outwards will be higher than the force pushing inwards — there's a net outwards force on the walls of the balloon. This causes the balloon to expand.
4) As the balloon expands, the gas particles inside it hit the walls less often. This causes the pressure inside the balloon to decrease.
5) Once the pressure inside the balloon has fallen back to the same level as atmospheric pressure, the balloon will stop expanding.
6) The opposite happens if you reduce the pressure inside the balloon. The pressure on the outside of the balloon will be bigger than the pressure on the inside, so there'll be a net inward force and the balloon will shrink.
7) This causes the pressure inside the container to rise, as the particles of the gas hit the walls of the container more often, until pressure inside = pressure outside again.
8) The same thing happens if you change the pressure acting on a gas from outside its container. E.g. you can compress a syringe filled with air by pushing hard on the plunger. The volume of the gas in the syringe will decrease until its pressure is equal to the pressure you're exerting on the plunger.

inward pressure from gas particles outside the balloon

outward pressure from gas particles inside the balloon

Doing Work on a Gas Can Increase its Temperature

1) Doing work on a gas can increase its internal energy (see page 15), which increases its temperature.
2) You can do work on a gas mechanically, e.g. with a bike pump.
3) The gas exerts pressure on the plunger of the pump, and so exerts a force on it. Work has to be done against this force to push down the plunger.
4) This transfers energy to the kinetic energy stores of the gas particles, so increases the internal energy and therefore the temperature.
5) If the pump is connected to e.g. a tyre, some of this energy is transferred from the gas to the thermal energy store of the tyre, and you'll feel the tyre getting warmer as you pump it up.

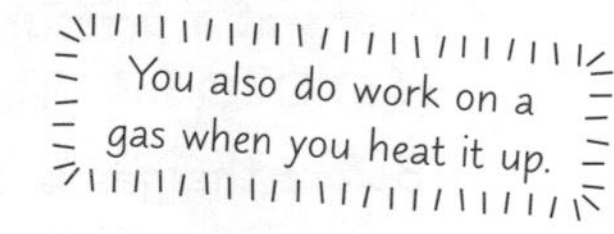

You also do work on a gas when you heat it up.

Hope the pressure's not getting to you...

Lots of facts to get into your head here I'm afraid, but you can do it, I believe in you.

Q1 Explain why pumping up a bike tyre increases the tyre's temperature. [3 marks]

Atmospheric Pressure and Liquid Pressure

The air in the atmosphere exerts pressure on us all the time. It's called atmospheric pressure, funnily enough.

Atmospheric Pressure is All Around Us All the Time

1) The Earth's atmosphere stretches to roughly 100 km above the Earth's surface. That's a lot of air.
2) The weight of the air high in the atmosphere pushes down on the air around us. This creates atmospheric pressure. Like the pressure in a tyre or a balloon, this pressure acts in all directions. Because it's always there, and because it's equal in every direction, we can't feel this pressure.
3) The lower you are, the more atmosphere there is above you, so the higher the atmospheric pressure is. If you gain height, there's less atmosphere above you, so the atmospheric pressure lowers. E.g. atmospheric pressure is over 100 000 Pa at sea level. But at the top of Mount Everest (8800 m above sea level) the atmospheric pressure is only around 33 000 Pa.
4) The graph shows how atmospheric pressure varies with height. It's curved because atmospheric pressure is affected by the density of the atmosphere, which also varies with height.
5) The density of the atmosphere gets higher the closer you are to sea level. This is because the weight of the air above pushes down on the air below it, compressing it — the closer to sea level you are, the more air there is above you, so the more the air around you is compressed.
6) Other factors like temperature also affect the density of air, but you can assume the density of the atmosphere is uniform at a given height.

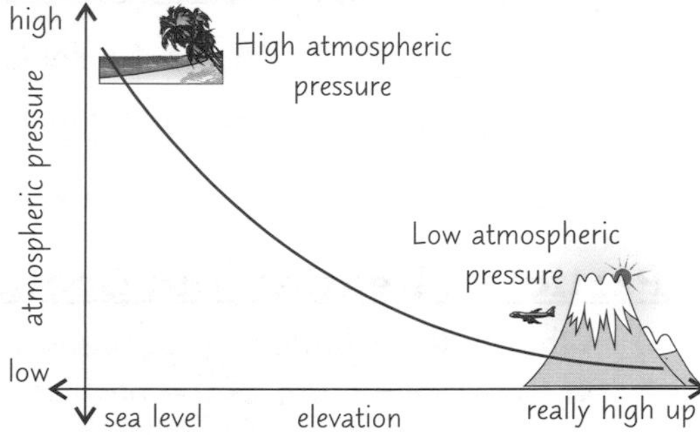

Liquid Pressure Causes Upthrust and Makes Things Float

1) If you submerge (or partially submerge) an object in a liquid, it experiences liquid pressure from all directions due to the particles of the liquid.
2) This pressure increases with depth, due to the weight of the 'column' of liquid directly above the object.
3) Liquids can't be compressed (or not very much), so their density is the same everywhere (unlike gases).
4) The pressure at a given depth (i.e. below a column of liquid of a given height) is given by the equation:

pressure due to a column of liquid (Pa) = height of column (m) × density of liquid (kg/m^3) × g (N/kg)

5) Here g is the gravitational field strength (see page 33). It's equal to about 10 N/kg.
6) You can also use this equation to find the difference in pressure between two depths — difference in pressure = difference in depth × density × g.
7) As pressure in a liquid increases with depth, the force pushing upwards on the bottom of an object due to the liquid pressure is greater than the force pushing down at the top of the object.
8) This causes an overall upwards force, called upthrust.
9) The upthrust acting on an object is equal to the weight of fluid it has displaced. If this upthrust is equal to the object's weight, then the object will float. If the upthrust is less than the object's weight, it will sink.
10) So, to make an object float, you need to make it less dense than the liquid you're trying to float it on — so it will have displaced a volume of water with a weight equal to its own weight before it's completely submerged.

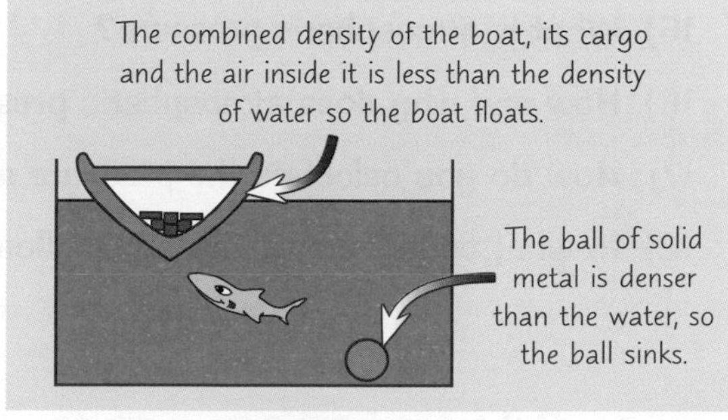

The combined density of the boat, its cargo and the air inside it is less than the density of water so the boat floats.
The ball of solid metal is denser than the water, so the ball sinks.

This upthrust stuff really floats my boat...

Upthrust is really hard to get your head around, so it's probably worth giving this page another read...

Q1 A submarine dives from a depth of 120 m to a depth of 320 m. Given that the density of water is 1000 kg/m^3, calculate the increase in liquid pressure acting on the submarine. [2 marks]

Q2 Explain why an object that's submerged in water will experience an upwards force. [3 marks]

Revision Questions for Topic P1

Well, that wraps up P1 — time to put yourself to the test and find out how much you really know.

- Try these questions and tick off each one when you get it right.
- When you've done all the questions under a heading and are completely happy with it, tick it off.

The Structure of the Atom (p.12)

1) a) Describe Rutherford's gold foil experiment.
   b) How did the results of this experiment disagree with the Thomson model of the atom?
2) How did Bohr's model of the atom differ from Rutherford's?
3) Roughly how big is an atom?

Density and States of Matter (p.13-14)

4) What is density? How is it calculated?
5) Describe solids, liquids, and gases in terms of the movements of their particles.
6) Explain what happens to the mass of a substance when it changes state.

Particles, Heating and Cooling (p.15-16)

7) What is the relationship between temperature and the energy in the kinetic store of the particles in a substance?
8) What is the specific heat capacity of a substance?
9) Describe an experiment to find the specific heat capacity of water.
10) A gas is cooled, until it becomes a liquid and eventually turns into a solid. Sketch a graph showing how the temperature of the substance changes over time, including labels to show the boiling point and the melting point, and label the changes of state.
11) What is meant by:
    a) the specific latent heat of fusion?
    b) the specific latent heat of vaporisation?

Volume, Temperature and Pressure (p.17-19)

12) What happens to the pressure of a gas in a sealed container of fixed volume when it is heated?
13) What is the relationship between pressure and volume at a constant temperature?
14) Describe how a change in external pressure can lead to a change in the volume of a gas in a sealed container.
15) What is atmospheric pressure?
16) How and why does atmospheric pressure change with height?
17) How do you calculate the pressure at different depths in a liquid?
18) In what conditions will an object float?

Speed and Velocity

This page will set you up for the rest of the topic. Learn it, don't forget it, and do the questions at the end.

Scalars are Just Numbers, but Vectors Have Direction Too

1) Distance and displacement are different things. They both measure how far something has travelled, but displacement also says which direction something has travelled in. For example, you could say a car has travelled a distance of 10 m, but it has a displacement of 10 m north.
2) To measure the speed of an object, you only need to measure how fast it's going — the direction is not important. E.g. speed = 30 mph.
3) Velocity is a more useful measure of motion, because it describes both the speed and direction. E.g. velocity = 30 mph due north.
4) Quantities like speed and distance, that are only numbers, are called scalar quantities. → Scalar quantities: speed, distance, mass, time, etc.

5) Quantities like velocity and displacement, that have a direction as well, are vector quantities. → Vector quantities: velocity, displacement, force, acceleration, etc.

When we use vectors, we often talk about there being a positive and a negative direction. E.g. a car moving in one direction could have a velocity of 3 m/s, but moving in the opposite direction it will have a velocity of –3 m/s. In this example, the car has a speed of 3 m/s in both directions. You can often pick a positive direction that makes the calculations easier.

Speed, Distance and Time — the Formula

You really ought to get pretty slick with this equation, it pops up a lot...

distance travelled (m) = speed (m/s) × time (s)

The equation for calculating displacement is: displacement (m) = velocity (m/s) × time (s).

A cat skulks 20 m in 50 s. Find: a) its speed, b) how long it takes to skulk 32 m.

1) Rearrange the equation above for speed, s. $s = \frac{d}{t} = 20 \div 50 = 0.4$ m/s
2) Now that the speed has been calculated, you can find the time, t, taken to travel a different distance at the same speed. $t = \frac{d}{s} = 32 \div 0.4 = 80$ s

You Need to be Able to Convert Between Units

When using any equation, it's important to have your quantities in the right units. E.g. in the speed equation above, the speed must be in m/s (metres per second), the distance must be in m (metres) and the time must be in s (seconds). You may need to convert e.g. between ms (milliseconds) and s, between km (kilometres) and m (metres).

To convert from miles to km, you multiply by 1.6.

To convert 16 km into m: multiply by 1000 — 16 × 1000 = 16 000 m
To convert 22 ms into s: divide by 1000 — 22 ÷ 1000 = 0.022 s

You can convert e.g. kilowatts to watts or milliamps to amps in the same way.

Getting hours and minutes into seconds is a little trickier:

To convert 8 hr (hours) into s:
Multiply 8 by 60 to find the number of minutes — 8 × 60 = 480 minutes
Then multiply 480 minutes by 60 to find the number of seconds — 480 × 60 = 28 800 s

A fairly easy way to start the section... — wait, whose cat is this?

Know the difference between vectors and scalars — scalars have a size, vectors have a size AND a direction.

Q1 A cyclist has a constant speed. Calculate their speed if they cycle 660 m in 2.0 minutes. [2 marks]

Q2 Find the distance travelled in 24 s by a car with a constant speed of 54 km/hr. [2 marks]

Acceleration

If an object is accelerating, its velocity is changing.

Acceleration is the Rate of Change of Velocity

1) Acceleration is how quickly the velocity is changing.
2) This change in velocity can be a CHANGE IN SPEED or a CHANGE IN DIRECTION or both.
3) You need to learn this equation for calculating acceleration:

$$\text{acceleration (m/s}^2) = \frac{\text{change in velocity (m/s)}}{\text{time (s)}}$$

4) To calculate the change in velocity, you must always do final velocity – initial velocity (and not initial velocity – final velocity).
5) Acceleration is like velocity — it's a vector and so can have a positive or negative value. If an object has a negative acceleration, it is either slowing down (decelerating), or speeding up in the negative direction.

An object travelling in a circle at a constant speed has a changing velocity (because it's always changing direction), so it's always accelerating.

EXAMPLE: A cyclist is in a race. As she approaches the finish line, she increases her speed from 11 m/s to 15 m/s in 25 s. Calculate her acceleration.

1) First find the change in velocity. change in velocity = final velocity – initial velocity = 15 – 11 = 4 m/s
2) Then substitute this into the acceleration equation. acceleration = change in velocity ÷ time
= 4 ÷ 25 = 0.16 m/s²

When the cyclist crosses the finish line, she immediately applies her brakes, and comes to a stop after 3 s. Calculate her acceleration after she crosses the finish line.

1) First find the change in velocity. change in velocity = final velocity – initial velocity = 0 – 15 = -15 m/s
2) Then substitute this into the acceleration equation. acceleration = change in velocity ÷ time
= -15 ÷ 3 = -5 m/s²

Calculating Distance or Velocity for Uniform Acceleration

For any object that is travelling with uniform acceleration (that's just a fancy way of saying its acceleration is constant), you can use the following equation:

This equation is really handy, so make sure you're comfortable with rearranging it and using it.

$$\underset{(\text{m/s})^2}{(\text{final velocity})^2} - \underset{(\text{m/s})^2}{(\text{initial velocity})^2} = 2 \times \underset{(\text{m/s}^2)}{\text{acceleration}} \times \underset{(\text{m})}{\text{distance}}$$

It might help you to remember the equation as $v^2 - u^2 = 2 \times a \times d$ (which is a bit shorter).

EXAMPLE: A horse is running with a constant acceleration of 0.45 m/s². It has an initial velocity of 8.0 m/s and runs a distance of 180 m. What is the horse's final velocity? Give your answer to 2 s.f.

1) Rearrange the equation for (final velocity)². (final velocity)² – (initial velocity)² = 2 × acceleration × distance
(final velocity)² = (2 × acceleration × distance) + (initial velocity)²
= (2 × 0.45 × 180) + 8.0² = 226
2) Take the square root of the answer. final velocity = $\sqrt{226}$ = 15.03... = 15 m/s (to 2 s.f.)

My dog's acceleration is negative when she gets closer to a bath...

Acceleration is odd — remember it's a measure of how fast an object's velocity is changing, and you'll be fine.

Q1 A cheetah with an acceleration of 8.25 m/s² takes 4.0 seconds to reach its maximum speed from rest. Calculate its maximum speed and the distance covered in this time. [4 marks]

Investigating Motion

PRACTICAL

Here's a simple experiment you can try out to investigate the relation between distance, speed and acceleration.

You can Investigate the Motion of a Trolley on a Ramp

1) Set up your apparatus as shown in the diagram below, and mark a line on the ramp just before the first light gate (see page 105) — this is to make sure the trolley starts from the same point each time.
2) Measure the distances between light gates 1 and 2, and 2 and 3.
3) Hold the trolley still at the start line, and then let go of it so that it starts to roll down the slope.
4) As it rolls down the ramp it will accelerate. When it reaches the runway, it will travel at a constant speed (ignoring any friction).

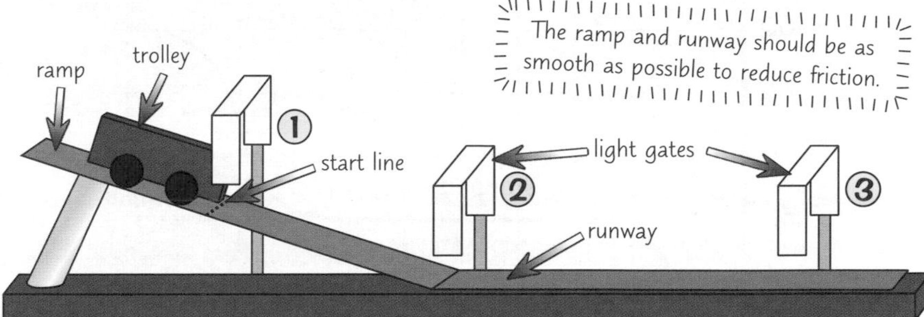

The ramp and runway should be as smooth as possible to reduce friction.

5) Each light gate will record the time when the trolley passes through it.
6) The time it takes to travel between gates 1 and 2 can be used to find the average speed on the ramp, and between gates 2 and 3 gives the speed on the runway (using speed = distance ÷ time).
7) The acceleration of the trolley on the ramp can be found using acceleration = change in speed ÷ time, with the following values:
   - the initial speed of the trolley (= 0 m/s),
   - the final speed of the trolley, which equals the speed of the trolley on the runway (ignoring friction),
   - the time it takes the trolley to travel between light gates 1 and 2.

You can also measure speed at a point using one light gate.

The trolley's acceleration on the ramp and its final speed on the runway will increase when the angle of the ramp increases, or the amount of friction between the ramp and the trolley decreases. Increasing the distance between the bottom of the ramp and where the trolley is released will also increase the final speed of the trolley.

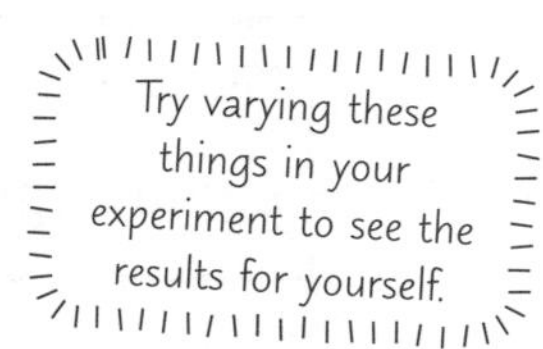

Try varying these things in your experiment to see the results for yourself.

You can use Different Equipment to Measure Distance and Time

Generally, you measure speed by measuring distance and time, and then calculating speed. You might need to use different methods for measuring distance and time depending on what you're investigating.

1) If possible, your measuring instrument should always be longer than the distance you're measuring with it — e.g. you shouldn't use a 30 cm ruler to measure something that's 45 cm long.
2) For experiments in the lab like the one above, the distances involved will generally be less than a metre, so you'll be able to measure them with a ruler or a metre stick.
3) If you're investigating e.g. how fast someone walks, you'll want to measure their speed over many metres, so you'll need a long tape measure, or a rolling tape measure (one of those clicky wheel things).
4) To measure time intervals longer than about e.g. 5 seconds, you can use a stopwatch.
5) To measure short intervals, like in the experiment above it's best to use e.g. light gates connected to a computer. Using a stopwatch involves human error, due to, for example, reaction times. This is more of a problem the shorter the interval you're timing, as the reaction time makes up a larger proportion of the interval.

If you want to investigate motion you'll need to invest in gates...

Think about it this way — say you were measuring the height of an elephant, you wouldn't use a 30 cm ruler, that would be daft. You'd be there forever. What experiment are you doing with an elephant anyway?

Q1 Explain how the speed of an object can be found using two light gates. [3 marks]

Q2 Explain why using light gates to measure short time intervals is more accurate than a stopwatch. [2 marks]

Distance-Time Graphs

A graph speaks a thousand words, so drawing one can be better than writing 'An object starts at rest, then moves at a steady speed of 10 m/s for 2 s until it reaches a distance of 20 m, then remains stationary for 5 s before increasing its velocity with a constant acceleration for 2.5 s.'

Distance-Time (d-t) Graphs Tell You How Far Something has Travelled

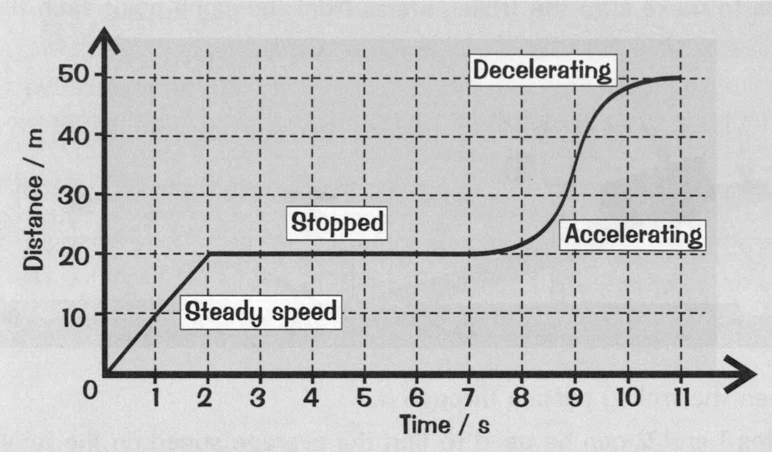

The different parts of a *d-t* graph describe the motion of an object:

- The gradient (slope) at any point gives the speed of the object.
- Flat sections are where it's stopped.
- A steeper graph means it's going faster.
- Curves represent acceleration.
- A steepening curve means it's speeding up (increasing gradient).
- A levelling off curve means it's slowing down (decreasing gradient).

The Speed of an Object can be Found From a Distance-Time Graph

1) The gradient of a distance-time graph at any point is equal to the speed of the object at that time.
2) If the graph is a straight line, the gradient at any point along the line is equal to $\frac{\text{change in the vertical}}{\text{change in the horizontal}}$.

> Example: In the graph above, the speed at any time between 0 s and 2 s is:
>
> $$\text{Speed} = \text{gradient} = \frac{\text{change in the vertical}}{\text{change in the horizontal}} = \frac{20}{2} = 10 \text{ m/s}$$

3) If the graph is curved, to find the speed at a certain time you need to draw a tangent to the curve at that point, and then find the gradient of the tangent.

A tangent is a line that is parallel to the curve at that point.

4) You can also calculate the average speed of an object when it has non-uniform motion (i.e. it's accelerating) by dividing the total distance travelled by the time it takes to travel that distance.

> Example: The graph shows the distance-time graph for a bike accelerating for 30 seconds and then travelling at a steady speed for 5 s. The speed of the bike at 25 s can be found by drawing a tangent to the curve (red line) at 25 s and then finding the gradient of the tangent:
>
> $$\text{gradient} = \frac{\text{change in the vertical}}{\text{change in the horizontal}} = \frac{170}{20} = 8.5 \text{ m/s}$$
>
> The average speed of the bike between 0 s and 30 s can also be calculated as:
>
> $$\text{average speed} = \frac{\text{total distance travelled}}{\text{time taken to travel}} = \frac{150}{30} = 5 \text{ m/s}$$
>
> Distance / m: 250, 200, 150, 100, 50, 0
> Time / s: 5, 10, 15, 20, 25, 30, 35

Tangent — a man who's just come back from holiday...

For practice, try sketching *d-t* graphs for different scenarios. Like cycling up a hill or running from a bear.

Q1 Sketch a distance-time graph for an object that initially accelerates, then travels at a constant speed, then decelerates to a stop. [2 marks]

Velocity-Time Graphs

Huzzah, more graphs. And they're velocity-time graphs too, you lucky thing. Keep an eye out for those negative gradients — they're not too tricky really, it just means the object has a negative acceleration.

Velocity-Time (v-t) Graphs can Be Used to Find Acceleration

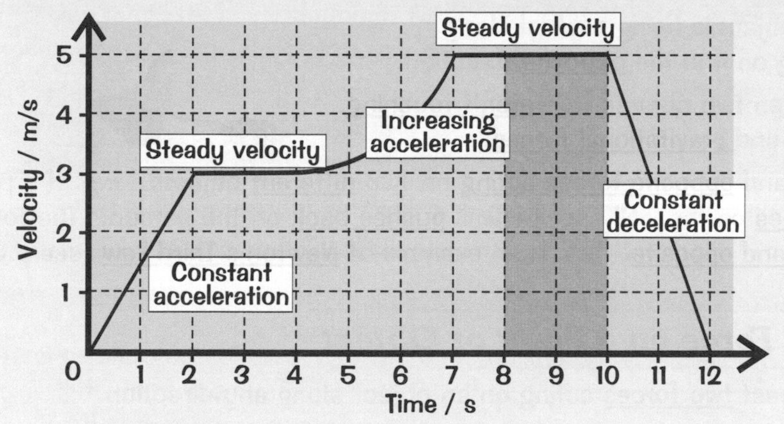

- Gradient = acceleration.
- Flat sections represent steady velocity.
- The steeper the graph, the greater the acceleration or deceleration.
- Uphill sections (/) are acceleration.
- Downhill sections (\) are deceleration.
- A curve means changing acceleration.
- The area under any section of the graph (or all of it) is equal to the distance travelled in that time interval.

You can find the acceleration, velocity and distance travelled from a velocity-time graph:

1) The acceleration represented between 0 s and 2 s on the graph is:

$$\text{Acceleration} = \text{gradient} = \frac{\text{change in the vertical}}{\text{change in the horizontal}} = \frac{3}{2} = 1.5 \text{ m/s}^2$$

2) The velocity at any time is simply found by reading the value off the velocity axis.
3) The distance travelled in any time interval is equal to the area under the graph. For example, the distance travelled between $t = 8$ s and $t = 10$ s is equal to the shaded area, which is 10 m (5 m/s × 2 s).

To find the acceleration at any point on a curved velocity-time graph, you draw a tangent to the curve and then find the gradient of the tangent (see page 24).

You can Use the Counting Squares Method To Find the Area Under the Graph

1) If an object has an increasing or decreasing acceleration (or deceleration), the graph is curved. You can estimate the distance travelled from the area under the graph by counting squares.
2) First you need to find out how much distance one square of the graph paper represents. To do this, multiply the width of square (in seconds) by the height of one square (in metres per second).
3) Then you just multiply this by the number of squares under the graph. If there are squares that are partly under the graph, you can add them together to make whole squares (see below).

The graph below is a velocity-time graph. You can estimate the distance travelled in the first 10 s by counting the number of squares under the graph (shown by the shaded area).

Total number of shaded squares = 32

Distance represented by one square
= width of square × height of square
= 1 s × 0.2 m/s = 0.2 m

So total distance travelled in 10 s
= 32 × 0.2 = 6.4 m

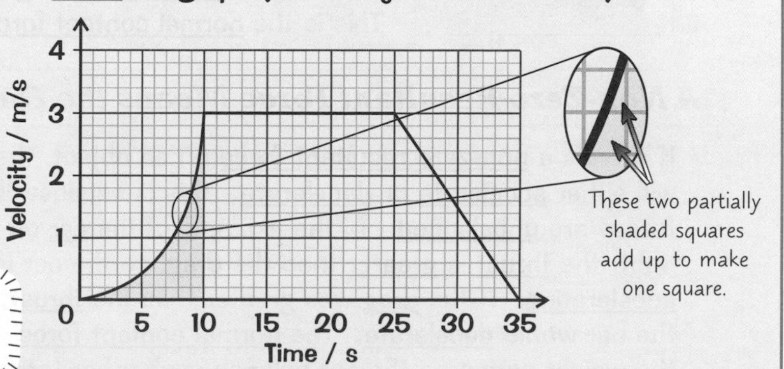

As you go through and count the squares, it helps to put a dot in the square once it's been counted. That way you don't lose track of what's been counted and what hasn't.

Anyone up for a game of squares?

Remember — the acceleration of an object on a velocity-time graph is the gradient of the curve at that time. And the total distance travelled within a time interval is the area under the graph for that time interval.

Q1 Sketch a velocity-time graph for a car that initially travels at a steady speed and then decelerates constantly to a stop. It is then stationary for a short time before accelerating with increasing acceleration. [3 marks]

Forces and Free Body Force Diagrams

Forces are everywhere, so it only makes sense that you should learn about them. Read on...

Forces can be Contact or Non-Contact

1) To exert a contact force, two objects must be touching, for example pushing or pulling an object.
2) Friction is a contact force — as an object is being pushed along a surface, there will be friction acting on it in the opposite direction.
3) Non-contact forces are forces between two objects that aren't touching. For example, electrostatic, magnetic and gravitational forces.
4) An interaction pair is a pair of equal and opposite forces acting on two different objects. E.g. if a person leans against a wall, the person pushes on the wall and the wall pushes back on the person. The forces on the person and the wall are equal and opposite. This is an example of Newton's Third Law (see p.30).

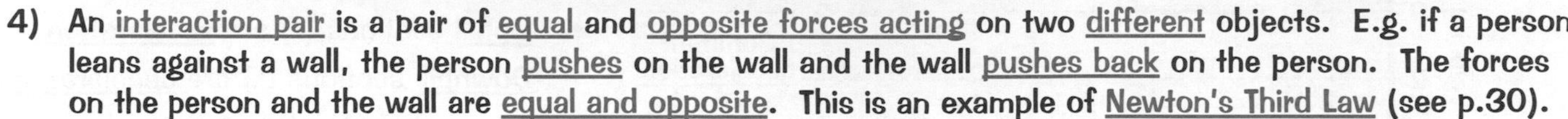

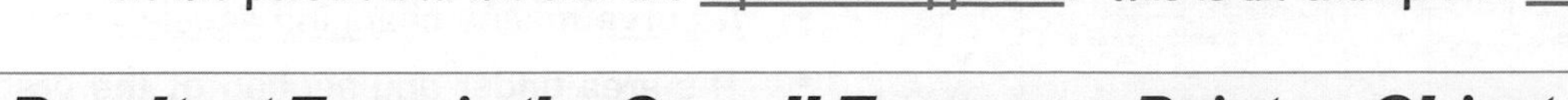

Resultant Force is the Overall Force on a Point or Object

1) In most real situations there are at least two forces acting on an object along any direction.
2) The overall effect of the forces decide whether the object accelerates, decelerates or has a steady speed.
3) If a number of forces act at a single point, you can replace them with a single force called the resultant force. The resultant force has the same effect on the motion as the original forces acting altogether.
4) If the forces all act along the same line (they're all parallel and act in the same or the opposite direction), the resultant force is found by just adding or subtracting them.

The diagram on the right shows a ball falling. Weight and air resistance are acting along the same line, so the resultant force acting on the ball = weight – air resistance = 8 – 3 = 5 N in the downwards direction.

Air resistance = 3 N

Weight = 8 N

Free Body Force Diagrams Show All the Forces Acting on a Body

Forces are vectors (see page 21) so they have a size and direction. A free body force diagram is a diagram of an object with arrows drawn to show the direction and size of the forces acting on the object.

A Resultant Force of Zero Means all the Forces are Balanced

An object with a zero resultant force will either be stationary or moving at a steady speed.

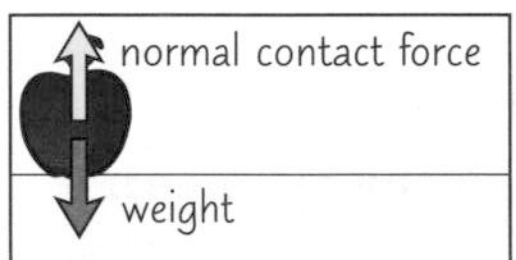

This diagram shows an apple sat on a table. The force due to gravity (its weight, see p.33) is acting downwards. The apple isn't moving because there's another force of the same size acting in the opposite direction to balance the weight. This is the normal contact force from the table top pushing up on the apple.

A Non-Zero Resultant Force Means the Forces are Unbalanced

If there's a non-zero resultant force on an object, then it will either accelerate or decelerate. This is because the forces are unbalanced. In the example of the car on the right, the thrust is greater than the drag, so the car is accelerating. If the drag was greater than the thrust, the car would decelerate. The normal contact force and the weight acting on the car balance each other (otherwise the car would go flying off or sink through the road).

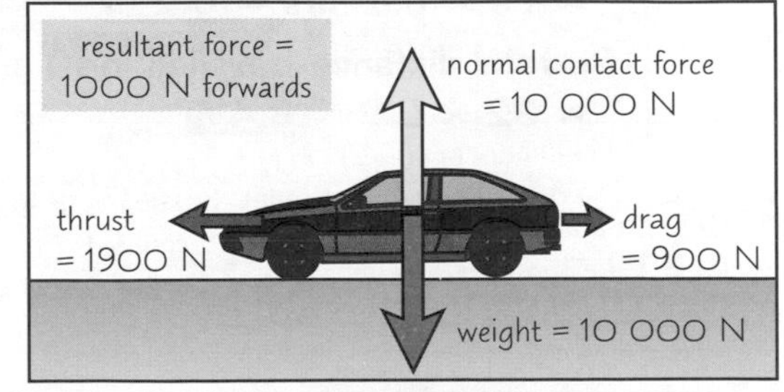

Drag yourself away from the TV and force yourself to revise...

The resultant force acting on an object will decide the motion of the object. If the resultant force is zero, the object is stationary or moving at a steady speed. If the resultant force is non-zero, it's accelerating. Easy.

Q1 Draw a free body diagram for: a) a book on a table b) an accelerating falling ball. [4 marks]

Scale Diagrams and Forces

You saw on the page 26 how to find the resultant force of two forces acting along the same line. Now here's what to do if they're at an angle to each other.

Use Scale Drawings to Find the Resultant Force

Resultant force can also be called the net force.

You can find the size and direction of the resultant force on an object using scale drawings. Draw the forces acting on the object to scale and 'tip-to-tail', then measure the length of the resultant force on the diagram. This is the line drawn from the start of the first force to the end of the last force.

EXAMPLE:

A man is on an electric bicycle that pushes him with a force of 4 N north. However, the wind is pushing him with a force of 3 N east. Find the magnitude of the resultant force.

1) Start by drawing a scale diagram to illustrate the forces acting on the man. Make sure you choose a sensible scale (e.g. 1 cm = 1 N).
2) Then just measure the missing side with a ruler.

If you were asked to find direction as well, you would just measure the angle θ with a protractor.

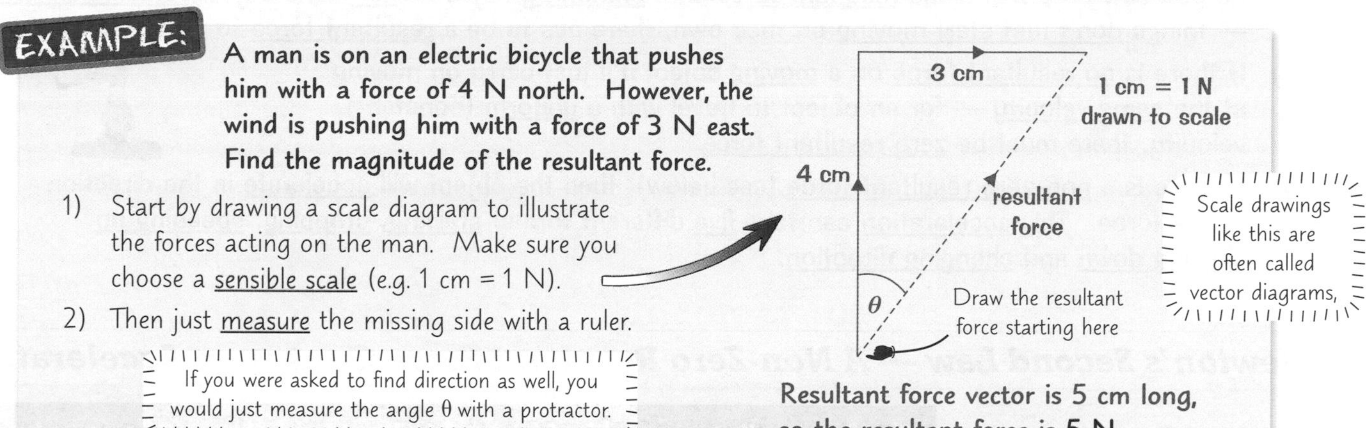

Scale drawings like this are often called vector diagrams.

Resultant force vector is 5 cm long, so the resultant force is 5 N.

An Object is in Equilibrium if all the Forces on it are Balanced

When an object has a zero resultant force, it is in equilibrium. All the forces on the object cancel each other out. You can use scale drawings to demonstrate this.

For example, look at the scale drawing of the three forces that are acting on the object on the right. If you draw all the forces tip-to-tail, you can see that they create a loop, so the resultant force is zero. The object is in equilibrium.

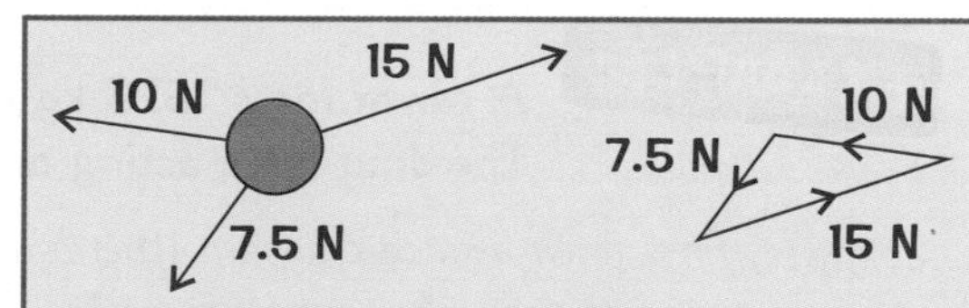

You May Need to Resolve Vectors

1) When you resolve a force, you split the force into two forces that are at right angles to each other. The two forces have the same overall effect as the original force.
2) You can resolve a force using a scale drawing — just draw two lines so that the original force becomes the longest side of a right-angled triangle (see example below).
3) Resolving forces is useful when you need to see the effect of a force along a particular line.

A toy train is being pulled along a track by a rope at an angle to the track. The scale drawing shows this force and the direction the train is moving.

The force can be resolved into a force acting horizontally and a force acting vertically. You just need to draw a right-angled triangle as shown on the scale drawing. The size of the vertical force is found by measuring the length of the vertical part of the triangle. Vertical length = 1.5 cm = 1.5 N.

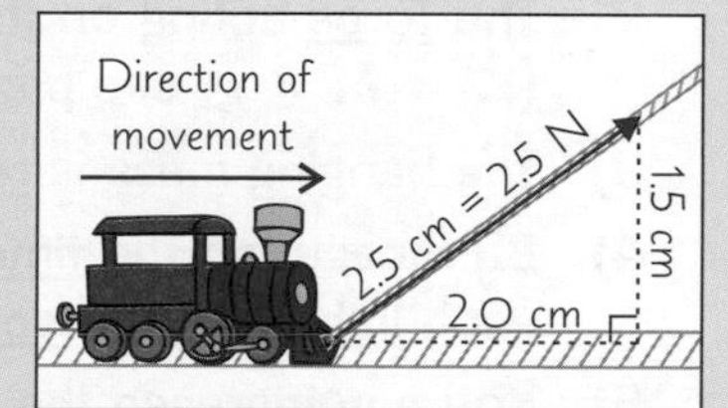

The size of the force acting horizontally can also be found by measuring the length of the horizontal part of the triangle. Horizontal length = 2 cm = 2 N. So 2 N is the size of the force that's pulling the train in its direction of movement.

Force yourself to revise this...oh wait, I've already done that pun...

If you're making a scale drawing, choose a sensible scale. It'll be no good if you need A0 paper to draw a triangle.

Q1 A boat is being pushed by its propeller with a driving force of 600 N south, and by the wind with a force of 450 N east. Use a scale drawing to find the size of the resultant force acting on the boat. [2 marks]

Newton's First and Second Laws of Motion

Clever chap Isaac Newton — he came up with three handy laws about motion. This page covers the first two.

Newton's First Law — No Resultant Force Means No Change in Velocity

1) Newton's First Law says that: **An object will remain stationary or at a constant velocity unless acted upon by an external force.**
2) As you saw on p.26, if the resultant force on a stationary object is zero, the object remains stationary — things don't just start moving on their own, there has to be a resultant force to get them started.
3) If there is no resultant force on a moving object it'll just carry on moving at the same velocity — for an object to travel with a uniform (constant) velocity, there must be zero resultant force.

4) If there is a non-zero resultant force (see below), then the object will accelerate in the direction of the force. This acceleration can take five different forms: starting, stopping, speeding up, slowing down and changing direction.

Newton's Second Law — A Non-Zero Resultant Force Causes an Acceleration

Newton's Second Law says: **The force acting on an object is equal to its rate of change of momentum.**

See page 31 for more on momentum.

But don't panic, this is roughly translated to — any resultant force will produce an acceleration, and the formula for it is:

force (N) = mass (kg) × acceleration (m/s^2) or $F = ma$

Remember that the F is always the resultant force — that's pretty important.

EXAMPLE:

A car of mass 1625 kg has an engine which provides a driving force of 5650 N. The drag force acting on the car is 450 N. Find its acceleration.

1) First draw a force diagram (there's no need to show the vertical forces).

2) Work out the resultant force. Resultant force = 5650 – 450 = 5200 N
3) Rearrange $F = ma$ to calculate the acceleration. $a = F \div m = 5200 \div 1625 = 3.2\ m/s^2$

A Simple Experiment Demonstrates Newton's Second Law

1) The acceleration of a trolley on an air track can be used to investigate Newton's Second Law.
2) The force acting on the trolley is equal to the weight ($W = M \times g$, see page 33) of the hanging mass.
3) The hanging mass is released, pulling the trolley along the track.
4) By measuring the time and speed at which the trolley passes each light gate, its acceleration can be calculated.
5) You can increase the force acting on the trolley by moving one of the masses from the trolley to the hanging mass, and repeating the experiment.
6) If you plot your results on a graph of force against acceleration, you should get a straight line, showing that $F = ma$.

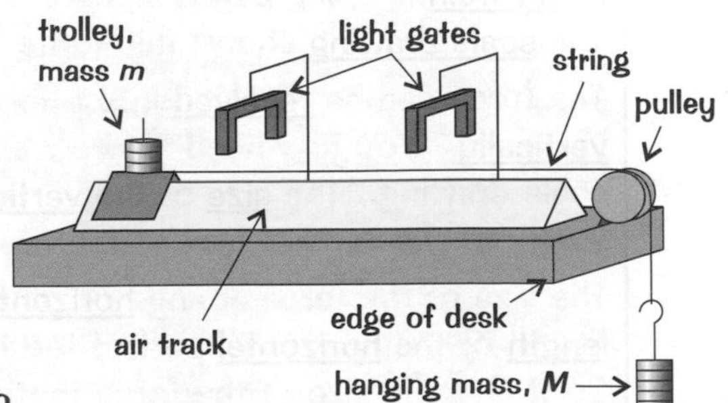

Air tracks and light gates — sounds like a band from the 80s...

Newton's First Law means that an object at a steady speed doesn't need a net force to keep moving. Remember that.

Q1 Calculate the resultant force acting on a 26 000 kg lorry with an acceleration of 1.5 m/s^2. [1 mark]

Friction and Terminal Velocity

Imagine a world without friction — you'd be sliding around all over the place. Weeeeeeeee.... Ouch.

Friction Will Slow Things Down

1) When an object is moving (or trying to move), friction acts in the direction that opposes movement.
2) Friction makes things slow down and stop, so you need a driving force to keep moving (e.g. thrust).
3) If the driving force is equal to the friction force, the object will move at a steady speed.
   If the driving force is greater than (>) the friction force, the object will accelerate.
   If the driving force is less than (<) the friction force, the object will decelerate.
4) Friction occurs between two surfaces in contact (e.g. tyres and the road), and drag occurs when an object passes through a fluid (e.g. a boat through water). Air resistance is a type of drag.

Moving Vehicles and Falling Objects Can Reach a Terminal Velocity

When objects first set off they have more driving force than friction force (resistance), so they accelerate. But the resistance is directly proportional to the velocity of the object — resistance $\propto$ velocity. So as the velocity increases, the resistance increases as well. This gradually reduces the acceleration until the friction force is equal to the driving force so it doesn't accelerate any more. The forces are balanced (there's no resultant force). The object will have reached its maximum velocity or terminal velocity.

1) A skydiver accelerates as weight due to gravity > air resistance.
2) But air resistance increases as velocity increases until weight = air resistance, and they reach terminal velocity.
3) The parachute opens and weight < air resistance, so they decelerate.
4) As velocity decreases, the air resistance also decreases until weight = air resistance — they reach a new terminal velocity (see below).

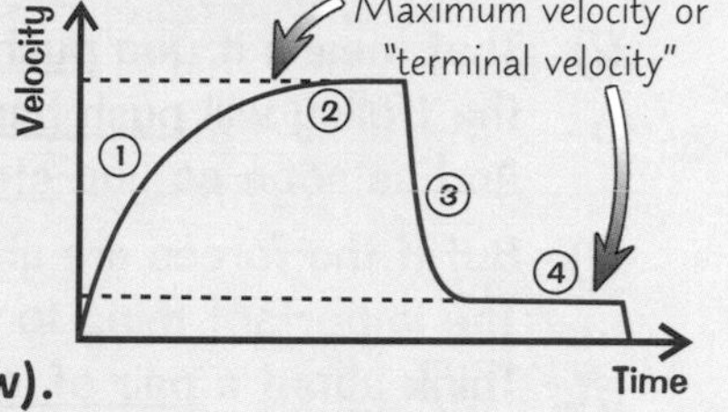

Terminal Velocity of Moving Objects Depends on Their Drag

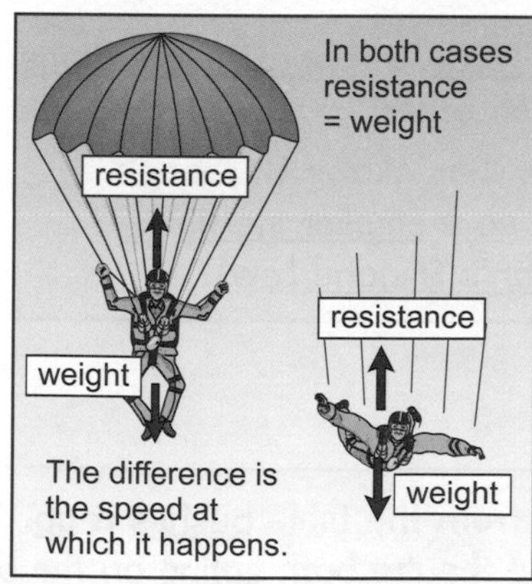

1) The greater the drag (or air resistance or friction), the lower the terminal velocity of an object, and drag depends on the object's shape and area.
2) For example, the driving force for a skydiver is his weight due to gravity and the drag (air resistance) depends on the skydiver's shape and area.
3) Without his parachute open, a skydiver's area is quite small. His terminal velocity is about 120 mph.
4) With the parachute open, there's more air resistance (at any given speed) because the skydiver's area is larger, but the driving force (his weight) is the same. This means his terminal velocity is much smaller (~15 mph), which is a safe speed to hit the ground at.
5) Decreasing drag makes things faster — streamlined cars have less drag.

To find the terminal velocity of a toy parachute — drop it from a sensible height in front of an object with regular vertical markings at set heights (e.g. 0.5 m markings on a wall), and measure the time at which it falls past each marking. Use the differences between times to find its average velocity between each pair of markings and plot your results on a graph of velocity against time. It should have a curved shape, like the graph above between points 1 and 2.

To measure the times accurately, you could film the parachute falling, then replay the video at a slower speed, and read the time the parachute passes each marking from the video.

Air resistance — it can be a real drag...

Make sure you can explain how an object reaches its terminal velocity in terms of forces. Then go skydiving.

Q1 A boat sets off with a constant thrust moving it forwards. After some time the boat reaches a terminal velocity. Explain the boat's motion in terms of the forces acting on the boat. [4 marks]

Inertia and Newton's Third Law of Motion

Another law eh? Isaac probably wasn't thinking about anyone having to revise them back in the 17th century.

Inertia Explains Why it's Harder to Move a Hammer Than a Feather

1) Inertia is the measure of how difficult it is to change an object's velocity.
2) It is dependent on the mass of the object — the larger the mass, the larger the inertia, and the harder it is to change the velocity of the object.
3) Imagine that a bowling ball and a golf ball roll towards you with the same velocity. It would require a larger force to stop the bowling ball than the golf ball in the same time. This is because the bowling ball has a larger mass and a larger inertia.
4) By rearranging the equation for Newton's Second Law (see page 28) you can show that mass is defined as the ratio of the force over acceleration: ➔ $\text{mass} = \frac{\text{force}}{\text{acceleration}}$
   So a larger mass requires a larger force to accelerate by a certain amount — i.e. it has a larger inertia.

Newton's Third Law — Reaction Forces are Equal and Opposite

1) Newton's Third Law says that:

   When two objects interact, the forces they exert on each other are equal and opposite.

2) That means if you push something, say a shopping trolley, the trolley will push back against you, just as hard. And as soon as you stop pushing, so does the trolley. Kinda clever really.

3) But if the forces are always equal, how does anything ever go anywhere? The important thing to remember is that the two forces are acting on different objects. Think about a pair of ice skaters:

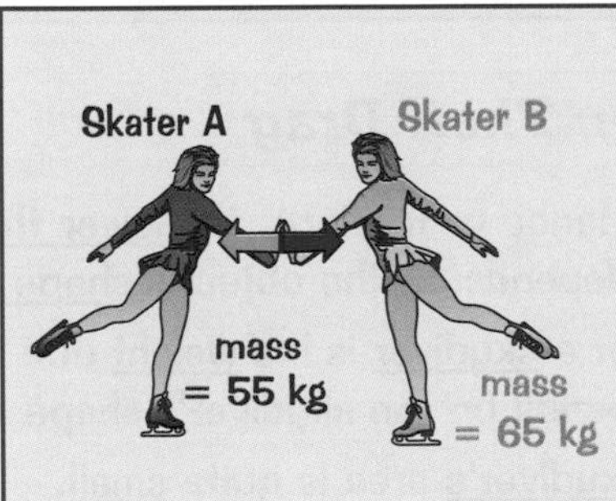

- When skater A pushes on skater B (the 'action' force), she feels an equal and opposite force from skater B's hand (the 'reaction' force).
- Both skaters feel the same sized force, in opposite directions, and so accelerate away from each other.
- Skater A will be accelerated more than skater B, though, because she has a smaller mass, so a smaller inertia — $a = F/m$ (from rearranging Newton's Second Law).

4) It's a bit more complicated for an object in equilibrium (see page 27). Imagine a book sat on a table:

The weight of the book pulls it down, and the normal reaction force from the table pushes it up. This is NOT Newton's Third Law. These forces are different types and they're both acting on the book.

The pairs of forces due to Newton's Third Law in this case are:

- The weight of book is pulled down by gravity from Earth (W_B) and the book also pulls back up on the Earth (W_E).
- The normal contact force from the table pushing up on the book (R_B) and the normal contact force from the book pushing down on the table (R_T).

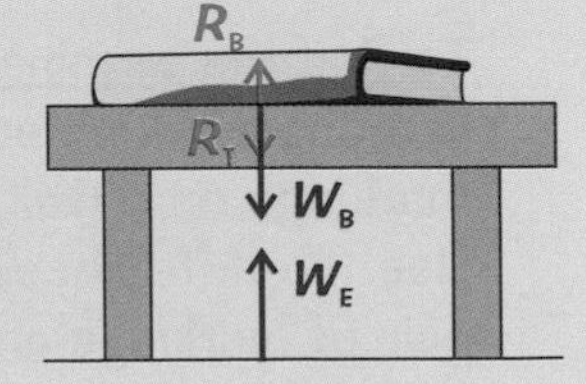

Newton's fourth law — revision must be done with cake...

Mmm... cake. A couple of tricky concepts here — inertia and Newton's Third Law. You can't say I don't spoil you.

Q1 A full shopping trolley and an empty one are moving at the same speed. Explain why it is easier to stop the empty trolley than the full trolley over the same amount of time. [1 mark]

Momentum

All moving objects have momentum. Like this book when I throw it across the room.

Momentum = Mass × Velocity

The greater the mass of an object and the greater its velocity, the more momentum the object has. They're linked by this equation:

momentum (kg m/s) = mass (kg) × velocity (m/s) or: $p = m \times v$

Momentum is a vector — it has size and direction.

EXAMPLE: A 65 kg kangaroo is moving in a straight line at 12 m/s. Calculate its momentum.

Momentum = mass × velocity = 65 × 12 = 780 kg m/s

Forces Cause Changes in Momentum

1) When a resultant force acts on an object for a certain amount of time, it causes a change in momentum. Newton's 2nd Law can explain this:
   - A resultant force on an object causes it to accelerate: force = mass × acceleration.
   - Acceleration is just change in velocity over time, so: force = $\frac{\text{mass} \times \text{change in velocity}}{\text{time}}$.
     This means a force applied to an object over any time interval will change the object's velocity.
   - Mass × change in velocity is equal to change in momentum, so you end up with the equation:

$$\text{force (N)} = \frac{\text{change in momentum (kg m/s)}}{\text{time (s)}} \quad \text{or} \quad F = \frac{p}{t}$$

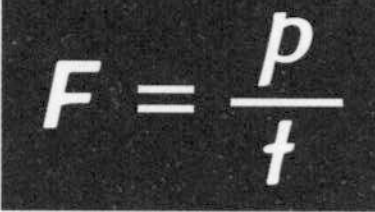

EXAMPLE: A rock of mass 1.0 kg is travelling through space at 15 m/s. A comet hits the rock, applying a force of 2500 N for 0.60 seconds. Calculate:
a) the rock's initial momentum
b) the change in the rock's momentum resulting from the impact.

a) Substitute into the equation for momentum: momentum = mass × velocity = 1.0 × 15 = 15 kg m/s

b) Use the equation for force and momentum to find what happens when the comet hits the rock. force = $\frac{\text{change in momentum}}{\text{time}}$ so:
change of momentum = force × time = 2500 × 0.60 = 1500 kg m/s

2) The faster a given change in momentum happens, the bigger the force causing the change must be (i.e. if t gets smaller in the equation above, F gets bigger).
3) So if someone's momentum changes very quickly, like in a car crash, the forces on the body will be very large, and more likely to cause injury. There's more about this on page 89.
4) You can also think of changes in momentum in collisions in terms of acceleration — a change in momentum normally involves a change in velocity, which is what acceleration is.
5) As you know, force = mass × acceleration, so the larger the acceleration (or deceleration), the larger the force needed to produce it.

Learn this stuff — it'll only take a moment... um...

Momentum is a pretty fundamental bit of physics — learn it well. Know the equations and know how to use them.

Q1 Calculate the momentum of a 220 000 kg aeroplane that is travelling at 250 m/s. [1 mark]

Q2 Calculate the force a tennis racket needs to apply to a 58 g tennis ball to accelerate it from rest to 34 m/s in 11.6 ms. [4 marks]

Conservation of Momentum

Momentum is always conserved. Easy peasy. Go squeeze some lemons.

Momentum Before = Momentum After

Make sure you learn the law of conservation of momentum:

> In a collision when no other external forces act, momentum is conserved — i.e. the total momentum after the collision is the same as it was before it.

1) Imagine a red snooker ball rolls towards a stationary yellow snooker ball with the same mass. If after the collision, the red ball stops and the yellow ball moves off, then the yellow ball will have the same velocity as the original velocity of the red ball (assuming there's no friction).
2) Conservation of momentum also explains rocket propulsion:

> When a rocket is stationary, it has zero velocity and so zero momentum. If the rocket's engines then fire, it'll chuck a load of exhaust gases out backwards (negative momentum). Since momentum is always conserved, this means the rocket has to move forwards (positive momentum), in order to keep the combined momentum of the gases and the rocket at zero.

3) You can use the idea of conservation of momentum to find the velocity of an object after a collision:

EXAMPLE: Ball A (mass = 0.08 kg) is moving at 9 m/s towards ball B (mass = 0.36 kg). Ball B is moving at 3 m/s in the same direction as ball A. The two balls collide. After the collision, ball A is stationary and ball B moves away. Calculate the velocity of ball B after the collision.

Before

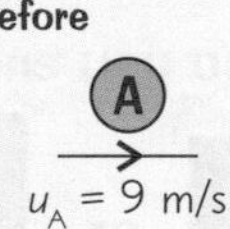

$u_A = 9$ m/s

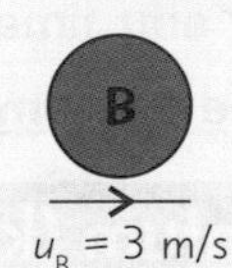

$u_B = 3$ m/s

After

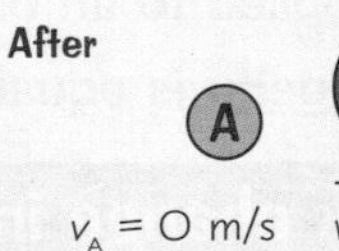

$v_A = 0$ m/s $v_B = ?$ m/s

1) First, calculate the total momentum before the collision.
   total momentum before = ball A's momentum + ball B's momentum $= (m_A \times u_A) + (m_B \times u_B)$ $= (0.08 \times 9) + (0.36 \times 3) = 1.8$ kg m/s
2) The total momentum before the collision is equal to the total momentum after the collision.
   total momentum after = total momentum before = 1.8 kg m/s
3) Write out the equation for the total momentum after the collision, and substitute in the values you know.
   total momentum after $= (m_A \times v_A) + (m_B \times v_B)$
   $1.8 = (0.08 \times 0) + (0.36 \times v_B)$
   $1.8 = 0 + (0.36 \times v_B)$
4) Rearrange and solve the equation.
   $v_B = 1.8 \div 0.36 = 5$ m/s

4) If two objects collide and join together, then the total momentum of both objects before the collision = momentum of the combined object after the collision. So in the example above, if the balls had joined together and moved away at a steady speed, you would have ended up with: total momentum after $= (m_A + m_B) \times v$.

Collisions can be Elastic or Inelastic

Momentum is conserved in both elastic and inelastic collisions.

1) An elastic collision is where the total energy in the kinetic energy stores of the objects colliding is the same before and after the collision — i.e. the energy in the kinetic energy stores is conserved.
2) An inelastic collision is where some of the energy in the kinetic energy stores is transferred to other stores. For example, energy can be transferred away by heating or by sound.

Homework this week — build a rocket to investigate momentum...

...*sigh* if only. It's probably to practise questions instead. Won't get you to the moon, but it'll help you in exams.

Q1 A 2.0 kg trolley travelling at 1.5 m/s collides with a 3.0 kg stationary trolley. They then move off together at a constant speed. Find the final velocity of the two trolleys. [3 marks]

Mass, Weight and Gravity

Gravity attracts everything with mass, but you only notice it when one of the masses is huge, like a planet.

Gravity is the Force of Attraction Between All Masses

1) Everything that is made of matter has a gravitational field around it. Everything. And a gravitational field attracts other masses.
2) The more massive the object is, the greater the strength of its gravitational field.
3) Earth has got a gravitational field that pulls us and everything else towards it.
4) The Moon is big enough that its gravitational field creates the tides on Earth.
5) Even you have a gravitational field, but it's so teeny tiny that it doesn't have any noticeable effect.

The Force due to Gravity is Called Weight

1) A planet's gravitational field makes all things accelerate towards the planet's surface, all with the same acceleration, g.
2) g is called the gravitational field strength. It's also known as the acceleration due to gravity (i.e. it's the acceleration an object will have when falling to Earth).
3) It has a value of about 10 N/kg (or 10 m/s^2) near the Earth's surface. This means that anything that falls or is dropped on Earth (i.e. an object in free fall) will have an acceleration of 10 m/s^2. The value of g is different on other planets, so an object in free fall on another planet will have a different acceleration.

4) The force acting on an object when it's in a gravitational field is called the weight, or gravity force. It's measured in newtons (N). You can calculate this force using the equation:

gravity force (N) = mass (kg) × gravitational field strength, g (N/kg)

5) Or in symbols, where W is the weight in N (i.e. the gravity force) and m is the mass in kg:

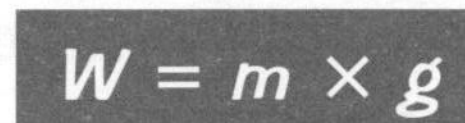

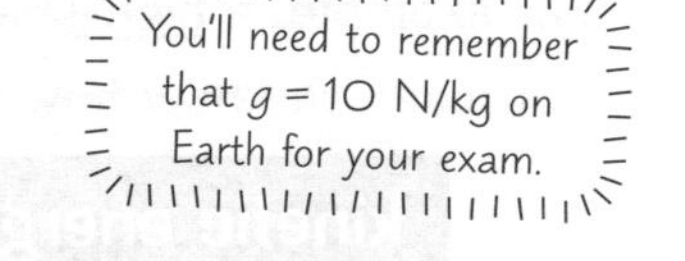

6) Remember, mass is not the same as weight. Mass is just the amount of 'stuff' in an object. For any given object this will have the same value anywhere in the Universe.
7) The more massive an object is, the larger its weight. Similarly, the stronger the gravitational field an object is in (e.g. the more massive the planet it is on), the higher the gravitational field strength and so the larger the object's weight.

EXAMPLE:

What is the weight, in newtons, of a 2.0 kg chicken, both on Earth (g = 10 N/kg) and on the Moon (g = 1.6 N/kg).

Weight is the same as gravity force.

1) Calculate the weight on Earth using the equation given above. weight = $m \times g$ = 2.0 × 10 = 20 N
2) Calculate the weight on the moon using its value of g. weight = $m \times g$ = 2.0 × 1.6 = 3.2 N

The chicken has a weight of 34 N on a mystery planet. What is the gravitational field strength of the planet?

1) Rearrange the equation for g. $g = w \div m$
2) Substitute the values in. = 34 ÷ 2.0 = 17 N/kg

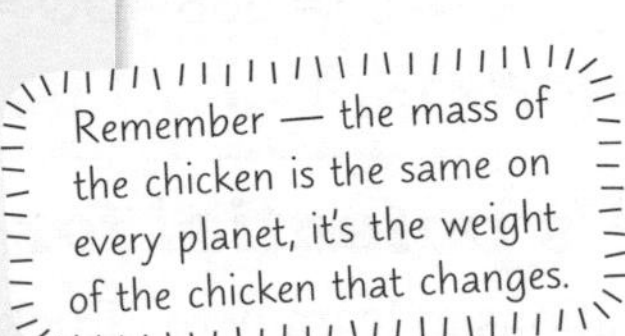

Remember — the mass of the chicken is the same on every planet, it's the weight of the chicken that changes.

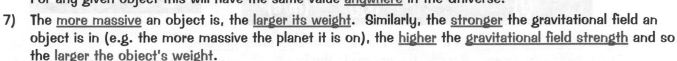

I'm always attracted to a shop with a sale on...

A common mistake is thinking that mass and weight are the same thing. They are not. Learn the difference.

Q1 Calculate the weight of a 67 kg mass on Earth. [1 mark]

Q2 A person has a weight of 820 N on Earth. Calculate their mass. [2 marks]

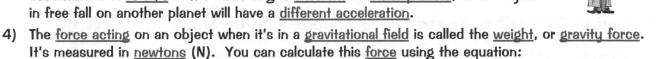

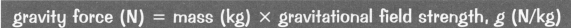

Mechanical Energy Stores

Take a sneaky peek at page 82 for more about energy stores. This page covers two types of energy stores and how to calculate how much energy is in them.

An Object at a Height has Energy in its Gravitational Potential Energy Store

1) When an object is at any height above the Earth's surface, it will have energy in its gravitational potential energy store.
2) You can calculate the amount of energy in the gravitational potential energy store using the equation:

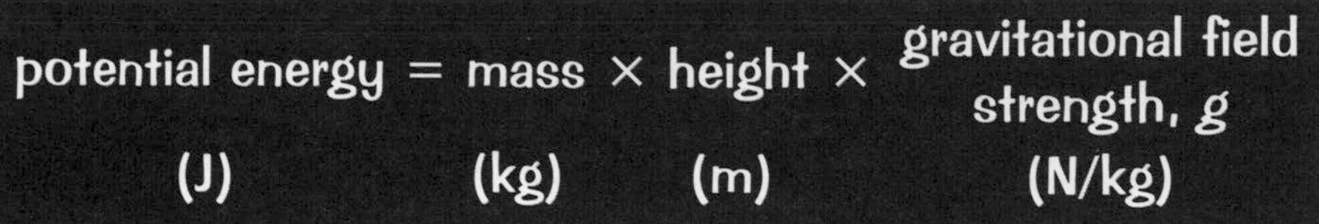

or $PE = m \times h \times g$

Calculate the energy in the gravitational potential energy store of a 1.2 kg book when it is 4.25 m above the ground.

potential energy = mass × height × g
= 1.2 × 4.25 × 10
= 51 J

A Moving Object has Energy in its Kinetic Energy Store

1) When an object is moving, it has energy in its kinetic energy store.
2) This energy depends on both the object's mass and velocity.
3) The greater its mass and the faster it's going, the more energy it has in its kinetic energy store.
4) For example, a high-speed train will have a lot more energy in its kinetic energy store than you running.
5) You need to know how to use the formula:

kinetic energy = 0.5 × mass × $(\text{speed})^2$
(J) (kg) $(\text{m/s})^2$

or $KE = \frac{1}{2} \times m \times v^2$

6) If you double the mass, the energy in the kinetic energy store doubles. If you double the speed, though, the energy in the kinetic energy store quadruples (increases by a factor of 4) — it's because of the '$(\text{speed})^2$' in the formula.

A car of mass 1450 kg is travelling at 28 m/s. Calculate the energy in its kinetic energy store, giving your answer to 2 s.f.

kinetic energy = 0.5 × mass × $(\text{speed})^2$
= 0.5 × 1450 × 28^2
= 568 400 = 570 000 J (to 2 s.f.)

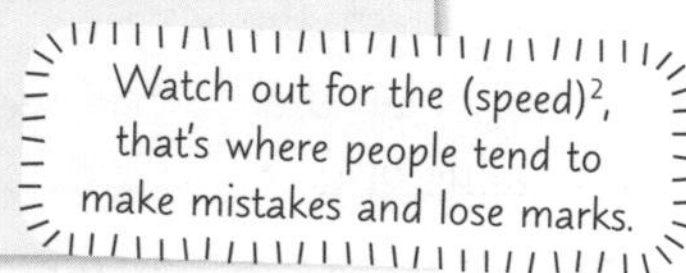

Watch out for the (speed)², that's where people tend to make mistakes and lose marks.

There's potential for a joke here somewhere...

More equations to learn here. Look on the bright side, at least you don't have to learn something like $-\frac{\hbar^2}{2m}\frac{d^2\Psi(x)}{dx^2} + U(x)\Psi(x) = E\Psi(x)$. And we all know what that equation is — altogether now, it's... erm...*

Q1 Calculate the energy in the gravitational potential energy store of a 0.80 kg ball at a height of 1.5 m above the Earth's surface. [1 mark]

Q2 An otter is swimming with a speed of 2.0 m/s. It has a mass of 4.9 kg. Calculate the energy in the otter's kinetic energy store. [1 mark]

*don't panic, you really don't need to know what this is.

Work Done and Power

Whenever I think of power, I have to stop myself from plotting world domination whilst stroking a cat.

Work is Done When a Force Moves an Object

When a FORCE makes an object MOVE, ENERGY IS TRANSFERRED and WORK IS DONE.

1) Whenever something moves, something else is providing some sort of effort to move it.
2) The thing putting the effort in needs a supply of energy (from fuel or food or electricity etc.).
3) It then does work by moving the object, and transfers the energy it receives (from fuel) to other stores.
4) Whether this energy is transferred usefully (e.g. by lifting a load) or wasted (e.g. dissipated by heating from friction), you still say that 'work is done'. 'Work done' and 'energy transferred' are the same.
5) The formula to calculate the amount of work done is:

work done (J) = force (N) × distance (m) or $W = F \times d$

The distance here is the distance moved along the line of action of the force (i.e. the distance moved in the direction of the force).

Work done is sometimes given in Nm, but it's the same as J, so converting between the two is easy, i.e. 5 Nm = 5 J.

Find the energy transferred when a tyre is dragged 5.0 m with a constant force of 340 N.

work done = force × distance = 340 × 5.0 = 1700 J

6) If a force is applied to move an object, the work done on the object will be equal to the energy transferred to the kinetic energy store of the object if there's no friction.
7) If an object is already moving and then a force (such as friction) slows it down, the energy transferred from the object's kinetic energy store is equal to the work done against the object's motion.
8) Work done on an object can also be transferred to other energy stores. E.g. the work done on lifting an object off the ground will be equal to the energy transferred to its gravitational potential energy store.

Power is the 'Rate of Doing Work' — i.e. How Much per Second

1) Power is a measure of how quickly work is being done. As work done = energy transferred, you can define power like this:

Power is the rate at which energy is transferred.

2) So, the power of a machine is the rate at which it transfers energy. For example, if an electric drill has a power of 700 W this means it can transfer 700 J of energy every second.
3) This is the very easy formula for power:
4) The proper unit of power is the watt (W). 1 W = 1 J of energy transferred per second (J/s).

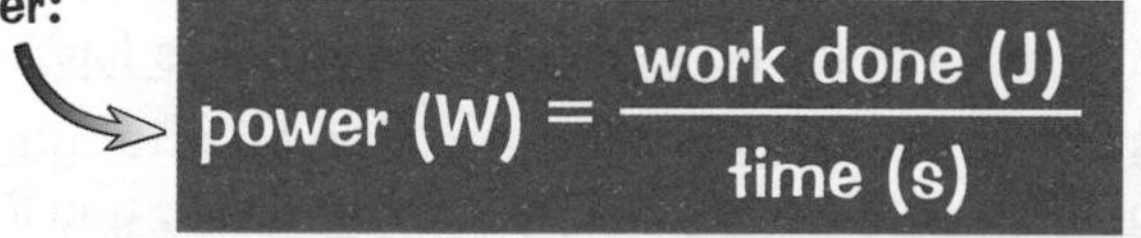

$$\text{power (W)} = \frac{\text{work done (J)}}{\text{time (s)}}$$

or

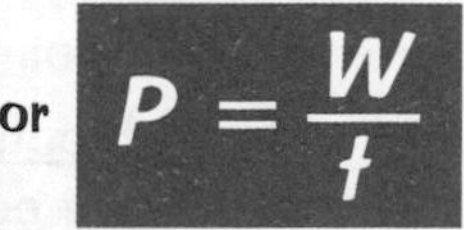

$$P = \frac{W}{t}$$

EXAMPLE:

A motor transfers 4.8 kJ of useful energy in 2 minutes. Find its power output.

1) Convert the values to the correct units first. 4.8 kJ = 4800 J and 2 mins = 120 s
2) Substitute the values into the power equation.

$$\text{power} = \frac{\text{work done}}{\text{time}} = \frac{4800}{120} = 40 \text{ W}$$

Watt's power? Power's watts...

Make sure you're happy with using both the equations on this page before you move on.

Q1 A book sliding across a table has 1.25 J of energy in its kinetic energy store. Friction from the table provides a constant force of 5.0 N. Calculate the distance travelled by the book before it stops. [2 marks]

Forces and Elasticity

Elasticity involves lots of physics and pinging elastic bands at people. Ok, maybe not that last one.

A Deformation can be Elastic or Plastic

1) When you apply forces to an object it can be stretched, compressed or bent — this is deformation.
2) To deform an object, you need at least two forces. Think of a spring — if you just pull one end of it, and there's no force at the other end, you'll just pull the spring along rather than stretching it.
3) If an object returns to its original shape after the forces are removed, it's an elastic deformation.
4) If the object doesn't return to its original shape when you remove the forces, it's a plastic deformation.

Extension is Directly Proportional to Force for an Elastic Deformation...

1) Imagine you have a vertical spring that is fixed at the top end and has a mass attached to the bottom.
2) When the spring and mass are in equilibrium (i.e. the spring isn't stretching any further), the downwards force on the mass (its weight) is equal in size to the upwards force that the spring exerts on the mass.
3) The extension of a spring (or any object that's deforming elastically) is directly proportional to the force that the spring exerts on the mass (up to a point, see below).
4) How much an elastically deforming object stretches for a given force depends on its spring constant. The spring constant depends on the material that you're stretching — the stiffer the material, the larger the spring constant.
5) The relationship between the extension of a spring and the force is called Hooke's law:

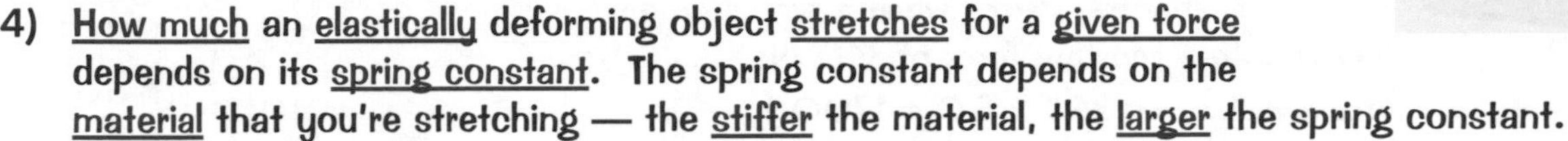

force exerted by a spring = extension × spring constant
(N) (m) (N/m)

or $F = x \times k$

This equation can be applied to any elastic object, not just springs.

...but this Stops Working when the Force is Great Enough

1) There's a limit to the amount of force you can apply to an object for the extension to keep on increasing proportionally.
2) The graph shows force against extension for an object being stretched.
3) For small forces, force and extension have a linear relationship. So the first part of the graph shows a straight-line (up to point P). This is where Hooke's law (see above) applies to the object.
4) The gradient of the straight line is equal to the spring constant of the object — the larger the spring constant, the steeper the gradient.
5) Beyond point P, the object no longer obeys Hooke's law.
6) Most objects still deform elastically for a little bit after you reach the limit of proportionality. But if you continue to increase the deforming force, you'll reach a point where its elasticity 'runs out' and it starts to deform plastically — the object won't spring back to its original shape after the stretching force has been removed.
7) The maximum force that can be applied to a material before this happens is called its elastic limit. For the graph here it'll be somewhere after point P (P is just where a material stops obeying Hooke's law).
8) For some objects, the elastic limit is so low that you'll never normally see them deforming elastically — you might see these called plastic materials. The relationship between force and extension for these materials is non-linear, so the force-extension graphs of these materials are curved.

I hope this stuff isn't stretching you too much...

The gradient of a force-extension graph for a material obeying Hooke's law is equal to its spring constant. Super.

Q1 A spring has a natural length of 0.16 m. When a force of 3.0 N is applied to the spring, its length becomes 0.20 m. Calculate the spring constant of the spring. [2 marks]

Investigating Hooke's Law

More springs here, but now you actually get to do some experiments with them. Hip hip hooray.

You can Investigate the Extension of a Spring

PRACTICAL

1) Hang your spring from a clamp stand, as shown in the diagram (without the masses, but with the hook the masses hang from), then measure the spring's length using the ruler — this is the spring's original length.
2) Weigh your masses and add them one at a time to the hook hanging from the spring, so the force on the spring increases.
3) After each mass is added, measure the new length of the spring, then calculate the extension:

   extension = new length – original length

4) Plot a graph of force (weight) against extension using your results and draw a line of best fit.

Spring
Clamp and clamp stand
Hook
Pointer (to help measure the length of the spring)
Masses
Ruler

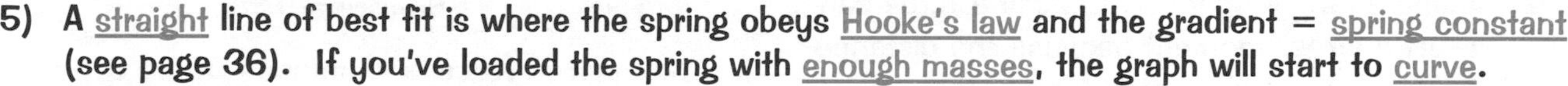

5) A straight line of best fit is where the spring obeys Hooke's law and the gradient = spring constant (see page 36). If you've loaded the spring with enough masses, the graph will start to curve.

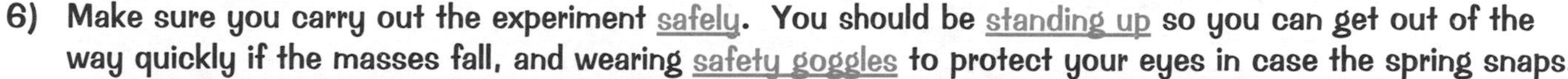

6) Make sure you carry out the experiment safely. You should be standing up so you can get out of the way quickly if the masses fall, and wearing safety goggles to protect your eyes in case the spring snaps.

When measuring the length of the spring, you should move yourself so the pointer on the hook is at eye level. Otherwise it could look like it is next to a different marking on the ruler. You also need to make sure the ruler is exactly vertical to get an accurate measurement, and that the spring isn't moving.

Work is Done to Deform an Object

1) When a force deforms an object, work is done to stretch, compress or bend the object.
2) If the deformation is elastic, this transfers energy to the object's elastic potential energy store.
3) The equation for the energy stored in an object's elastic potential energy store is:

energy transferred in stretching (J) = 0.5 × spring constant (N/m) × (extension)^2 (m)^2

4) You can also write this in symbols. It's: $E = 0.5 \times k \times x^2$
5) This also works for objects that are being compressed elastically. Just use the compression instead of extension.

The compression of an object is how much shorter it gets when it's squashed.

EXAMPLE: A spring has a spring constant of 32 N/m. Calculate the work done on the spring if it is stretched elastically from 0.40 m to 0.45 m.

Remember: work done = energy transferred.

extension = new length – original length = 0.45 – 0.40 = 0.05 m

energy transferred in stretching = 0.5 × spring constant × (extension)^2 = 0.5 × 32 × 0.05^2 = 0.04 J

6) You can also find the energy transferred when an object deforms elastically from its force-extension graph. The energy transferred is equal to the area under the graph up to its current extension.
7) You can find this area by counting squares, or if the graph is linear, by finding the area of the triangle.

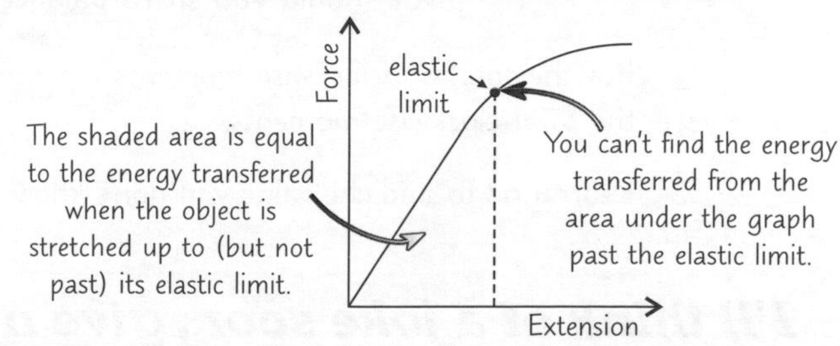

Force
elastic limit
Extension
The shaded area is equal to the energy transferred when the object is stretched up to (but not past) its elastic limit.
You can't find the energy transferred from the area under the graph past the elastic limit.

Tell your parents you need to buy a trampoline for your revision...

More energy transfers — you'd better get used to them, there's more of them coming up later on in the book.

Q1 A 1.2 m long spring (k = 54 N/m) extends elastically to 1.3 m. Calculate the work done. [2 marks]

Moments

Once you can calculate moments, you can work out if a seesaw is balanced. Useful thing, physics.

A Moment is the Turning Effect of a Force

If a force acts on an object with a pivot, it can cause the object to rotate around the pivot — like pushing open a door on a hinge. The size of the moment of the force is given by:

moment of a force (Nm) = force (N) × distance (m) or $M = F \times d$

The distance here is the normal (perpendicular) distance between the pivot and the line of action of the force (the direction of the force, see below).

1) The force on the spanner causes a turning effect or moment on the nut (which acts as a pivot). A larger force would mean a larger moment.

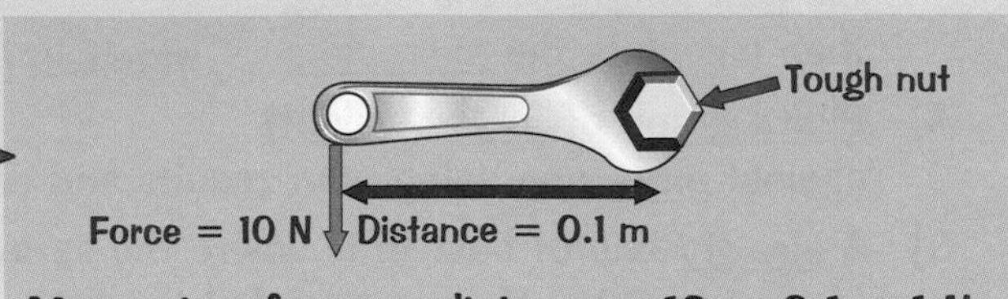

2) Using a longer spanner, the same force can exert a larger moment because the distance from the pivot is greater.

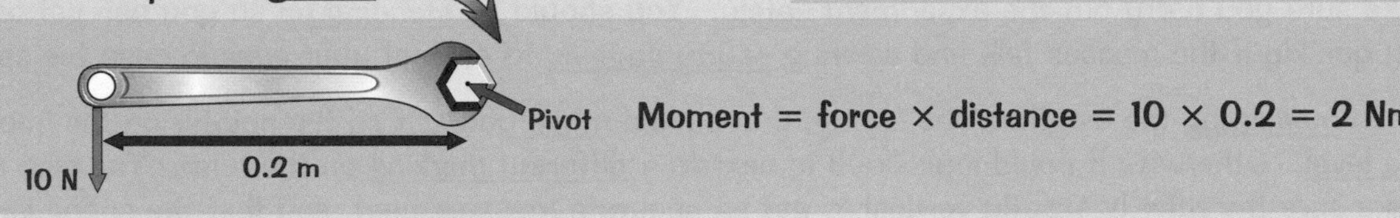

3) To get the maximum moment you need to push at right angles (perpendicular) to the pivot.
4) Pushing at any other angle means a smaller moment because the perpendicular distance between the line of action and the pivot is smaller.

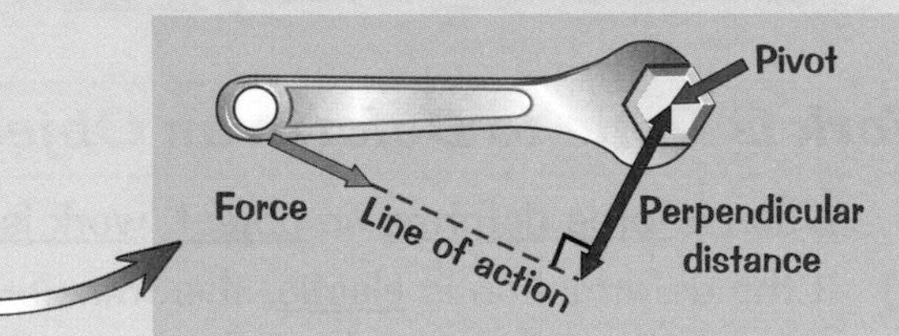

A force can either cause an object with a pivot to rotate clockwise or anticlockwise. The direction of the rotation depends on the direction of the force and which side of the pivot the force is on. Just imagine the object is in front of you and you're applying the force to work out which direction the rotation is in.

A Question of Balance — Are the Moments Equal?

If the anticlockwise moments are equal to the clockwise moments, an object won't turn. Balanced objects obey the principle of moments:

Total anticlockwise moments = Total clockwise moments

Your younger brother weighs 350 N and sits 2 m from the pivot of a seesaw. You sit on the other side of the pivot. If you weigh 700 N, how far from the pivot should you sit to balance the seesaw?

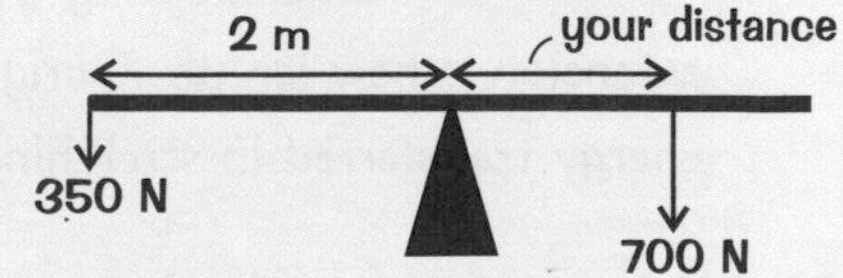

1) Put the total anticlockwise moments equal to the total clockwise moments.

anticlockwise moments = clockwise moments

350 × 2 = 700 × your distance

2) Rearrange to find the value you don't know.

your distance = (350 × 2) ÷ 700 = 1 m

I'll think of a joke soon, give me a moment...

Don't forget — the distance in the equation at the top of this page is the perpendicular distance to the line of action.

Q1 Three people are sat on a seesaw. Jonnie weighs 360 N and is sat 1.50 m to the right of the pivot. Conor weighs 540 N and is sat 0.75 m to the right of the pivot. Evan weighs 420 N. How far to the left of the pivot should Evan sit to balance out the seesaw? [2 marks]

Levers and Gears

I have good news — there are no equations to learn on this page. Savour this moment because it won't last.

Levers act as Force Multipliers

1) Levers transfer the turning effect of a force — push one end of a lever down and the rotation around the pivot causes the other end to rise.
2) You saw on p.38 that the moment due to a force depends on the distance of the force from the pivot.
3) Levers increase the distance from the pivot that the force is applied, so less input force is needed to get the same moment. This moment provides an output force to a load.
4) Levers are known as force multipliers — they reduce the force needed to get the same moment. Some examples of when levers act as force multipliers are:

Scissors use a combination of two levers.

Long sticks or bars:

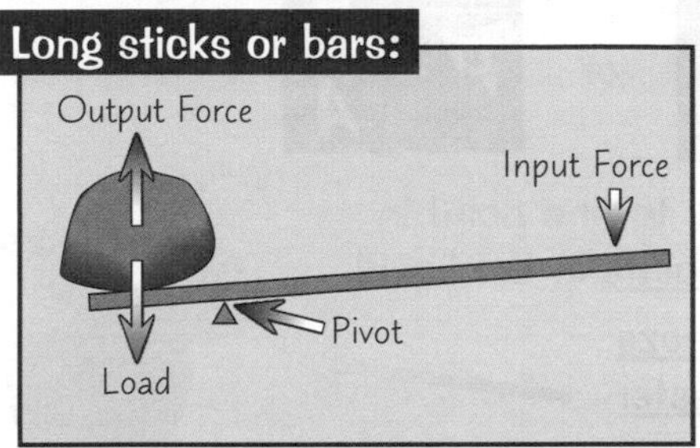

Wheelbarrows:

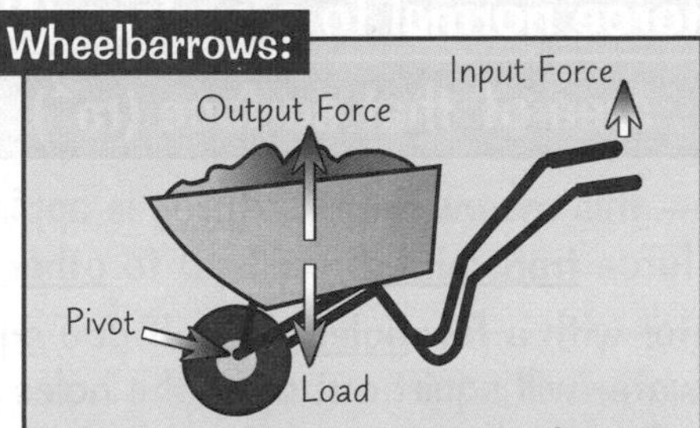

Scissors:

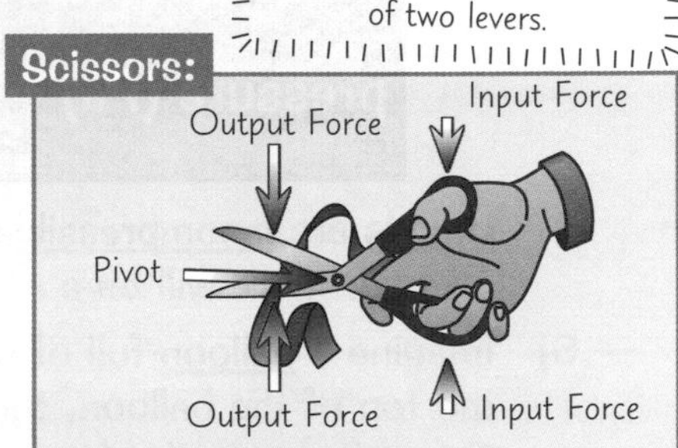

5) The moment of the input force (the force you apply) equals the moment of the output force (which is applied to the load). Moment = force × distance, which means you can write:

$$\frac{\text{input force}}{\text{output force}} = \frac{\text{distance of output force from pivot}}{\text{distance of input force from pivot}}$$

Gears Fit Together to Transfer Turning Effects

1) Gears are circular cogs with 'teeth' around their edge.
2) The teeth of different gears can interlock so that turning one gear causes another to turn as well. Because of how they are linked together, a gear spinning clockwise will make the next gear spin anticlockwise. This then alternates as you go from gear to gear.
3) A force applied to a small gear creates a small moment. The small gear applies this force to the gear next to it. If this second gear is larger, the force is being applied further from the pivot (of the larger gear), so the moment of the second gear is larger.
4) A series of gears that get bigger from gear to gear will multiply the moment of the first, smallest gear.
5) Interlocked gears will rotate at different speeds, depending on their size — the larger the gear, the slower it spins. (Think of a large gear and a small gear turning together. For every complete turn of the small gear, the large gear has only turned a small amount.)

You can work out how the speeds and moments will change between gears by looking at the gear ratios.

For example, look at the three gears above. The largest gear has 16 teeth and the medium gear has 8 teeth. The ratio of teeth between the largest and medium gear is 16 : 8 = 2 : 1.
This means that for every 1 turn the largest gear does, the medium gear will do 2 turns.

Because moment = force × distance, and the forces applied to each gear are the same, the ratio of moments of two gears is equal to the ratio of the gears' radii, and therefore equal to the ratio of teeth. For the gears above, the moment of the largest gear to the medium gear is also 2 : 1 — so the moment gets doubled.

A gear's radius is equal to the distance of the applied force from the pivot.

What did one cog say to the other? Gear we go again...

If a cog turns clockwise, then a cog next to it will turn anticlockwise, and a cog next to that will turn clockwise etc.

Q1 Cog A has 9 teeth and cog B has 6 teeth. How many times will cog B turn for one turn of cog A? [1 mark]

Hydraulics

Hydraulics is all about how we can use the properties of liquids to our advantage. Mwahaha.

Pressure is the Force per Unit Area

1) Pressure in a fluid (liquid or gas) is caused by the particles in the fluid moving around and bumping into the sides of its container. You met this on page 17.
2) This pressure causes a net force at right-angles to all surfaces that the fluid is in contact with:

> Pressure in a fluid is transmitted equally in all directions and it causes a force at right-angles to any surface.

3) You can calculate pressure from the force and the area of the surface that the force is being exerted on:

$$\text{pressure (Pa)} = \frac{\text{force normal to a surface (N)}}{\text{area of that surface (m}^2\text{)}} \quad \text{or} \quad P = \frac{F}{A}$$

4) Liquids are incompressible — this means that if a force is applied to one point in a liquid, there will be a net force transmitted (passed) to other points in the liquid.
5) Imagine a balloon full of water with a few holes in it. If you squeeze the top of the balloon, the water will squirt out of all the holes faster. This is because the force applied to the water at the top of the balloon is transmitted to the water in other parts of the balloon.

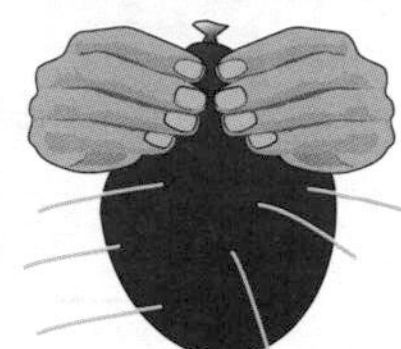

The Pressure in Liquids can be Used in Hydraulic Systems

1) Hydraulic systems are used as force multipliers — they use a small force to produce a bigger force.
2) The diagram to the right shows a simple hydraulic system.
3) The system has two pistons, one with a smaller cross-sectional area than the other. Pressure is transmitted equally through a liquid — so the pressure at both pistons is the same.
4) $P = F \div A$, so at the 1st piston, a pressure is exerted on the liquid using a small force over a small area. This pressure is transmitted to the 2nd piston.
5) The 2nd piston has a larger area, and so as $F = P \times A$, there will be a larger force.

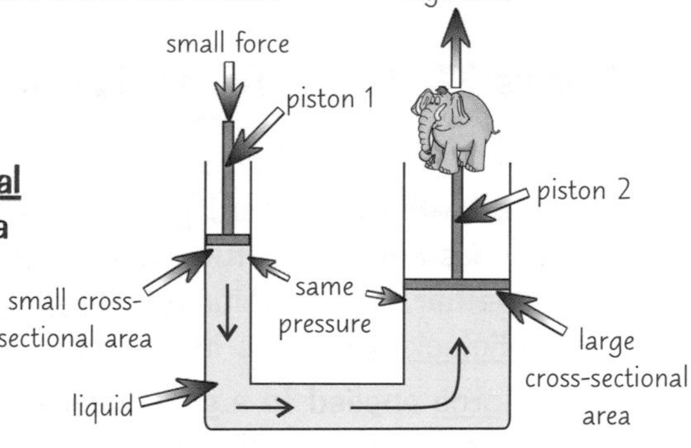

EXAMPLE:

The diagram on the right shows a simple hydraulic system. A force of 15 N is applied to the first piston which has a cross-sectional area of 0.00025 m^2.

a) Calculate the pressure created on the first piston.

b) Calculate the force acting on the second piston if its cross-sectional area is 0.0012 m^2.

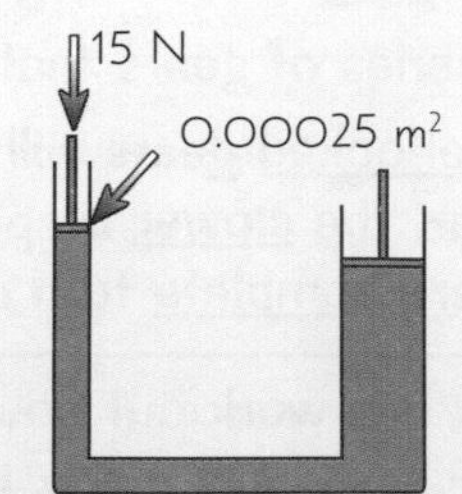

1) Calculate the pressure at the first piston, using the force and cross-sectional area of the first piston.

a) $P = \frac{F}{A} = \frac{15}{0.00025} = 60\,000$ Pa

2) Rearrange the pressure equation for force. The pressure at the first piston is the same as the pressure at the second piston, so use the answer from a) for the value of pressure.

b) $F = P \times A = 60\,000 \times 0.0012 = 72$ N

With all this talk of hydraulics, I'm really feeling under pressure...

Don't forget — the pressure in a fluid is always at right-angles to any surface that it's in contact with.

Q1 In a hydraulic system, piston 1 has a cross-sectional area of 0.2 m^2. A force of 3 N is applied to piston 1, which creates a force of 90 N at piston 2. Calculate the cross-sectional area of piston 2. [2 marks]

Revision Questions for Topic P2

Phew that was a lot of information — time to see what you've learnt and what needs revisiting.

- Try these questions and tick off each one when you get it right.
- When you've done all the questions under a heading and are completely happy with it, tick it off.

Motion (p.21-25)

1) What is the difference between a scalar and a vector quantity? Give two examples of each.
2) Define acceleration in terms of velocity.
3) Explain why an object travelling in a circle at a constant speed is accelerating.
4) Describe an experiment to investigate the acceleration of a trolley down a ramp.
5) How is the speed of an object found from its distance-time graph?
6) What does a flat section on a velocity-time graph represent?
7) How is the distance travelled by an object found from its velocity-time graph?

Forces, Newton's Laws and Momentum (p.26-33)

8) What is meant by the 'resultant force' acting on an object?
9) What will happen to an object that has a zero resultant force?
10) What will happen to an object that has a non-zero resultant force?
11) What is Newton's First Law of motion?
12) Give the equation for Newton's Second Law.
13) Explain how a car moving with a constant driving force will reach terminal velocity.
14) What is inertia?
15) What is Newton's Third Law of motion? Give an example of it in action.
16) Give the equation for momentum in terms of mass and velocity.
17) What is an elastic collision?
18) What is the difference between mass and weight. How can weight be calculated?

Energy and Elasticity (p.34-37)

19) Give the equation for the energy in an object's gravitational potential energy store.
20) Give the equation for the energy in the kinetic energy store of a moving object.
21) Give the equation for the work done on an object when it's moved a certain distance by a force.
22) What is meant by power? How is power calculated?
23) Give the equation that is known as Hooke's law.
24) What constant can be found from calculating the gradient of a force-extension graph for a material obeying Hooke's law?
25) What is the difference between an elastic deformation and a plastic deformation?
26) Describe a simple experiment to investigate Hooke's law.
27) Give the equation for calculating the energy transferred to a spring when it's stretched.

Moments and Forces (p.38-40)

28) Give the equation for a moment of a force.
29) How can a lever be used as a force multiplier?
30) How does the size of a gear in a series of interlocked gears affect its speed compared to other gears?
31) Give the equation for pressure in terms of force and the area of the surface the force is applied to.

Static Electricity

Static electricity builds up when electrons are transferred between things that rub together.

Build-up of Static is Caused by Transferring Electrons

All matter contains charge — atoms contain positive protons and negative electrons. Neutral matter contains an equal number of positive and negative charges, so their effects cancel each other out (the matter has zero net charge). But in some situations charge can build up on objects — this is static electricity:

1) When two materials are rubbed together, electrons are transferred from one to the other.
2) If the materials are conductors, the electrons will flow back into or out of them, so they stay neutral. But if the materials are insulators, electrons can't flow, so a positive static charge is left on the object that lost electrons and a negative static charge is left on the object that gained electrons.
3) It's always negative charges (electrons) that move. The direction of electron transfer depends on the materials:
4) If enough charge builds up, it can suddenly move, causing sparks or shocks.

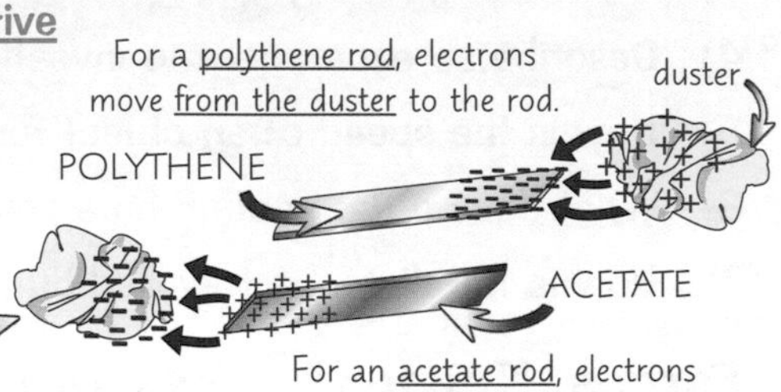

For a polythene rod, electrons move from the duster to the rod.
duster
POLYTHENE
ACETATE
For an acetate rod, electrons move from the rod to the duster.

Like Charges Repel, Opposite Charges Attract

1) Electrically charged objects exert a force on one another.
2) These forces get weaker the further apart the two objects are.
3) Things with opposite electric charges attract each other, things with the same electric charge repel.
4) The force between two charged objects is known as electrostatic attraction (if they attract each other), or electrostatic repulsion (if they repel). It's a non-contact force — the objects don't need to touch.
5) If you hang a charged rod from a string and put an object with the same charge near the rod, the rod will move away from the object. An oppositely-charged object will attract the rod towards it.

You Need to Know How to Test Whether an Object is Charged

1) Electrically charged objects attract small neutral objects placed near them. E.g. if you hold a charged rod above some small scraps of paper the scraps will 'jump' towards it.
2) This happens because the charged rod induces a charge in the paper — if the rod is positively charged, it attracts the electrons in the paper towards it, and if it's negatively charged it repels the electrons. This gives the surface of the paper near the rod an opposite charge to the rod, so the rod and the paper are attracted together.

Negative charges in the paper are repelled by the negatively charged rod...

...this means the parts of the paper nearest the rod have a positive charge. They're attracted to the rod.

3) You can also test if a rod is charged by holding it near a stream of water from a tap. The rod will induce a charge in the water, so the stream will be attracted to the rod and bend towards it.

You can also test for charge using a gold leaf electroscope:

- If a negatively charged insulator touches the zinc plate, some of its charge is transferred to the electroscope, and conducted down to the metal stem and gold leaf. This negatively charges both the stem and the gold leaf, which repel each other. This makes the gold leaf rise.
- If you touch the plate with a positively charged insulator, electrons flow into it from the plate, stem and leaf. Again, the stem and leaf will have the same charge and the leaf will rise.

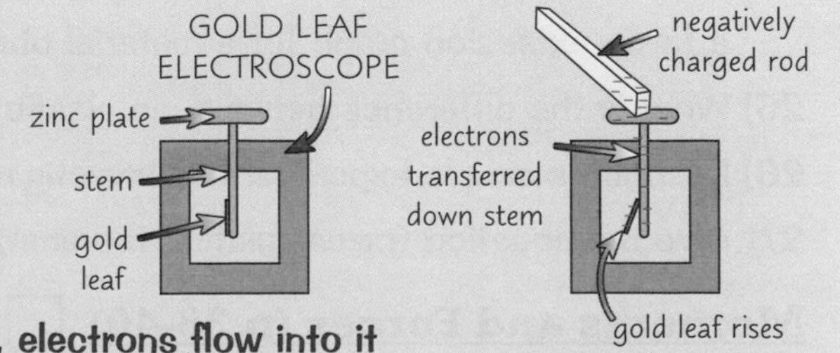

Come on, think positive...

The methods above are just a couple of ways of testing if an object is charged — you might see another in the exams.

Q1 Describe one way of demonstrating that an insulating object is carrying a static charge. [2 marks]

Electric Fields

Electric fields can help you to explain the forces that charged objects will exert on each other in different situations. They're also an excellent excuse to draw some pictures...

Electric Charges Have an Electric Field

1) Like magnets have magnetic fields, charged objects have electric fields, which you can show with electric field lines.
2) Electric field lines go from positive to negative. They're always at a right angle to the surface of the object at the point where they touch the surface.
3) The closer together the field lines are, the stronger the field, and the stronger the force a charged object in the field experiences.
4) For charged spheres, like the ones on the right, field lines get further apart the further from the sphere you are, so the force another charged object feels due to an electric field decreases with distance.

Isolated means it's not interacting with anything.

Here are the field lines around isolated, uniformly charged spheres:

positive charge:

negative charge:

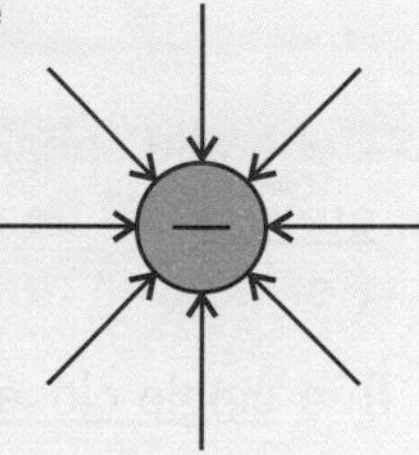

Electric Fields Cause Electrostatic Forces

1) When the electric fields around two charged objects interact, a force is produced.
2) If the field lines between the charged objects point in the same direction, the field lines 'join up' and the objects are attracted to each other. This happens when the two charges are opposite, e.g.: If the charges are free to move, the field lines will straighten and shorten as the charges move together.
3) When the field lines between the charged objects point in opposite directions, the field lines 'push against' each other and the objects repel each other. This happens when the two charges are the same type, e.g.:

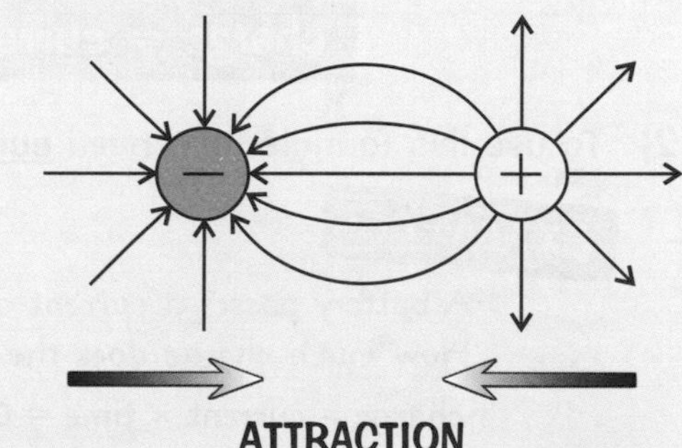

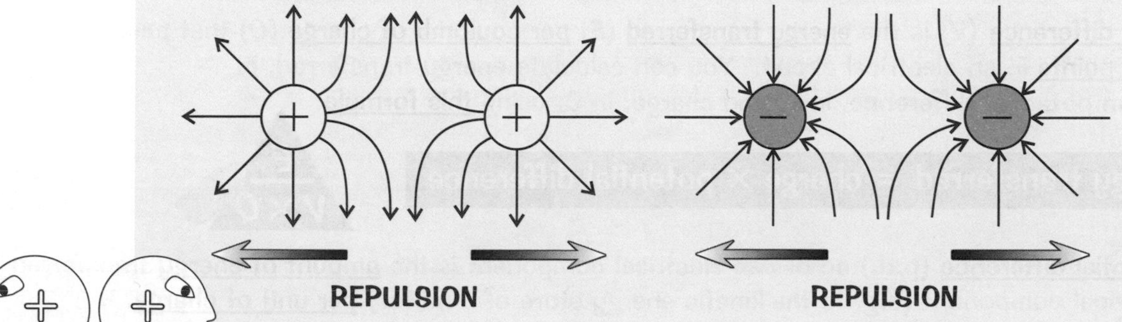

If you need to draw electric fields, don't forget the arrows on your field lines.

Electric felines — lines between charged cats...

Electric fields may seem a little bit weird at first, but the good news is that they're very similar to magnetic fields — so if you understand one of them, you can understand them both.

Q1 State what will happen to the strength of the electric field around a uniformly charged sphere as you move towards the sphere. [1 mark]

Q2 Draw the field lines surrounding an isolated, uniform, positively-charged sphere. [2 marks]

Current and Potential Difference

When charge moves, you get a current. Currents transfer energy around a circuit.

A Potential Difference Pushes a Current Through a Resistance

1) Current is the rate of flow of electric charge (electrons) around the circuit. Current will only flow through an electrical component if there is a potential difference across that component, and if the circuit is complete (closed). Unit: ampere, A.
2) Potential Difference is the driving force that pushes the current round. Unit: volt, V.
3) Resistance is a measure of how easily charge can flow. Unit: ohm, Ω.

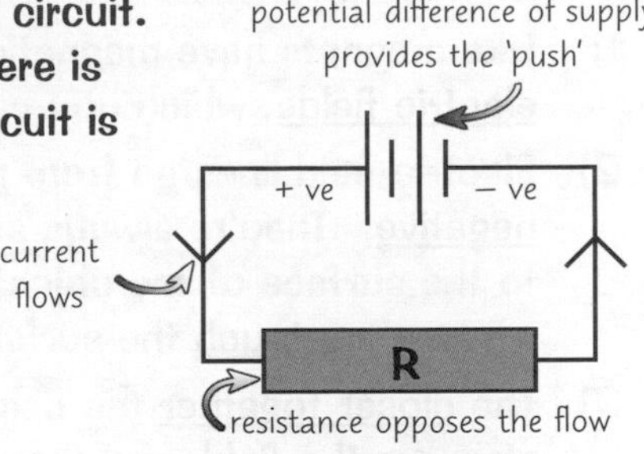

Generally speaking, the higher the potential difference across a given component, the higher the current will be. And the greater the resistance of a component, the smaller the current that flows (for a given potential difference across the component). There's more on resistance on page 46.

In a single closed loop (like the one in the diagram above) the current will have the same value at any point.

Total Charge Through a Circuit Depends on Current and Time

1) Current is the rate of flow of charge. If a current (I) flows past a point in a circuit for a length of time (t), then the charge (Q) that has passed this point is given by this formula:

charge = current × time

$$\frac{Q}{I \times t}$$

More charge passes around the circuit in a given time when a greater current flows.

2) To use this formula, you need current in amperes, A, charge in coulombs, C and time in seconds, s.

EXAMPLE:

A battery passes a current of 0.25 A through a light bulb over a period of 4 hours. How much charge does the battery transfer through the bulb altogether?

charge = current × time = 0.25 × (4 × 60 × 60) = 3600 C

Watch out for units — your time needs to be in seconds if you're calculating charge.

Potential Difference is the Energy Transferred Per Unit Charge

1) The potential difference (V) is the energy transferred (E) per coulomb of charge (Q) that passes between two points in an electrical circuit. You can calculate energy transferred, in joules, J, from potential difference, in V, and charge, in C, using this formula:

energy transferred = charge × potential difference

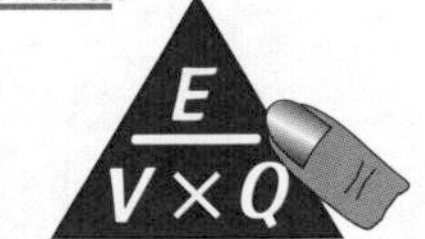

2) So, the potential difference (p.d.) across an electrical component is the amount of energy transferred by that electrical component (e.g. to the kinetic energy store of a motor) per unit of charge.
3) Potential difference is sometimes called voltage. They're the same thing.

I think it's about time you took charge...

Electrons in circuits actually move from –ve to +ve, but it's conventional to draw current as though it's flowing from +ve to –ve. It's what early physicists thought (before they found out about the electrons), and it's stuck.

Q1 Calculate how long it takes a current of 2.5 A to transfer a charge of 120 C. [2 marks]

Q2 A current flowing through a resistor transfers 360 J of energy when 75 C of charge are passed through it. Calculate the potential difference across the resistor. [2 marks]

Circuits — the Basics

That's enough theory for a minute, time to get practical...

Circuit Symbols You Should Know

there's more about a.c. and d.c. on p.95.

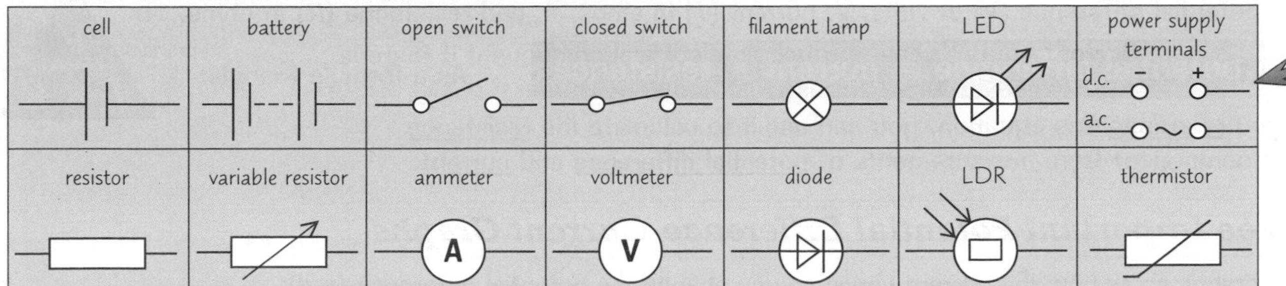

Some resistors have a fixed resistance, but for other resistors their resistance varies depending on the current that's flowing through them.

The Standard Test Circuit

You can use this circuit to investigate components — e.g. how their resistance changes with current and potential difference.

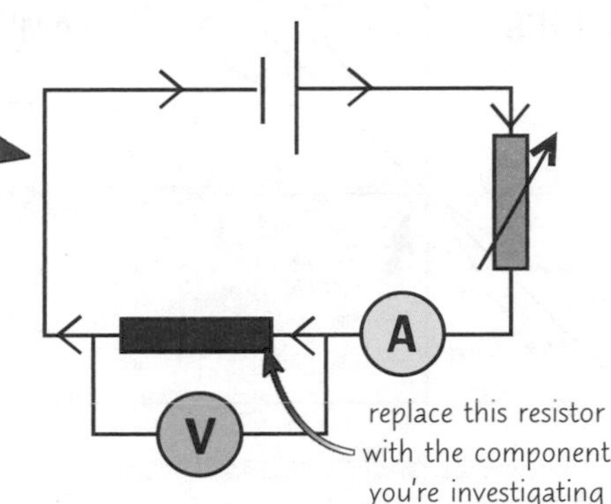

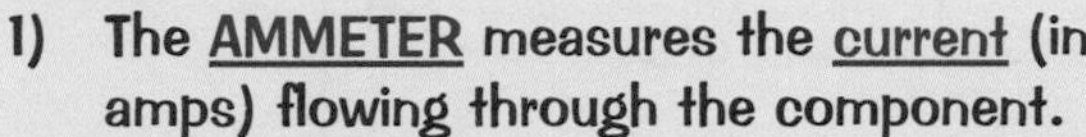

1) The AMMETER measures the current (in amps) flowing through the component.
2) Must be placed in series (in line with) the component.
3) Can be put anywhere in series in the main circuit, but never in parallel like the voltmeter.

1) The VOLTMETER measures the potential difference across the component.
2) Must be placed in parallel with the component under test, NOT the variable resistor or battery (so it can compare the energy the charge has before and after passing through the component).

PRACTICAL

You can use this circuit to produce *I-V* graphs (see p.46) for different components.

1) Connect the circuit as shown above. The component, the ammeter and the variable resistor are all in series, which means they can be put in any order in the main circuit. (Remember the voltmeter must be in parallel around the component under test.)
2) Begin to vary the resistance of the variable resistor. This alters the current flowing through the circuit and the potential difference across the component.
3) Take several pairs of readings from the ammeter and voltmeter to see how the potential difference across the component varies as the current changes.
4) Plot the current against the potential difference to get *I-V* graphs like the ones on page 46.
5) You can use this data to work out the resistance for each measurement of *I* and *V*, using the formula on page 46 — so you can see if the resistance of the component changes as *I* and *V* change.
6) Make sure the circuit doesn't get too hot over the course of your experiment, as this will mess up your results. If the circuit starts to warm up, disconnect it for a while between readings so it can cool down. And, like any experiment, you should do repeats and calculate averages.

Measure gymnastics — use a vaultmeter...

Learn all those circuit symbols — you could be asked to draw a circuit using one or more of them in your exams.

Q1 Draw the circuit symbol for an LED. [1 mark]

Q2 Draw a circuit you could use to create an *I-V* graph for a thermistor. [2 marks]

Resistance and $V = I \times R$

With your current and your potential difference measured, you can now make some sweet graphs...

Resistance, Potential Difference and Current: $V = I \times R$

For potential difference (V) in volts, V, current (I) in amps, A, and resistance (R) in ohms, Ω:

potential difference = current × resistance

As a formula triangle:

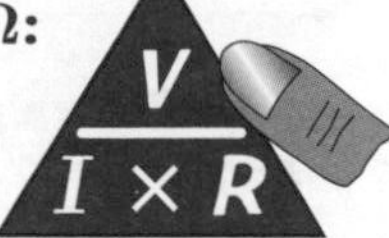

If you rearrange this equation, you can use it to calculate the resistance of a component from measurements of potential difference and current.

Three Important Potential Difference-Current Graphs

I-V graphs show how the current varies as you change the potential difference (p.d). Here are three examples, plotted from experiments like the one on page 45:

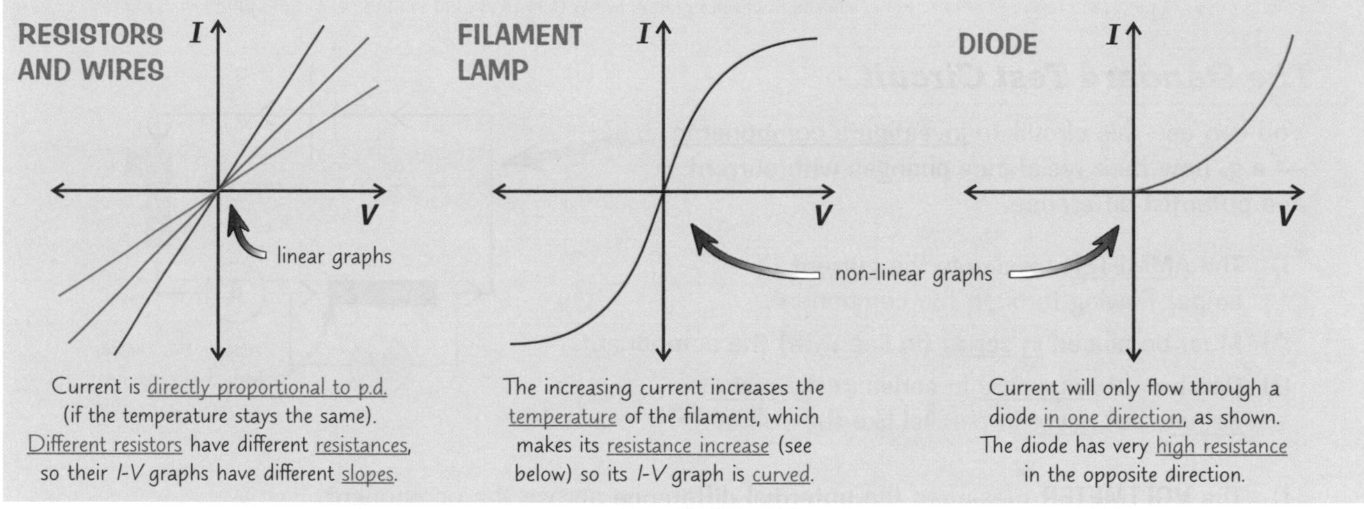

Current is directly proportional to p.d. (if the temperature stays the same). Different resistors have different resistances, so their I-V graphs have different slopes.

The increasing current increases the temperature of the filament, which makes its resistance increase (see below) so its I-V graph is curved.

Current will only flow through a diode in one direction, as shown. The diode has very high resistance in the opposite direction.

1) You can find the resistance for any point on any I-V graph by reading the p.d. and current at that point and sticking them in the formula above.
2) A resistor or wire has a constant resistance (i.e. it doesn't change with current or p.d.), so its I-V graph is linear. If the line goes through the origin, the resistance of the component equals the inverse of the gradient of the line, or "1/gradient". The steeper the graph, the lower the resistance.
3) For some components, the resistance changes as the current and p.d. change — the I-V graph curves.

Resistance Increases with Temperature (Usually)

1) When an electron flows through a resistor, some of its energy is transferred to the thermal energy store of the resistor, heating it up.
2) As you know from p.14, the thermal energy store of a substance is really just the kinetic energy store of its particles. So as the resistor heats up its particles start to vibrate more. With the particles jiggling around it's more difficult for the charge-carrying electrons to get through the resistor — the current can't flow as easily and the resistance increases.
3) For most resistors there's a limit to the current that can flow. More current means an increase in temperature, which means an increase in resistance, which means the current decreases again.
4) This is why the graph for the filament lamp levels off at high currents.

Thermistors (see page 47) are different — their resistance decreases with increasing temperature.

In the end you'll have to learn this — resistance is futile...

You may get given an I-V graph in your exam that you haven't seen before. Make sure you understand why these graphs have the shape they do, and you'll be ready for anything they throw at you.

Q1 A potential difference of 4.25 V is applied across a resistor, causing a current of 0.25 A to flow. Calculate the resistance, in ohms, of the resistor. [1 mark]

Circuit Devices

Lamps and resistors are all very well and good, but diodes, LDRs and thermistors are where the fun's really at.

Current Only Flows in One Direction through a Diode

1) A diode is a special device made from semiconductor material such as silicon.
2) It lets current flow freely through it in one direction, but not in the other (i.e. there's a very high resistance in the reverse direction).
3) This turns out to be really useful in various electronic circuits, e.g. in radio receivers. Diodes can also be used to get direct current from an alternating supply (see page 95).

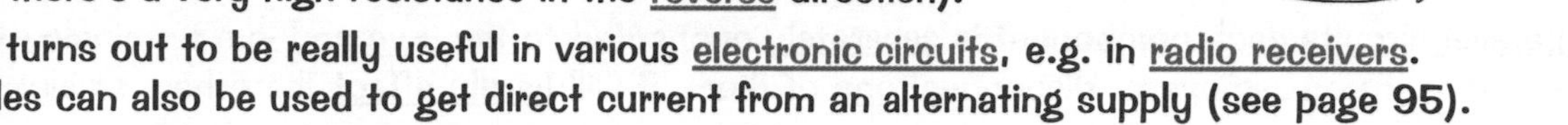

A Light-Dependent Resistor or "LDR" to You

1) An LDR is a resistor that's dependent on the intensity of light.
2) In darkness, the resistance is highest. As light levels increase the resistance falls so (for a given p.d.) the current through the LDR increases.
3) They have lots of applications including automatic night lights, outdoor lighting and burglar detectors.

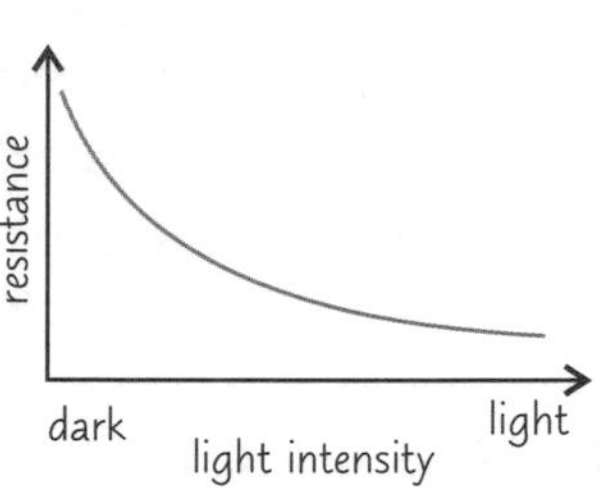

A Thermistor is a Temperature-Dependent Resistor

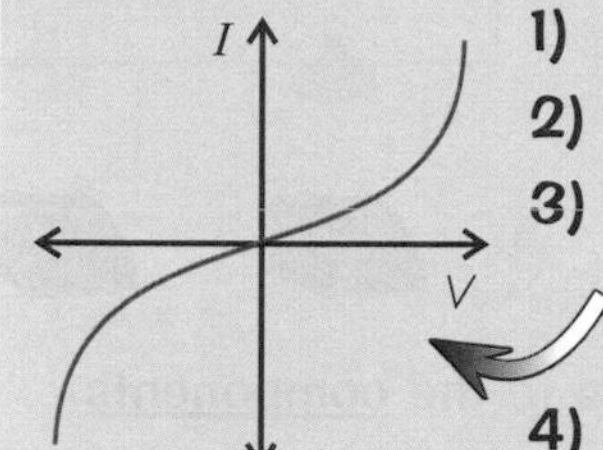

1) In hot conditions, the resistance of a thermistor drops.
2) In cool conditions, the resistance goes up.
3) In constant conditions, their *I-V* graphs are curved — as the current increases, the thermistor warms up, so the resistance decreases.
4) They're used as temperature detectors, in e.g. thermostats, irons and car engines.

resistance

cool temperature hot

You Can Use LDRs and Thermistors in Sensing Circuits

1) Sensing circuits can be used to turn on or increase the power to components depending on the conditions that they are in.
2) The circuit on the right is a sensing circuit.
3) The fixed resistor and the fan will always have the same potential difference across them (because they're connected in parallel — see page 48).
4) The p.d. of the power supply is shared out between the thermistor and the loop made up of the fixed resistor and the fan according to their resistances — the bigger a component's resistance, the more of the p.d. it takes.
5) As the room gets hotter, the resistance of the thermistor decreases and it takes a smaller share of the p.d. from the power supply. So the p.d. across the fixed resistor and the fan rises, making the fan go faster.

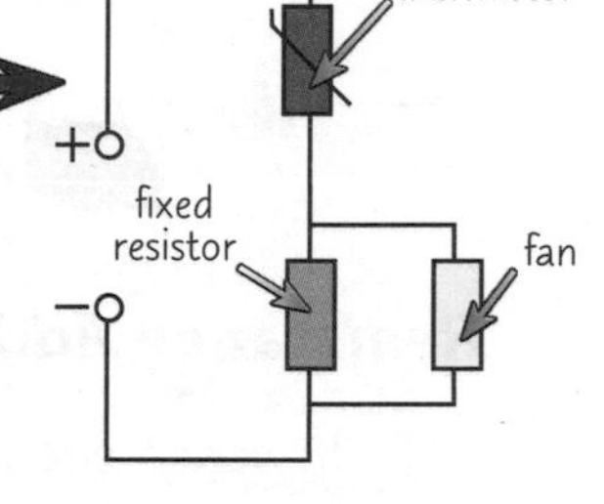

You can also connect the component across the variable resistor instead.
For example, if you connect a bulb in parallel to an LDR, the p.d. across both the LDR and the bulb will be high when it's dark and the LDR's resistance is high.
The greater the p.d. across a component, the more energy it gets.
So a bulb connected across an LDR would get brighter as the room got darker.

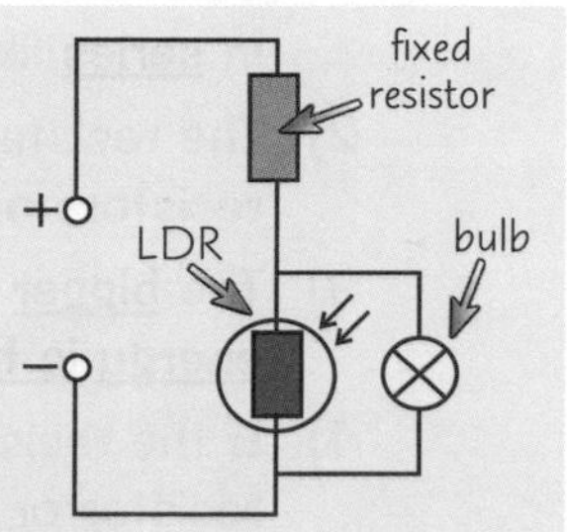

Permistors — resistance decreases with curliness of hair...

Bonus fact — circuits like the one above are called potential dividers (because they divide up potential difference).

Q1 a) Sketch an *I-V* graph for a thermistor in constant conditions. [1 mark]
b) Explain the shape of the graph you drew in part a). [2 marks]

Series and Parallel Circuits

Wiring a circuit in series or parallel can have a big difference on its behaviour.

Series and Parallel Circuits are Connected Differently

1) In series circuits, the different components are connected in a line, end to end, between the +ve and –ve terminals of the power supply. Current has to flow through all of the components to get round the circuit, so if you remove one of them it can have a big effect on the others.
2) In parallel circuits each component is separately connected to the +ve and –ve terminals of the supply. This means if you remove or disconnect one of them, it will hardly affect the others at all.
3) Parallel circuits are usually the most sensible way to connect things, for example in cars and in household electrics, where you have to be able to switch everything on and off separately. But you need to know all about both types of circuit I'm afraid.
4) If you add more cells to any circuit, connect them in series, not parallel. Connecting several cells in series, all the same way (+ to –) gives a bigger total p.d. — because each charge in the circuit passes through each cell and gets a 'push' from each one. So two 1.5 V cells in series would supply 3 V in total.

Series Circuits — Everything in a Line

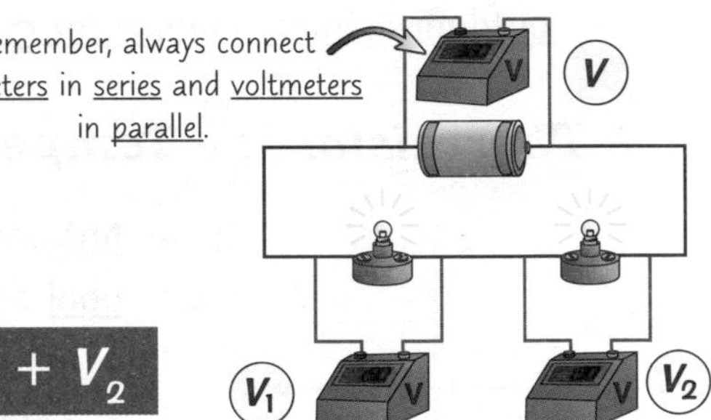

Remember, always connect ammeters in series and voltmeters in parallel.
V
V1
V2

Potential Difference is Shared

1) In series circuits, the total potential difference (p.d.) of the supply is shared between the various components. So the p.d.s round a series circuit always add up to equal the p.d. across the power supply: $V = V_1 + V_2$
2) This is because the total energy transferred to the charges in the circuit by the power supply equals the total energy transferred from the charges to the components.

Current is the Same Everywhere

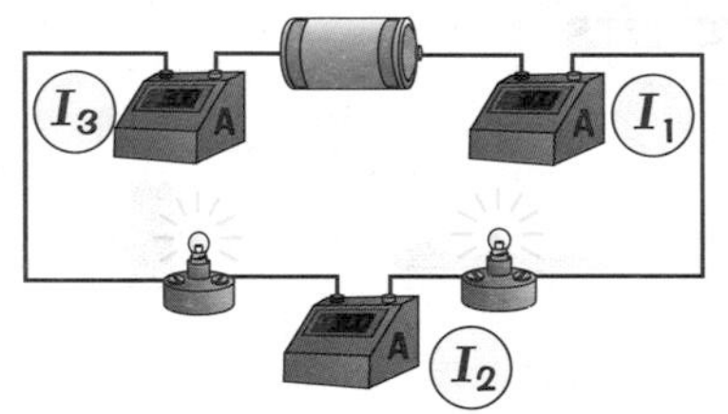

1) In series circuits the same current flows through all parts of the circuit: $I_1 = I_2 = I_3$
2) The size of the current is determined by the total p.d. of the power supply and the total resistance of the circuit: i.e. $I = V/R$.

Resistance Adds Up

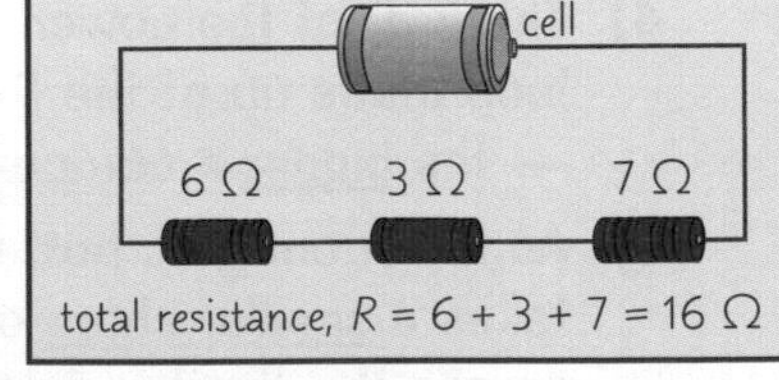

1) In series circuits, the total resistance is just the sum of the individual resistances: $R = R_1 + R_2 + R_3$
You can treat multiple resistors connected in series like this as a single resistor with equivalent resistance R.
2) The resistance of two (or more) resistors in series is bigger than the resistance of just one of the resistors on its own because the battery has to push each charge through all of them.
3) The bigger the resistance of a component, the bigger its share of the total p.d. because more energy is transferred from the charge when moving through a large resistance than a small one).
4) If the resistance of one component changes (e.g. if it's a variable resistor, light-dependent resistor or thermistor) then the potential difference across all the components will change too.

I like series circuits so much I bought the box set...

Series circuits are simple to make, but a real pain — if one of the bulbs in the diagrams above blew, it'd break the circuit, so they'd all go out. That's one of the reasons they're not as popular as parallel circuits.

Q1 Three identical filament bulbs are connected in series to a power supply of 3.6 V. Calculate the p.d. across each bulb. [1 mark]

More on Series and Parallel Circuits

Parallel Circuits — Independence and Isolation

Potential Difference is the Same Across All Branches

1) In parallel circuits all branches get the full source p.d., so the p.d. is the same across all branches:

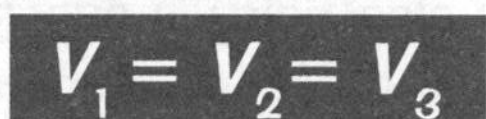

$$V_1 = V_2 = V_3$$

2) This is because each charge can only pass down one branch of the circuit, so it must transfer all the energy supplied to it by the source p.d. to whatever's on that branch (see page 50).

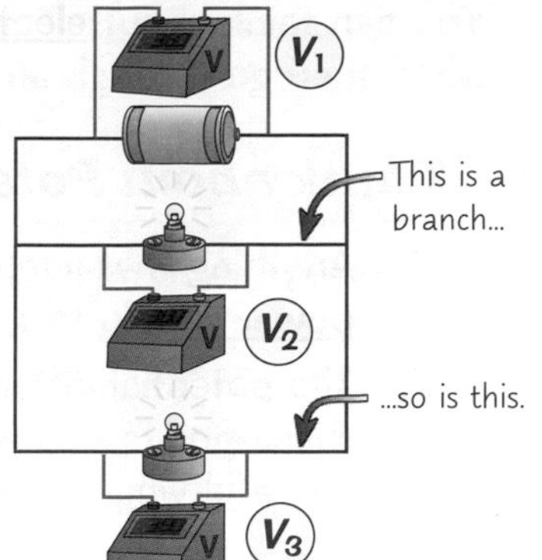

Current is Shared Between Branches

1) In parallel circuits the total current flowing round the circuit equals the total of all the currents through the separate branches.

$$I = I_1 + I_2$$

2) You can find the current in a branch using $I = V/R$, where V is the p.d. across the branch (which is equal to the source p.d.) and R is the resistance of the component on the branch (or the equivalent resistance of the branch if there's more than one component on it).
3) In a parallel circuit, there are junctions where the current either splits or rejoins. The total current going into a junction has to equal the total current leaving.

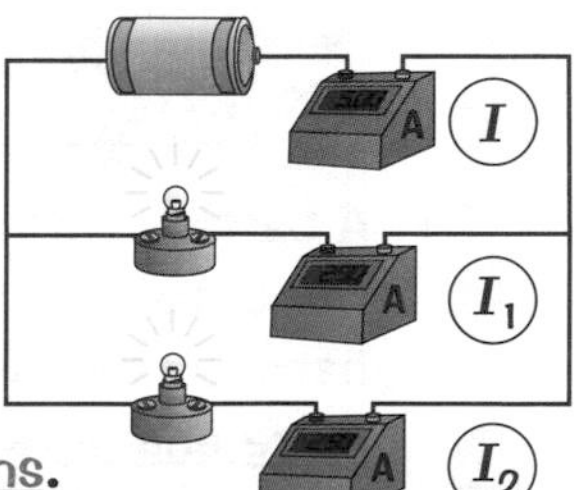

Resistance Is Tricky

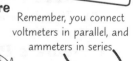

1) The total resistance of a parallel circuit is tricky to work out, but it's always less than that of the branch with the smallest resistance.
2) The resistance is lower because the charge has more than one branch to take — only some of the charge will flow along each branch.
3) A circuit with two resistors in parallel will have a lower resistance than a circuit with either of the resistors by themselves — which means the parallel circuit will have a higher total current.

R_1 R_2

total $R < R_1$ and total $R < R_2$

You Can Investigate Series and Parallel Circuits using Bulbs

PRACTICAL

1) Set up a circuit consisting of a power supply and a bulb. Use a voltmeter to measure the p.d. across the bulb, and an ammeter to measure the current in the circuit.
2) Add a second bulb in series with the first. Measure the current flowing through the circuit and the p.d. across each bulb. The bulbs should both look dimmer.
3) Add a third bulb in series with the first two. All three will look even dimmer. Again, measure the p.d. across each bulb, and the current through the circuit.
4) You'll find that each time you add a bulb, the p.d. across each bulb falls — this is because the p.d.s across the bulbs in the circuit need to add up to the source p.d.

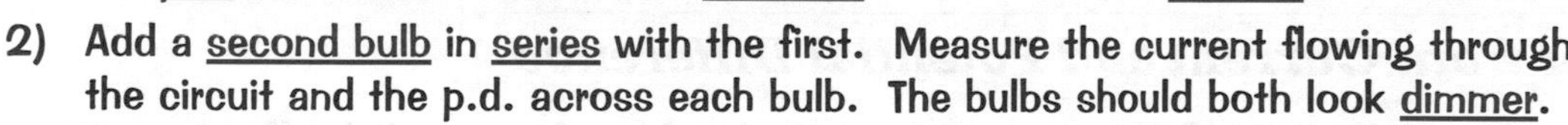

5) The current also falls each time you add a bulb, because you're increasing the resistance of the circuit.
6) Less current and less p.d. means the bulbs get dimmer (i.e. the power of each bulb is decreasing).
7) Repeat the experiment, this time adding each bulb in parallel on a new branch. You'll need to measure the current on each branch each time you add a bulb.
8) You should find that the bulbs don't get dimmer as you add more to the circuit.
9) The p.d. across each bulb is equal to the source p.d., no matter how many bulbs there are.
10) The current on each branch is the same, and doesn't change when you add more bulbs, because the resistance of each branch stays the same.

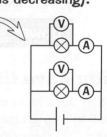

Remember, you connect voltmeters in parallel, and ammeters in series.

A current shared is a current halved...

Remember, in parallel circuits, each branch has the same p.d., but the total current is shared between branches.

Q1 If 3 identical bulbs are connected in parallel to a 3.5 V battery, state the p.d. across each bulb. [1 mark]

Energy and Power in Circuits

You can think about electrical circuits in terms of energy transfer — the charges travel around the circuit, and when they go through an electrical component energy is transferred to make the component work.

Think about Potential Difference in Terms of Energy and Charges

1) Anything that supplies electricity is supplying energy — an electrical current transfers energy from the power supply (e.g. cells, batteries, generators etc) to the components of the circuit.
2) The potential difference between two points is the energy transferred by one coulomb of charge between these points — energy = charge × potential difference (p.44). This gives you a useful way of thinking about how electric circuits actually work:
    - Energy is supplied to the charge at the power source to 'raise' it through a potential.
    - The charge gives up this energy when it 'falls' through a potential drop in any components elsewhere in the circuit.

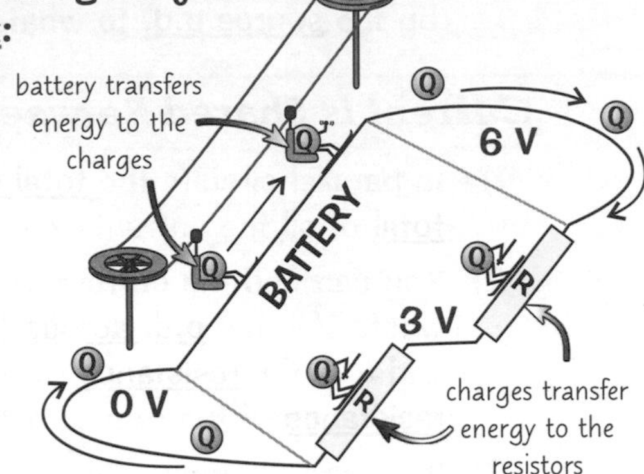

3) A battery with a bigger p.d. will supply more energy to the circuit for every coulomb of charge which flows round it, because the charge is raised up "higher" at the start — and more energy will be transferred in the circuit too.
4) The greater the resistance of a component, the more energy the charge has to transfer to it to pass through, so the bigger the drop in p.d.

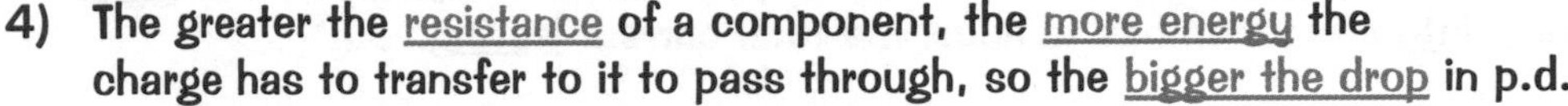

Power is the Rate of Energy Transfer

1) The power of a component tells you how much energy it transfers per second. Energy (E) and power (P) are related by the formula:

energy transferred = power × time

(energy transferred in joules (J), power in watts (W), time in seconds (s))

$E = P \times t$

2) Energy is usually given in joules, but you may also see it given in kilowatt-hours.
3) A kilowatt-hour (kWh) is the amount of energy a device with a power of 1 kW (1000 W) transfers in 1 hour of operation. It's much bigger than a joule, so it's useful for when you're dealing with large amounts of energy.
4) To calculate the energy transferred in kWh, you need power in kilowatts, kW, and the time in hours, h.

Calculate Power from Current and Potential Difference

1) You can calculate electrical power of a component in watts, W, from the potential difference across it in volts, V, and the current through it in amperes, A, using the formula:

power = potential difference × current

$P = V \times I$

2) You know that potential difference = current × resistance. If you substitute this into the formula above, you get another handy way to calculate power:

power = current^2 × resistance   or, in symbols: $P = I^2R$

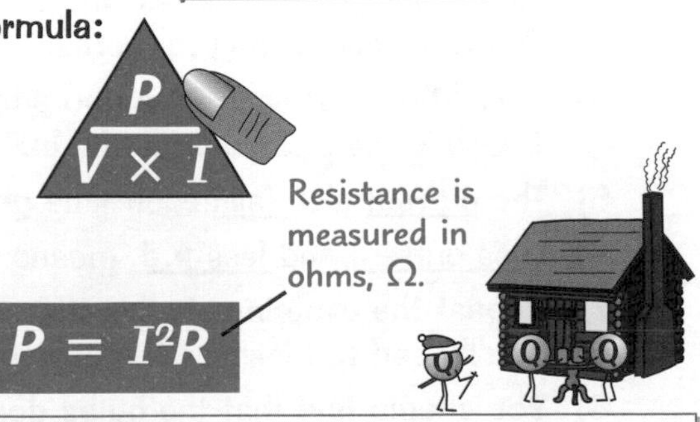

You have the power — now use your potential...

There are a lot of equations to learn here I'm afraid. You could try writing them out and sticking them to your wall to help get them firmly lodged in your brain. If not, at least you'll have some funky new wallpaper.

Q1 A 1.5×10^3 W hairdryer is turned on for 11 minutes. Calculate the energy transferred, in J. [2 marks]

Q2 A p.d. of 2.5 V is applied across a resistor with a power of 8.5 W. Calculate the current flowing through the resistor. [2 marks]

Q3 A 15 Ω resistor transfers energy at a rate of 375 W. Calculate the current through the resistor. [2 marks]

Revision Questions for Topic P3

Topic P3 — it was a tough ride but we got through it. Now let's see how much of it stuck...

- Try these questions and tick off each one when you get it right.
- When you've done all the questions under a heading and are completely happy with it, tick it off.

Static Electricity and Electric Fields (p.42-43)

1) Why aren't the effects of charge seen in neutral matter?
2) Explain how static electricity builds up on a polythene rod when it's rubbed with a duster.
3) Explain why a charged rod will attract small pieces of paper.
4) Draw diagrams to show the electric field between:
   a) two negative uniformly-charged spheres,
   b) a negative uniformly-charged sphere and a positive uniformly-charged sphere.

Electricity and Circuits (p.44-47)

5) What conditions are needed for a current to flow in a circuit?
6) What are the units of: a) current, b) charge, c) potential difference?
7) What is the equation linking current, charge and time?
8) Define potential difference in terms of energy and charge.
9) Draw the circuit symbols for:
   a) a battery, b) a filament lamp, c) a thermistor, d) an LDR.
10) Sketch a standard test circuit. Describe how you could use it to draw an I-V graph for a resistor.
11) Sketch the I-V graph of: a) a filament lamp, b) a wire, c) a diode.
12) Describe how to calculate the resistance of a component for a particular current and potential difference from an I-V graph.
13) Describe how the resistance of an LDR changes with light-level.

Series and Parallel Circuits (p.48-49)

14) Sketch a circuit diagram showing three resistors connected in series.
15) What is the rule relating the p.d.s across the components of a series circuit to the source p.d.?
16) What is the rule for current in a series circuit?
17) What is the total resistance of a series circuit equal to?
18) Sketch a circuit diagram showing three resistors connected in parallel.
19) State the rule relating the p.d.s across the components of a parallel circuit to the source p.d.
20) What is the rule for current in a parallel circuit?

Energy and Power in Circuits (p.50)

21) What is the power of a circuit component? How is power related to energy and time?
22) Explain what a kilowatt-hour is.
23) Write equations linking power to: a) potential difference and current, b) current and resistance.

Magnets and Magnetic Fields

I think magnetism is an attractive subject, but don't get repelled by the exam — revise.

Magnets Have Magnetic Fields

1) All magnets have two poles — north and south.
2) A magnetic field is a region where a magnetic material (iron, nickel or cobalt) experiences a force.
3) Magnetic field lines (or "lines of force") are used to show the size and direction of magnetic fields. They always point from NORTH to SOUTH.
4) The closer the field lines are to each other, the stronger the magnetic field at that point.

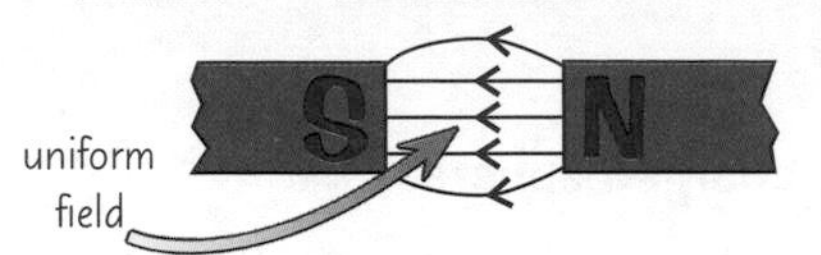

5) The strength of the magnetic field is called the magnetic flux density and is measured in teslas (T).
6) Placing the north and south poles of two permanent bar magnets near each other creates a uniform field between these two poles.

There Are Different Ways to See Magnetic Field Patterns

1) You can use iron filings to see magnetic field patterns of a magnet. Just put the magnet under a piece of paper and scatter the iron filings on top. The iron filings will align themselves with the field lines, e.g.:
2) You can also use a compass to plot magnetic field patterns:
   - Put the magnet on a piece of paper and place the compass on the paper, next to the magnet. The compass needle will point in the direction of the field line at this position. Mark the direction that the compass needle is pointing in by marking two dots on the paper, one at each end of the needle.
   - Move the compass so that the tail end of the needle is where the tip of the needle was previously. Repeat this and then join up the marks you've made — you will end up with a drawing of one field line around the magnet.
   - Repeat this method at different points around the magnet to get several field lines.
3) Using a compass is better than iron filings as the drawing of the field will still be there after the magnet has been removed, and the drawing also shows the direction of the field lines. Also, iron filings are quite messy to work with — they're a nightmare if you drop them and incredibly difficult to take off a magnet if they get in contact with it.
4) Compasses will always point North when they aren't near a magnet. This is evidence that the Earth has a magnetic north and south pole and therefore must have a magnetic core.

Magnets Affect Magnetic Materials and Other Magnets

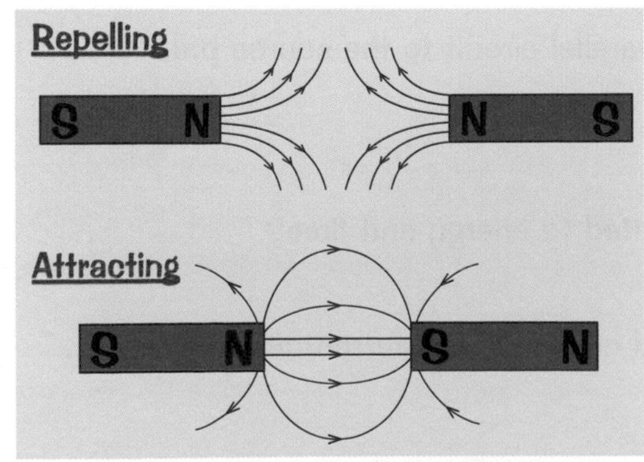

1) Like poles repel each other and unlike (opposite) poles attract.
2) Both poles attract magnetic materials (that aren't magnets).
3) When a magnet is brought near a magnetic material then that material acts as a magnet.
4) This magnetism has been induced by the original magnet. The closer the two get, the stronger the induced magnetism.
5) The difference between permanent and induced magnets is that induced magnets will (usually) lose their magnetism once the magnet has been moved away.

Magnets are like farmers — surrounded by fields...

Lots of fun diagrams here, so get arty and practise drawing field lines around and between magnets.

Q1 Describe how to plot the magnetic field lines of a bar magnet with a compass. [4 marks]

Q2 Explain why a piece of copper is not attracted to or repelled by a magnet. [1 mark]

Electromagnetism

It would be really handy if you could turn a magnetic field on and off. Entrance stage left — electromagnetism.

A Current-Carrying Wire has a Magnetic Effect

1) An electric current in a material produces a magnetic field around it.
2) The larger the electric current, the stronger the magnetic field.

The wire that carries the current doesn't have to be a magnetic material — it can be any metal.

The Magnetic Field Around a Straight Wire

1) A magnetic field around a straight, current-carrying wire is made up of concentric circles with the wire in the centre. You can find the direction of the field with the right-hand rule.

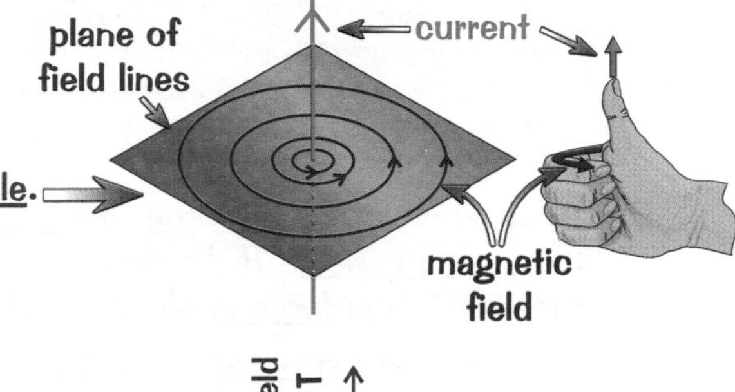

2) You could show that there's a magnetic field around a current-carrying wire by using compasses. They can also be used to find the direction of the magnetic field.
3) The further away from the wire, the weaker the magnetic field (shown by the field lines getting further apart). A graph of magnetic field strength against distance from wire would look like this:
It's a non-linear relationship — the strength decreases quickly at first, but this slows down with an increasing distance.

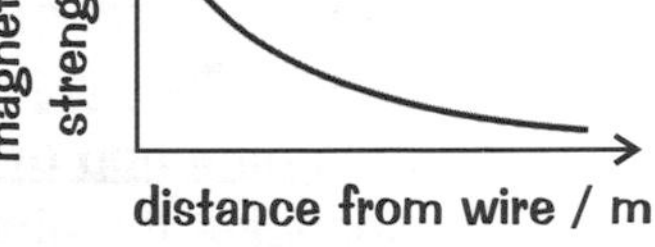

The Magnetic Field Around a Flat Circular Coil

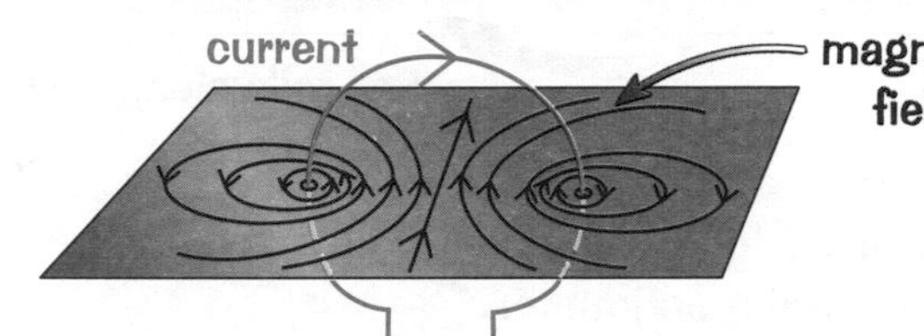

1) The magnetic field in the centre of a flat circular coil of wire is similar to that of a bar magnet.
2) There are concentric ellipses (stretched circles) of magnetic field lines around the coil.

The Magnetic Field Around a Solenoid

1) If you have lots of coils of wire joined together to make a solenoid, the magnetic effect is increased. The magnetic field inside a current-carrying solenoid is strong and uniform.
2) Outside the coil, the field is just like the one around a bar magnet.
3) This means that the ends of a solenoid act like the north pole and south pole of a bar magnet. This type of magnet is called an electromagnet.

You can work out which end of the solenoid is the north pole and which is the south pole using the right-hand rule shown above.

The magnetic effect at the ends of the solenoid will increase if:

- the current in the wire is increased
- the number of turns (i.e. the number of coils) of wire is increased, but the length stays the same
- the cross-sectional area of the solenoid is decreased
- the length of the solenoid is decreased (but the number of turns stays the same)
- an iron core is added inside the solenoid.

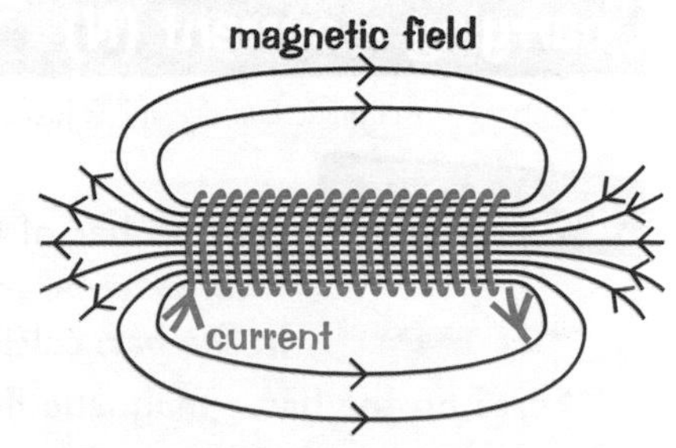

Give me one good raisin why I should make the currant joke...

Remember — the closer to the current-carrying wire or solenoid, the stronger the magnetic field.

Q1 Sketch the magnetic field lines produced by each of the following.
Include the direction of both the current and the field lines in your answer.
a) A straight current-carrying wire. b) A current-carrying solenoid. [4 marks]

Magnetic Forces

If you put a current-carrying conductor into a magnetic field, you have two magnetic fields combining.

A Current in a Magnetic Field Experiences a Force

When a current-carrying conductor (e.g. a wire) is put between magnetic poles, the two magnetic fields affect one another. The result is a force on the wire.

This is an aerial view. The red dot represents a wire carrying current "out of the page" (towards you). (If it was a cross ('×') then that would mean the current was going into the page.)

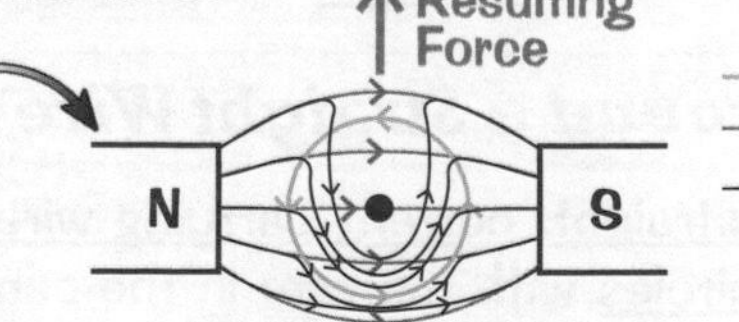

→ Normal magnetic field of wire
→ Normal magnetic field of magnets
→ Deviated magnetic field of magnets

The wire also exerts an equal and opposite force on the magnet, but here we're just looking at the force on the wire.

1) To experience the full force, the wire has to be at 90° (right angles) to the magnetic field. If the wire runs along the magnetic field, it won't experience any force at all. At angles in between, it'll feel some force.
2) The force gets stronger if either the current or the magnetic field is made stronger.
3) The force always acts in the same direction relative to the magnetic field of the magnets and the direction of the current in the wire. So changing the direction of either the magnetic field or the current will change the direction of the force.
4) A good way of showing the direction of the force is to apply a current to a set of rails inside a horseshoe magnet (as shown). A bar is placed on the rails, which completes the circuit. This generates a force that rolls the bar along the rails.

N S F

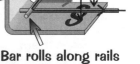

→ Current
→ Magnetic field
→ Force

Horseshoe magnet

Bar rolls along rails when current is applied

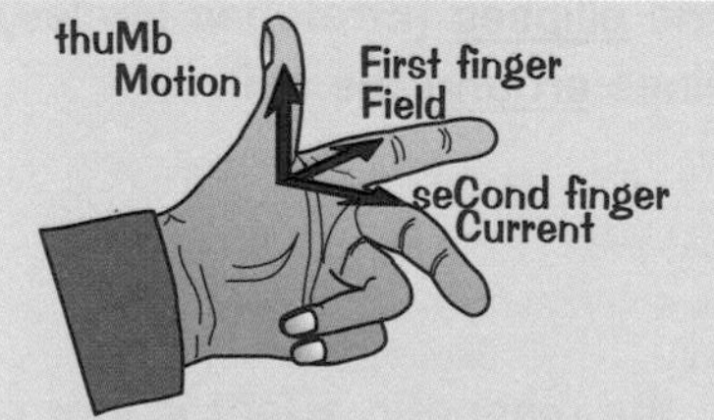

1) Fleming's left-hand rule is used to find the direction of the force on a current-carrying conductor.
2) Using your left hand, point your First finger in the direction of the magnetic Field and your seCond finger in the direction of the Current.
3) Your thuMb will then point in the direction of the force (Motion).

You can Calculate the Force Acting on a Current-Carrying Conductor

The equation used to calculate the force on a current-carrying conductor (e.g. a wire) when it's at right-angles to a magnetic field is:

Force on a conductor carrying a current (N) = magnetic flux density (T) × current (A) × length (m) or $F = B \times I \times L$

Remember — 'magnetic flux density' is just a fancy term for magnetic field strength.

An iron bar of length 0.20 m is connected in a circuit so a current of 15 A flows through it. If an external magnetic field of 0.18 T is placed at right angles to the direction of the current in the bar, calculate the force acting on the iron bar due to the presence of the magnetic field.

Force on the bar = magnetic flux density × current × bar length = 0.18 × 15 × 0.20 = 0.54 N

A current-carrying conductor — a ticket inspector eating sultanas...*

Learn the left-hand rule and use it — don't be scared of looking like a muppet in the exam.

Q1 State what the thumb, first finger and second finger each represent in Fleming's left-hand rule. [3 marks]

Q2 A 35 cm long piece of wire is at 90° to an external magnetic field. The wire experiences a force of 9.8 N when a current of 5.0 A is flowing through it. Calculate the magnetic flux density of the field. [2 marks]

*OK, so I did make the currant joke. Again.

Motors and Loudspeakers

This lot might look a bit tricky, but really it's just applying the stuff you learnt on the previous page.

A Simple Electric Motor uses Magnets and a Current-Carrying Coil

1) In a simple d.c. motor, a current-carrying coil sits between two opposite poles of a magnet.
2) Because the current is flowing in different directions on each side of the coil, and each side of the coil is perpendicular to the magnetic field, each side will experience forces in opposite directions.
3) Because the coil is on a spindle, and the forces act in opposite directions on each side, it rotates.
4) The split-ring commutator is a clever way of swapping the contacts every half turn to keep the motor rotating in the same direction.
5) The direction of the motor can be reversed either by swapping the polarity of the d.c. supply (reversing the current) or swapping the magnetic poles over (reversing the field).

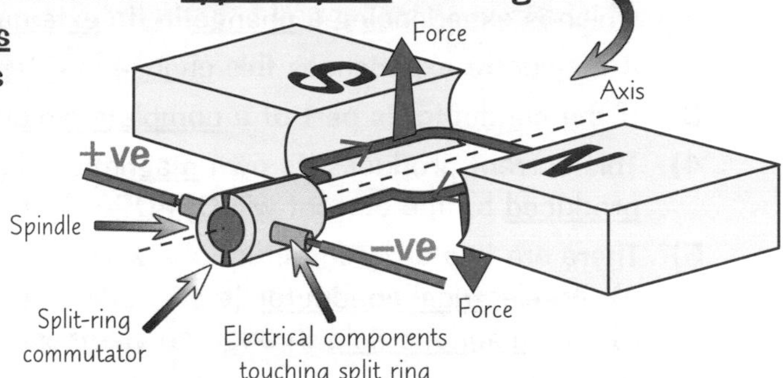

To speed up the motor, increase the current, add more turns to the coil or increase the magnetic flux density.

You can use Fleming's left-hand rule (see page 54) to figure out whether a coil like the one below is rotating clockwise or anticlockwise:

1) Draw in arrows to show the direction of the magnetic field lines and the current.

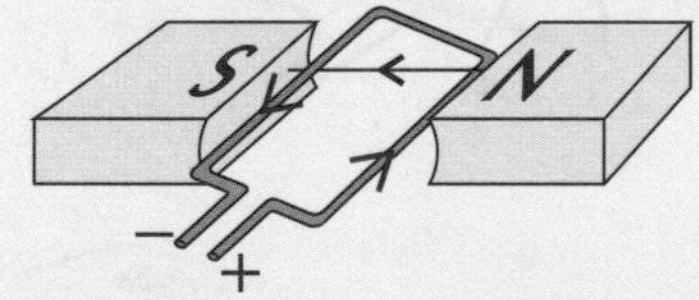

(Remember, current goes from positive to negative.)

2) Use Fleming's LHR on one side of the coil (here we've used the right-hand side).

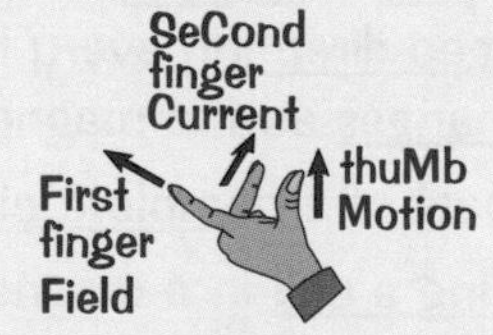

3) Draw in the direction of the force (motion) for this side of the coil.

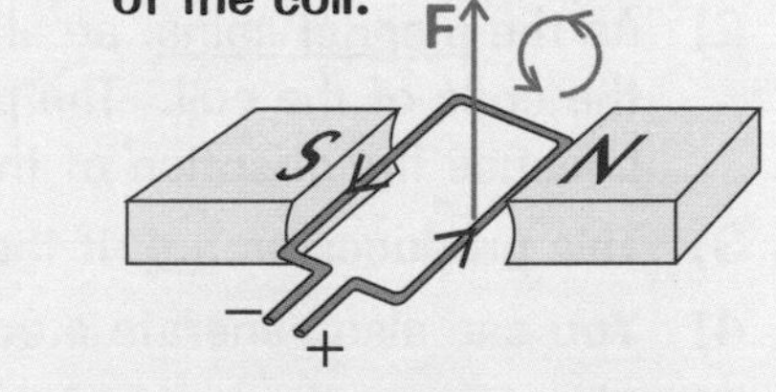

So — the coil is turning anticlockwise.

Loudspeakers Use Magnets and a Coil of Wire

1) As well as rotation, the force between a current-carrying coil of wire and a magnetic field can be used to make things move back and forth, like in a loudspeaker.
2) A loudspeaker contains a coil of wire which is surrounded by one magnet. Another magnet is inside the coil.
3) A.c. (alternating current) electrical signals are fed to the coil of wire, which is wrapped around the base of a cone.
4) The interaction between the magnetic field and the current in the coil forces the coil to move in one direction. As it's an alternating current, the current changes direction, forcing the coil back in the other direction. As the current continues to alternate, the coil moves back and forth.
5) These movements make the cone vibrate. This creates pressure variations in the air, i.e. sound.

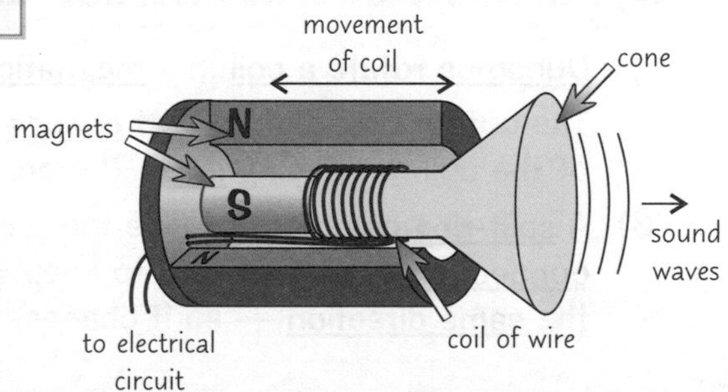

The coil and cone will move more if the force acting on the coil is larger.

What makes the world go round? Not an electric motor. Or love...

Practise using Fleming's LHR rule on coils, so you're super confident in working out which way they will turn.

Q1 State two properties that could be changed to decrease the speed of an electric motor. [2 marks]

Electromagnetic Induction

Electromagnetic induction is a pretty fancy piece of physics that helps to generate electricity.

A Changing Magnetic Field Induces a Potential Difference in a Conductor

1) Electromagnetic induction is when a potential difference (p.d.) is induced across a conductor which is experiencing a change in its external magnetic field.
2) A conductor experiences this change in external magnetic field when it passes through magnetic field lines.
3) If the conductor is part of a complete circuit, the induced p.d. will result in a current in the circuit.
4) This current produces its own magnetic field too. The p.d. is always induced so that the magnetic field produced by the current will OPPOSE the original change in the external magnetic field.
5) There are two different situations where you get electromagnetic induction:
   a) An electrical conductor (e.g. a coil of wire) and a magnetic field move relative to each other.
   b) The magnetic field through an electrical conductor changes (gets bigger or smaller or reverses).
6) Generators are the opposite of motors — they use the relative motion of a conductor and magnetic field to induce a p.d. and a current. For any generator:

   If the direction of rotation is reversed, then the direction of the induced p.d./current reverses too.

   The current induced in an alternator or dynamo will be greater if there are more turns on the coil, the magnetic flux density is increased or if the speed of rotation is increased.

7) ALTERNATORS and DYNAMOS are types of generators.

Alternators Generate Alternating Current

1) Some alternators rotate a magnet in a coil of wire.
2) As the magnet spins, an alternating p.d. is induced across the ends of the coil. The p.d. changes direction every half turn because the direction of the field changes as the magnet rotates.
3) This produces an a.c. if the coil is part of a complete circuit.
4) You can also generate a.c. by rotating a coil in a magnetic field.
5) Slip rings at the ends of the coil remain in contact with brushes that are connected to the rest of the circuit. This means the contacts don't swap every half turn, so they also produce a.c..

rotating magnet
axis
N
S
coil of wire
applied force
rest of circuit

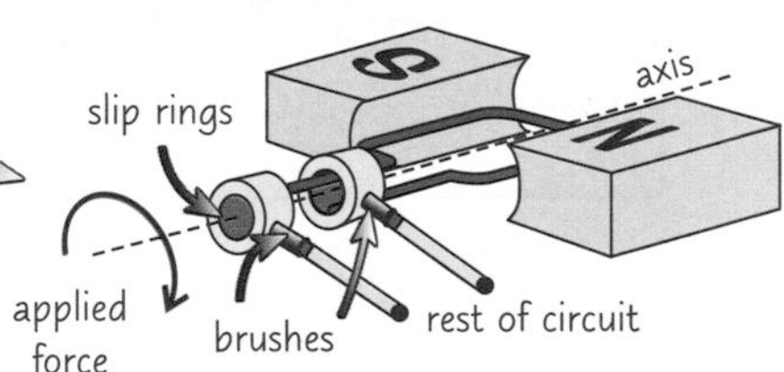

Dynamos Generate Direct Current

1) Dynamos rotate a coil in a magnetic field.
2) The output p.d. and current change direction with every half rotation of the coil, producing a.c.. The coil is part of a complete circuit.
3) A split-ring commutator (like the one on p.55) swaps the connection every half turn to keep the current flowing in the same direction — so it changes a.c. to d.c..

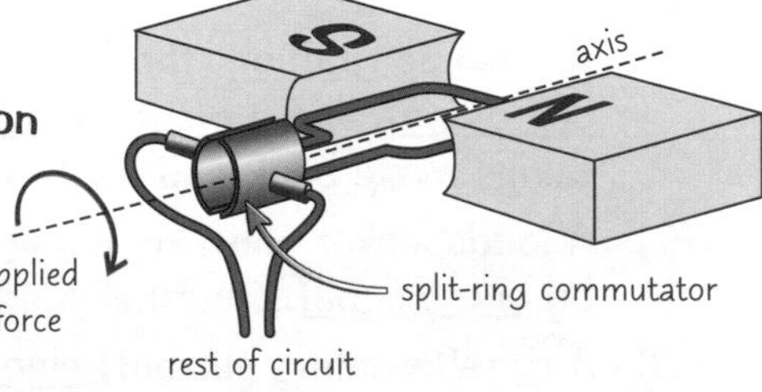

Microphones Work due to Electromagnetic Induction

1) A dynamic microphone's structure is like a loudspeaker (p.55), but the cone is replaced by a diaphragm.
2) Sound waves (pressure variations in air) cause the diaphragm to move back and forth when hit by them.
3) As the diaphragm moves, the coil of wire moves, inducing a p.d. across the ends of the coil of wire.
4) The coil is part of a circuit, so the induced p.d. means variations in current in the electrical circuit.

Breaking news — page is attacked by overload of information...

Electromagnetic induction is weird and funky. Make sure you get your head around this page before moving on.

Q1 State what is different about the current produced by alternators and dynamos. [1 mark]

Transformers

Transformers only work with an alternating current. Try it with a standard battery and you'll be there for days.

Transformers Change the Potential Difference

> You must be careful using transformers as they can produce very high voltages — the risk of injury can be reduced by insulating the coils.

1) Transformers change the size of the potential difference (p.d.) of an alternating current.
2) They all have two coils, the primary and the secondary coils, joined with an iron core.
3) When an alternating p.d. is applied across the primary coil, it produces an alternating magnetic field.
4) As iron is a magnetic material, the core also becomes magnetised. Because the coil is producing an alternating magnetic field, the magnetisation in the core also alternates.
5) A changing magnetic field induces a p.d. in the secondary coil.
6) The power of a primary coil is given by power = p.d. × current. Transformers are nearly 100% efficient, so power in primary coil = power in secondary coil. This means that if the secondary coil has more turns, the p.d. increases and the current decreases, or vice versa (see p.95 for more on transformers).

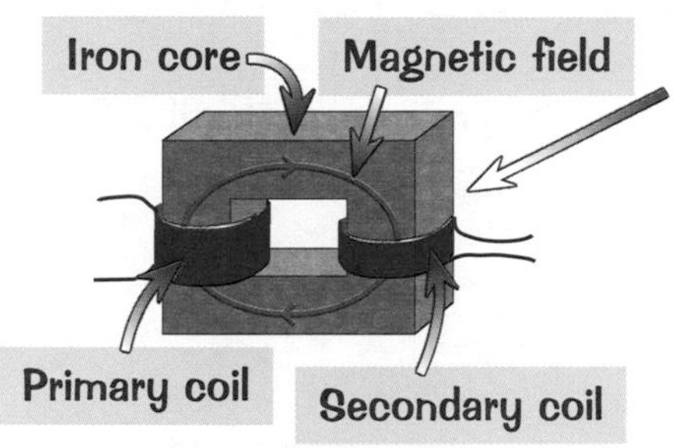

STEP-DOWN TRANSFORMERS step the voltage down. They have more turns on the primary coil than the secondary coil.

STEP-UP TRANSFORMERS step the voltage up. They have more turns on the secondary coil than the primary coil.

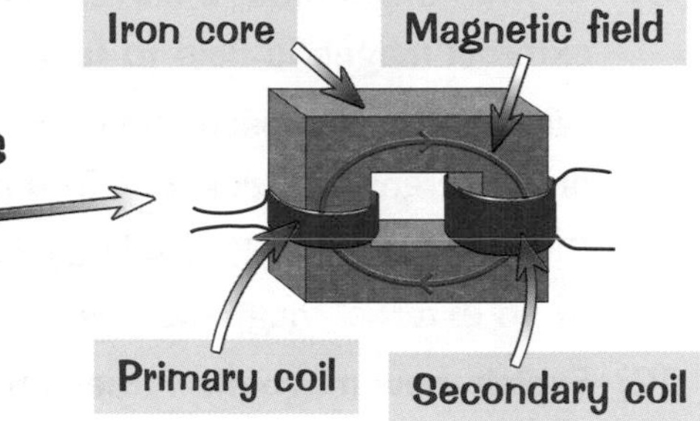

The Transformer Equation — Use it Either Way Up

The number of turns in a coil affects the size of the induced potential difference across it. The ratio between the potential differences across the primary and secondary coils is the same as the ratio between the number of turns in the primary and secondary coils.

$$\frac{\text{p.d. across primary coil (V)}}{\text{p.d. across secondary coil (V)}} = \frac{\text{number of turns in primary coil}}{\text{number of turns in secondary coil}}$$

or

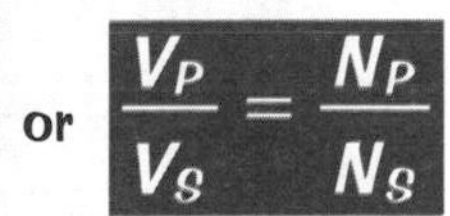

$$\frac{V_P}{V_S} = \frac{N_P}{N_S}$$

This equation can be used either way up — there's less rearranging to do if you put whatever you're trying to calculate (the unknown) on the top.

A step-down transformer has a primary coil with 3900 turns and a secondary coil with 2400 turns. If the input voltage is 6.5 V, what is the output voltage?

1) Rearrange the ratio equation for V_S. $V_S = V_P \times \frac{N_S}{N_P}$

2) Substitute the numbers in. $V_S = 6.5 \times \frac{2400}{3900} = 4.0 \text{ V}$

> The input voltage is the p.d. across the primary coil and the output voltage is the p.d. across the secondary coil.

I once had a dream about transforming into a hamster...

...but that's a story for another time. For now, get revising what transformers do, and why they're useful. You'll need to learn that equation linking the p.d. and the number of turns in the primary secondary coils too. Sigh...

Q1 A step-down transformer has a primary coil with 22 000 turns and an input voltage of 1.6 V. The output voltage is 0.40 V. Calculate the number of turns on the secondary coil. [2 marks]

Revision Questions for Topic P4

Well, that wraps up Topic P4 — now test yourself on everything you've learnt over the last few pages.

- Try these questions and tick off each one when you get it right.
- When you've done all the questions under a heading and are completely happy with it, tick it off.

Magnetic Fields (p.52-53)

1) Give the three magnetic materials.
2) In which direction do magnetic field lines always point?
3) Sketch the field lines (including their direction) around a bar magnet.
4) What does the distance between field lines tell you about a magnetic field?
5) What is the magnetic flux density and what unit is it measured in?
6) What is the difference between a permanent magnet and an induced magnet?
7) Describe what happens to magnetic field strength as you get further from a current-carrying wire.

Magnetic Forces (p.54-55)

8) Why could a magnet and a current-carrying conductor feel a force when they're near each other?
9) At what angle must a current-carrying wire be to an external magnetic field to feel the maximum force?
10) What is the rule used to find the direction of the force acting on a current-carrying wire in a magnetic field?
11) Give the equation that relates the force on a current-carrying conductor, the magnetic flux density of an external magnetic field, the current in the conductor and the length of the conductor.
12) Explain how magnetic forces are used in: a) electric motors, b) loudspeakers.

Electromagnetic Induction (p.56-57)

13) What is electromagnetic induction?
14) What type of current does an alternator produce?
15) What would happen to the current produced by a dynamo if the direction of rotation of the coil was reversed?
16) Explain how a dynamic microphone converts sound waves to electrical signals.
17) What type of current is required for a transformer to work?
18) Explain how a transformer works.
19) What is the difference between a step-up transformer and a step-down transformer?
20) Give the equation relating the potential differences across the coils in a transformer and the number of turns in each coil.

Wave Basics

Waves transfer energy from one place to another without transferring any matter (stuff). Clever so and so's.

Waves Transfer Energy in the Direction they are Travelling

When waves travel through a medium, the particles of the medium vibrate and transfer energy between each other. BUT overall, the particles stay in the same place — only energy is transferred.

> For example, if you drop a twig into a calm pool of water, ripples form on the water's surface. The ripples don't carry the water (or the twig) away with them though.
> Similarly, if you strum a guitar string and create sound waves, the sound waves don't carry the air away from the guitar and create a vacuum.

1) The amplitude of a wave is the displacement from the rest position to a crest or trough.
2) The wavelength is the length of a full cycle of the wave, e.g. from crest to crest (or from compression to compression — see below).
3) Frequency is the number of complete waves or cycles passing a certain point per second. Frequency is measured in hertz (Hz). 1 Hz is 1 wave per second.
4) The period of a wave is the number of seconds it takes for one full cycle. Period = 1 ÷ frequency.

amplitude
crest
wavelength
rest position
wavelength
trough

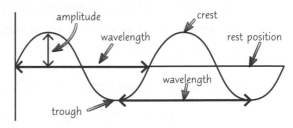

Transverse Waves Have Sideways Vibrations

In transverse waves, the vibrations are perpendicular (at 90°) to the direction the wave travels. Most waves are transverse, including:

1) All electromagnetic waves, e.g. light (p.66).
2) S waves (see p.101).
3) Ripples and waves in water.

A spring wiggled up and down gives a transverse wave.
wave travels this way
vibrations go up and down

Water waves, sound waves, P and S waves and waves in springs are all examples of mechanical waves.

Longitudinal Waves Have Parallel Vibrations

1) In longitudinal waves, the vibrations are parallel to the direction the wave travels.
2) Examples are sound waves (p.64) and P waves (p.101).
3) Longitudinal waves squash up and stretch out the arrangement of particles in the medium they pass through, making compressions (high pressure, lots of particles) and rarefactions (low pressure, fewer particles).

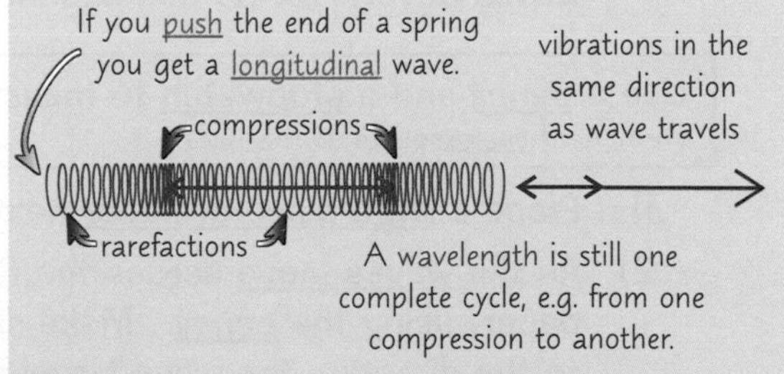

If you push the end of a spring you get a longitudinal wave.
vibrations in the same direction as wave travels
compressions
rarefactions
A wavelength is still one complete cycle, e.g. from one compression to another.

Learn the Wave Speed Equation

wave speed (m/s) = frequency (Hz) × wavelength (m)

Or:

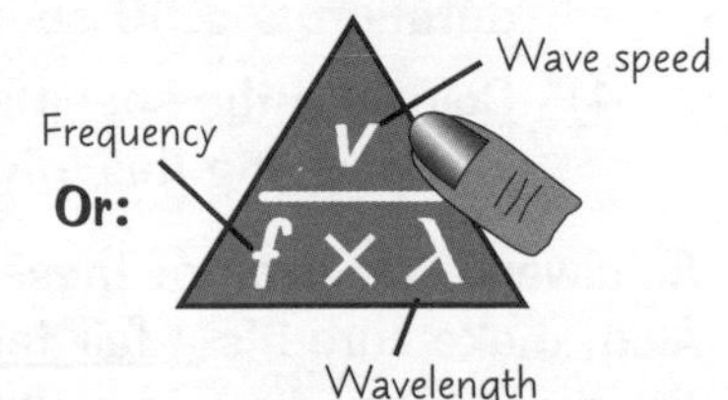

Wave frequencies are often given in kHz (kilohertz) or MHz (megahertz). Change them to Hz to use them in the equation.
1 kHz = 1000 Hz and 1 MHz = 1 000 000 Hz.

What about Mexican waves...

You won't get far unless you understand these wave basics. Try a question to test your knowledge.

Q1 A wave has a speed of 0.15 m/s and a wavelength of 7.5 cm. Calculate its frequency. [3 marks]

Wave Experiments

Time to experiment. Microphones and ripple tanks — sounds like fun, just don't mix them together...

Use an Oscilloscope to Measure the Speed of Sound

By attaching a signal generator to a speaker you can generate sounds with a specific frequency. You can use two microphones and an oscilloscope to find the wavelength of the sound waves generated.

1) Set up the oscilloscope so the detected waves at each microphone are shown as separate waves.
2) Start with both microphones next to the speaker, then slowly move one away until the two waves are aligned on the display, but have moved exactly one wavelength apart.

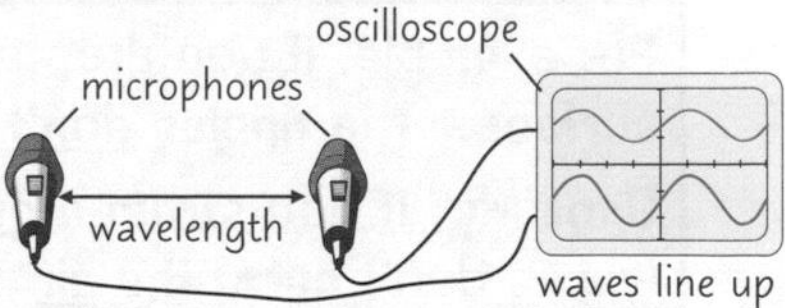

3) Measure the distance between the microphones to find one wavelength (λ).
4) You can then use the formula $v = f\lambda$ to find the speed (v) of the sound waves passing through the air — the frequency (f) is whatever you set the signal generator to in the first place.

Measure Speed, Frequency and Wavelength with a Ripple Tank

PRACTICAL

You can generate waves in a ripple tank using a signal generator attached to a dipper. The signal generator moves the dipper up and down to create water waves at a fixed frequency.

To measure the frequency, you'll need a cork and a stopwatch:

1) Float the cork in the ripple tank. It should bob up and down as the waves pass it.
2) When the cork is at the top of a 'bob', start the stopwatch.
3) Count how many times the cork bobs in, e.g. 20 seconds.
4) Divide this number by your time interval (how long you counted for) to get the number of 'bobs' per second — this is the frequency of the wave.

dipper attached to signal generator
ripple tank
cork bobs up and down

To measure the wavelength, use a strobe light:

1) Place a card covered with centimetre-squared paper behind the ripple tank.
2) Turn on the strobe light and adjust its frequency until the waves appear to 'freeze'.

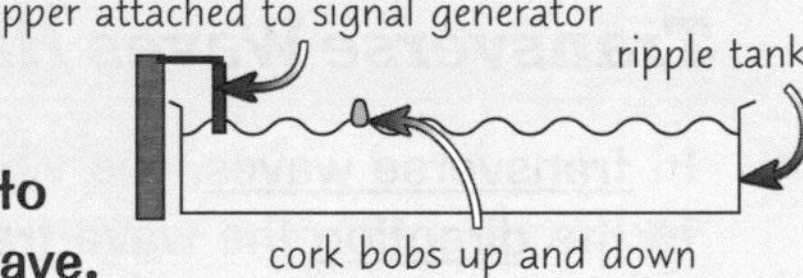

3) Using the squared paper, measure the distance that, e.g. five waves cover. Divide this distance by the number of waves to get an average wavelength.

Use a pencil and a stopwatch to measure the wave speed:
(You'll need two people to do this one.)

As $v = f\lambda$, you could measure two of these quantities and calculate the third.

1) Place a large piece of paper next to the tank.
2) As the waves move across the tank, one of you should track the path of one of the crests on the paper, using the pencil. Make sure your line is straight, and parallel to the direction the wave travels. You could use a ruler to help you.
3) The other should time how long the first has been drawing for. Pick a duration, e.g. 10 seconds, and stop drawing when this time has passed.
4) Calculate the speed of the wave by measuring the length of the line and plugging this into the formula distance travelled = speed × time.

pencil tracks this wave crest
line drawn along the paper as the crest moves

As always, for each of these experiments make sure you do at least three repeats and take an average. Also, make sure it's a fair test — keep the equipment the same and the variables you aren't testing the same every time, e.g. the position of the dipper, the amplitude of the waves, the depth of the water...

Disco time in the physics lab...

Sound waves and ripples on water are model longitudinal and transverse waves because they're easy to work with.

Q1 Describe an experiment to measure the frequency of a water wave. [3 marks]

Reflection and Refraction

All waves reflect and refract. 'What does that mean', you say? Read on...

Waves Are Absorbed, Transmitted and Reflected at Boundaries

When a wave meets a boundary between two materials (a material interface), three things can happen:

1) The wave may be absorbed by the second material, transferring energy to the material's energy stores (this is how a microwave works — see page 67).
2) The wave may be transmitted — it carries on travelling through the new material, often at a different speed (velocity), which can lead to refraction (see below)
3) The wave may reflect off the boundary. This is where the incoming ray is neither absorbed or transmitted, but 'sent back' away from the second material (see below).

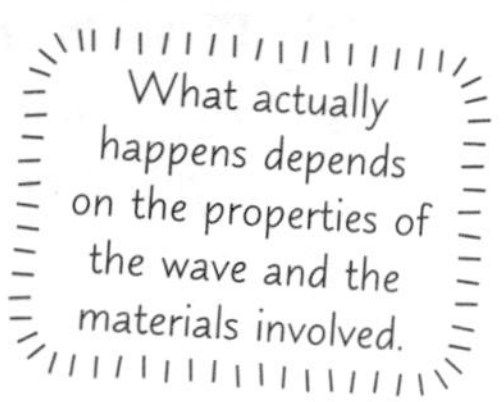

What actually happens depends on the properties of the wave and the materials involved.

Reflection of Light Lets Us See Things

There's one simple rule for all reflected waves:

Angle of Incidence = Angle of Reflection

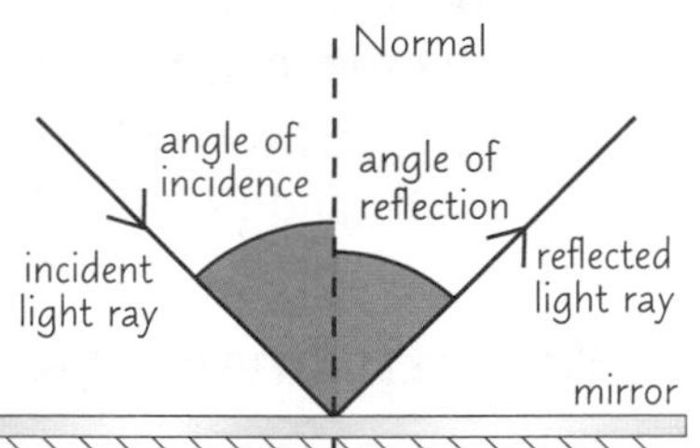

Each angle is measured from the normal — an imaginary line that's at right angles to the surface at the point the light hits it (drawn with a dotty line).

1) The reflection of visible light is what let's us see things — light bounces off objects and into our eyes.
2) Light rays reflect off smooth surfaces (e.g. a mirror) all in the same direction, giving a clear reflection.
3) But light rays reflect off rough surfaces (e.g. paper) in all different directions. The angle of incidence still equals the angle of reflection for each ray, but the rough surface means each ray hits the surface at a different angle, and so is reflected at a different angle, scattering the light.
4) White light is a mixture of all the different colours of light, which all have a different wavelength.
5) All the colours of light in white light are reflected at the same angle — white light doesn't split into the different colours when it reflects, as all the wavelengths follow the rule above.

Refraction is When Waves Bend

For light, when we say density we mean optical density — how the material affects the speed of light.

1) Waves travel at different speeds in materials with different densities. So when a wave crosses a boundary between materials, e.g. from glass to air, it changes speed.
2) The frequency of the wave stays the same when it crosses a boundary. As $v = f\lambda$, this means the wavelength changes — the wavelength decreases if the wave slows down, and increases if it speeds up.
3) If the wave hits the boundary at an angle to the normal, this change in speed (and wavelength) makes the wave bend — this is called refraction. The greater the change in speed, the more it bends.

If the wave is travelling along the normal, it doesn't bend (but it still changes speed).

4) If the wave slows down, it will bend towards the normal. If it speeds up it will bend away from the normal.
5) Sound generally travels faster in denser material. So going to water from air, its wavelength increases.
6) Electromagnetic (EM) waves like light usually travel more slowly in denser materials. So going from air to glass, their wavelength would decrease, and they would bend towards the normal (if they refracted).
7) How much an EM wave refracts can be affected by its wavelength — shorter wavelengths bend more:

The colours of light all have slightly different wavelengths — shortest to longest it goes violet, indigo, blue, green, yellow, orange, red.
They travel at the same speed in air, but when they enter a denser substance (e.g. glass), the shorter wavelengths slow down more and so refract (bend) more.

air
glass
violet (most)
red (least)

Red light bends the least — it should try yoga...

Hooray, a light mnemonic — Richard of York gave battle in vain (red, orange, yellow, green, blue, indigo, violet).

Q1 A light ray enters air from water at 50° to the normal. How does it bend relative to the normal? [1 mark]

More on Reflection

Light reflects off lots of stuff. Which is pretty useful, or you wouldn't be able to read this book.

Reflection can be Specular or Scattered

1) Waves are reflected by different boundaries in different ways.
2) Specular reflection is when waves are reflected in a single direction by a smooth surface.
3) This means you get a clear reflection, e.g. when light is reflected by a mirror.
4) Scattering occurs when waves are reflected by a rough surface (e.g. paper) and the waves are reflected in all directions.
5) This happens because the normal is different for each incident ray, so each ray has a different angle of incidence. The rule angle of incidence = angle of reflection still applies.
6) When light is reflected by something rough, the surface looks matt, and you don't get a clear reflection.

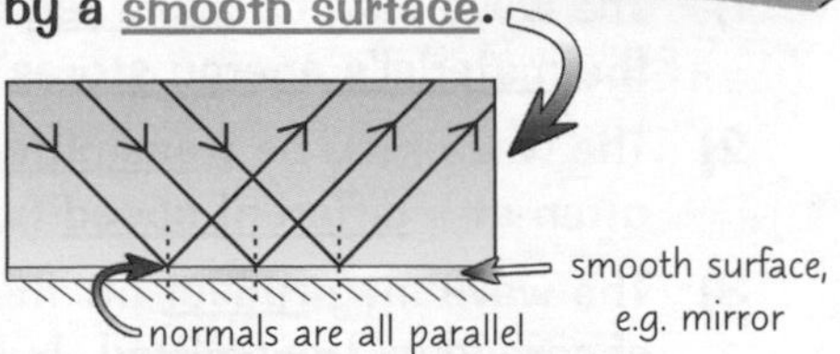

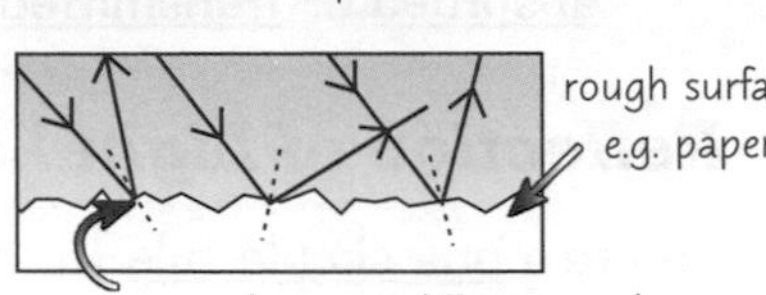

You can Investigate Reflection Using a Ray Box and a Mirror

PRACTICAL

1) Take a piece of paper and draw a solid line across it using a ruler. Then draw a dotted line at 90° to the solid line (your normal).
2) Place a plane (flat) mirror so it lines up with the solid line.
3) Using a ray box, shine a thin beam of white light at the mirror, so the light hits the mirror where the normal meets the mirror.
4) Trace the incident and reflected light rays.
5) Measure the angle between the incident ray and the normal (the angle of incidence) and the angle between the reflected ray and the normal (the angle of reflection) using a protractor.
6) Repeat these steps, varying the angle of incidence. You should find that no matter its value, the angle of incidence ALWAYS equals the angle of reflection.
7) You should see that the reflected ray is as thin and bright as the incident ray — a plane mirror gives a clear reflection and none of the light is absorbed.
8) You could repeat this experiment for different colours of light by using colour filters. You should find that for any colour the angle of incidence still always equals the angle of reflection.
9) As always, keep your test fair by keeping other variables the same, e.g. same mirror, same width and brightness of beam.

angle of incidence, angle of reflection, ray box, incident ray, reflected ray, paper, line, mirror, normal

Do this experiment in a dark room. Keep the light levels the same throughout your experiment.

You Need to Be Able to Draw Ray Diagrams for Reflection

1) Draw a normal to your surface and a light ray that meets the normal at the surface — this is your incident ray.
2) Now draw the reflected ray, remembering that the angle of incidence must always equal the angle of reflection.
3) If there are multiple rays which are parallel (e.g. the light source is distant) and they're reflecting off a smooth surface, then the reflected rays will also all be parallel to each other.
4) Remember to use a ruler (and protractor if required) and always put arrows on your rays.

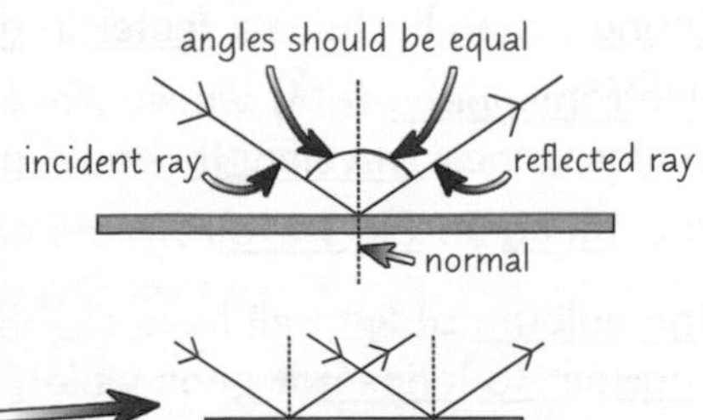

If you struggled with this page, take a moment to reflect on it...

Remember, the angle of incidence always equals the angle of reflection. Carve it on your brain (or just learn it).

Q1 Sketch a ray diagram showing parallel rays of red and violet light reflecting off a mirror at roughly 45° to the normal. [2 marks]

More on Refraction

Remember refraction from page 61? Well, here's some more stuff you need to know about it.

You Need to Be Able to Draw Ray Diagrams for Refraction

1) Draw a normal where any ray meets a boundary.
2) If the light ray is travelling into a MORE dense material, it will slow DOWN, making it bend TOWARDS the normal.
3) If the light ray is travelling into a LESS dense material, it will speed UP, making it bend AWAY from the normal.
4) If a light ray is travelling through a rectangular block, the emerging ray and the incident ray will be parallel.
5) Remember to use a ruler and add arrows to your rays to show direction.

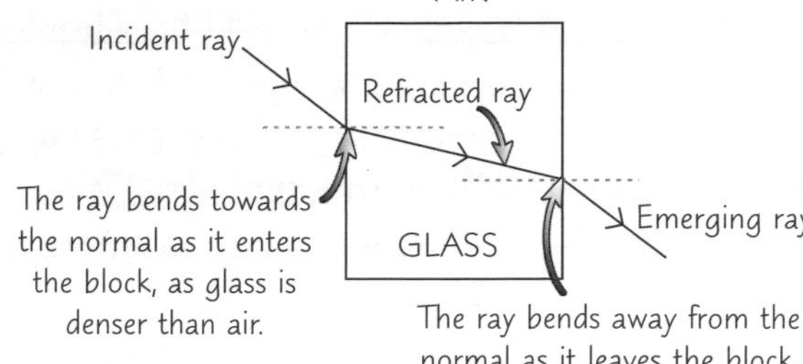

1) The angle of incidence is between the incident ray and the normal.
2) The angle of refraction is between the refracted ray and the normal.
3) The angle of refraction varies with the angle of incidence. It also depends on the light's wavelength — the shorter the wavelength, the more it refracts. And it depends on the materials either side of the boundary, e.g. glass refracts light more than water.

angle of incidence

angle of refraction

Triangular Prisms Disperse White Light

Different wavelengths (colours) of light travel at different speeds in glass, so they refract by different amounts. So when white light passes through a triangular prism, you get a rainbow:

You don't get a rainbow like this with a rectangular block because it has parallel boundaries, so the different colours bend by the same amount when they leave as when they entered — the rays emerge parallel.

1. The light bends towards the normal as it enters the prism, as glass is denser than air. Different wavelengths (colours) of light bend by different amounts — red bends the least, violet bends the most.
2. Light bends away from the normal as it leaves the prism. Again, different colours bend by different amounts. Because of the prism's shape, this spreads the wavelengths out even more.
3. On the far side of the prism, you see a spectrum (rainbow).

They said prism, Dave.

You can Investigate the Refraction of Light using a Prism

PRACTICAL

You'll need a light source (e.g. a ray box), coloured filters, and a triangular glass prism on a piece of paper:

1) Place a red filter in front of the ray box, then shine a thin light beam into the prism at an angle to the normal. (Some light will be reflected.)
2) Trace the incident and emerging rays onto the paper and remove the prism.
3) Draw the refracted ray by joining the ends of the other two rays with a straight line. (You could measure the angles of incidence and refraction.)
4) Repeat using a blue filter (keeping the angle of incidence the same) — you should see that the blue light refracts more at each boundary.
5) You could repeat this with more colours (wavelengths) of light — the shorter the wavelength, the more it should refract). Or without filters, so the white light disperses (as shown above).
6) You could also try changing the shape or material of the prism.

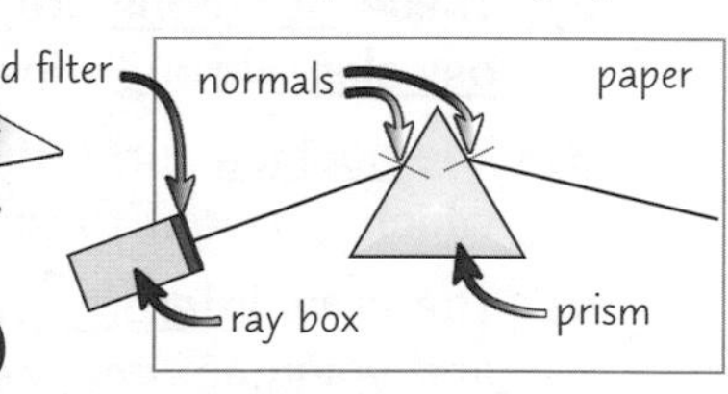

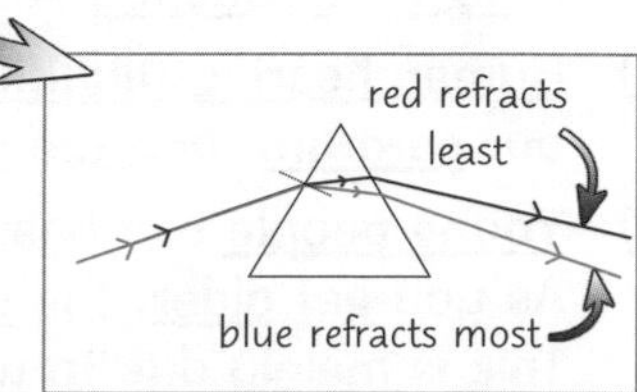

Lights, camera, refraction...

When light goes into a denser material, it slows down and bends towards the normal. But when it goes into a less dense material, it speeds up and bends away from the normal. Get it, got it, good!

Q1 Sketch a ray diagram showing parallel rays of red and violet light travelling through a rectangular glass block from air. Include the emerging rays on your diagram. [3 marks]

Sound Waves and Hearing

We hear sounds when vibrations reach our eardrums. I'm picking up good vibrations about this page...

Sound Travels as a Wave

1) Sound waves are caused by vibrating objects.
2) These vibrations are passed through the surrounding medium as a series of compressions and rarefactions. They're a type of longitudinal wave (see page 59).

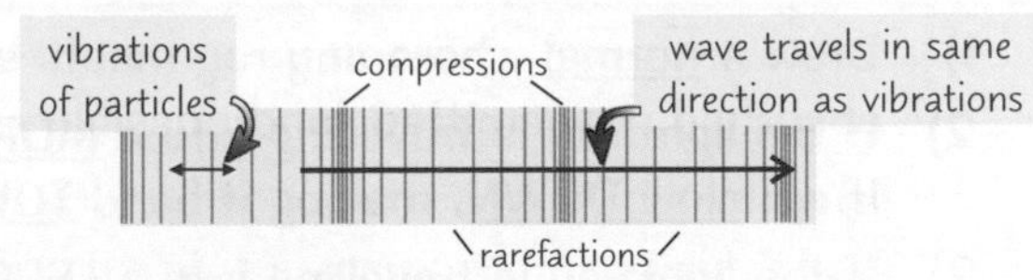

3) When a sound wave travels through a solid it does so by causing vibrations of the particles in that solid.

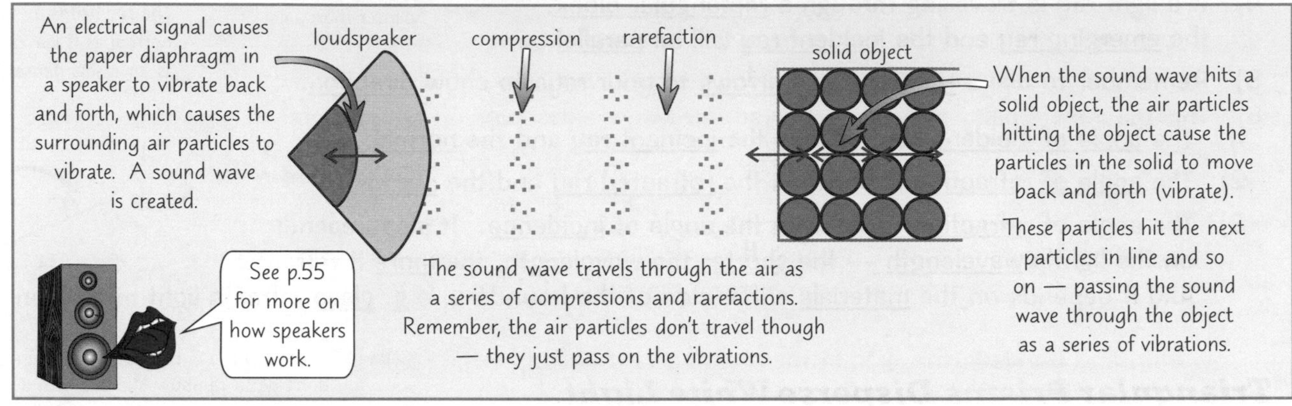

An electrical signal causes the paper diaphragm in a speaker to vibrate back and forth, which causes the surrounding air particles to vibrate. A sound wave is created.
loudspeaker
compression
rarefaction
solid object
When the sound wave hits a solid object, the air particles hitting the object cause the particles in the solid to move back and forth (vibrate).
These particles hit the next particles in line and so on — passing the sound wave through the object as a series of vibrations.
See p.55 for more on how speakers work.
The sound wave travels through the air as a series of compressions and rarefactions. Remember, the air particles don't travel though — they just pass on the vibrations.

4) Sound travels at different speeds in different media — it generally travels faster in solids than in liquids, and faster in liquids than in gases.
5) The frequency of sound doesn't change when it passes from one medium into another. But because $v = f\lambda$, the wavelength does change — it gets longer when it speeds up, and shorter when it slows down.
6) So sound waves can refract as they enter different media.
(However, since sound waves are always spreading out, the change in direction is hard to spot under normal circumstances.)
7) Sound waves will be reflected by hard flat surfaces. Echoes are just reflected sound waves.
8) Sound can't travel in space because it's mostly a vacuum (there are no particles to move or vibrate).

You Hear Sound When Your Eardrum Vibrates

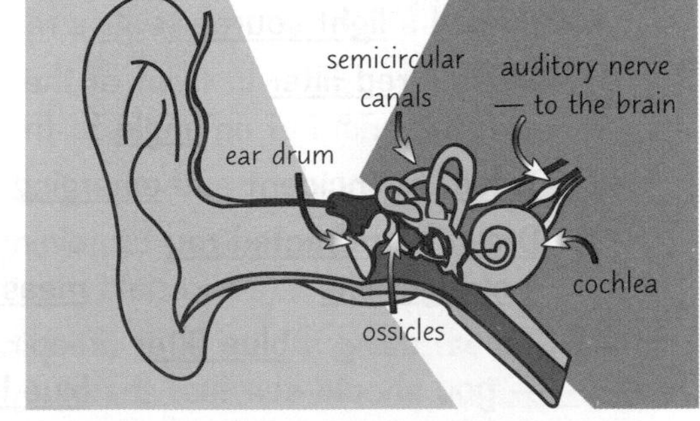

1) Sound waves that reach your eardrum cause it to vibrate.
2) These vibrations are passed on to tiny bones in your ear called ossicles, through the semicircular canal and to the cochlea.
3) The cochlea turns these vibrations into electrical signals which get sent to your brain.
4) The brain interprets the signals as sounds of different pitches and volumes, depending on their frequency and intensity. A higher frequency sound wave has a higher pitch.
5) Human hearing (audition) is limited by the size and shape of our eardrum, and the structure of all the parts within the ear that vibrate to transmit the sound wave.
6) Young people can hear frequencies ranging from about 20 Hz (low pitch) up to 20 000 Hz (high pitch). As you get older, the upper limit decreases, and sounds may need to be louder for you to hear them. This is mainly due to wear and tear of the cochlea or auditory nerve.

Sorry, listening to the radio doesn't count as revision...

A microphone is like a loudspeaker in reverse — sound waves make it vibrate, generating an electrical signal.

Q1 Explain why you wouldn't hear an explosion in space. [2 marks]

Q2 Explain how your ears allow you to hear sounds. [3 marks]

Sonar and Ultrasound

Sound's great for hearing, but we can use it for seeing things too. Crazy stuff...

Waves Get Partially Reflected at Boundaries

1) When a wave reaches a boundary between two media it can be absorbed, transmitted (and possibly refracted) or reflected (see p.61).
2) If a wave is transmitted, some of the wave is usually reflected off the boundary too. This is partial reflection.
3) So if you point a pulse of waves at a boundary, some of the wave will get reflected back, and some will carry on.
4) If you know the speed of the wave in the medium, you can use the time it takes for the reflections to reach a detector and the formula distance = speed × time to find how far away the boundary is.
5) This means we can use ultrasound (sound with frequencies above 20 kHz) to 'see' hidden things.

How much is reflected and how much is transmitted depends on the media and the wavelength of the waves.

Ultrasound is used in Medicine and Industry...

1) Ultrasound waves can pass through the body, but are partially reflected at boundaries between different tissues (e.g. between the muscles in a pregnant woman's stomach and the fluid in her womb, and between the fluid in the womb and the skin of the foetus).
2) If you know the speed of ultrasound in the different tissues, you can calculate the distance to the different boundaries.
3) The reflections are processed by a computer to produce an image.
4) So ultrasound can be used to form an image of a developing foetus. It's also used to examine soft tissues and organs like the kidneys, liver and bladder.
5) So far as we know, ultrasound imaging like this is completely safe.

ultrasound transmitter/receiver
partial reflection
womb filled with fluid
mother
foetus

1) Ultrasound can also be used to find flaws in objects such as pipes or materials such as wood or metal.
2) Ultrasound waves entering a material will usually be reflected by the far side of the material.
3) If there is a flaw such as a crack inside the object, the wave will be reflected sooner.

ultrasound waves reflected by far side of material
crack causes early reflection of waves

...and in Sonar

Sonar is used by boats and submarines to find out the distance to the seabed or to locate objects in deep water. There's more about it on page 101.

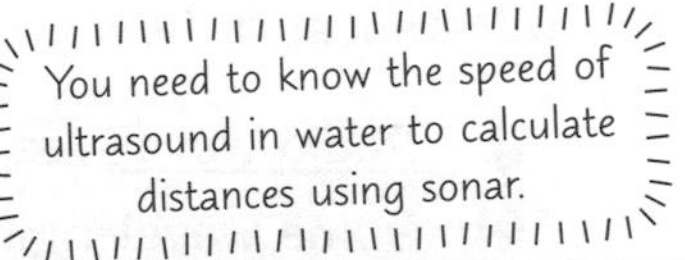

You need to know the speed of ultrasound in water to calculate distances using sonar.

A pulse of ultrasound takes 4.5 seconds to travel from a submarine to the seabed and back again. If the speed of sound in seawater is 1520 m/s, how far away is the submarine from the seabed?

1) The formula is of course distance = speed × time
2) But this is a reflection question, so the 4.5 s is the time taken for the wave to travel there and back. So you need to halve the distance.

total distance travelled = $1520 \times 4.5 = 6840$

distance to seabed = $6840 \div 2 = 3420$ m

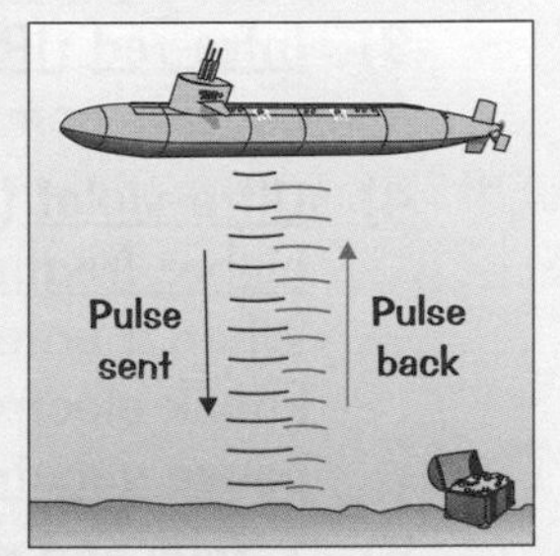

Partially reflected — completely revised...

Ultrasound waves are really useful, so make sure you can describe how to use the time taken for them to be reflected to calculate distances and 'see' things — like inside of your body (fun) or a pipe (less fun).

Q1 Calculate how long it takes for an ultrasound pulse to return to a submarine from the seabed, if the speed of sound in seawater is 1520 m/s and the submarine is 2500 m above the seabed. [3 marks]

Electromagnetic Waves

You've learned a lot about light so far, but light's just one small part of the EM spectrum...

There's a Continuous Spectrum of EM Waves

1) Electromagnetic (EM) waves are transverse waves (see page 59).
2) They all travel at the same speed (velocity) through air or space (a vacuum). But they travel at different speeds in different materials.
3) EM waves vary in wavelength from around 10^{-15} m to more than 10^4 m, and those with shorter wavelengths have higher frequencies (from $v = f\lambda$).
4) We group them based on their wavelength and frequency — there are seven basic types, but the different groups merge to form a continuous spectrum.
5) Our eyes can only detect a small part of this spectrum — visible light. Different colours of light have different wavelengths. From longest to shortest — red, orange, yellow, green, blue, indigo, violet.

Electromagnetic waves are vibrations of electric and magnetic fields (rather than vibrations of particles). This means they can travel through a vacuum.

	RADIO WAVES	MICRO WAVES	INFRA RED	VISIBLE LIGHT	ULTRA VIOLET	X-RAYS	GAMMA RAYS
wavelength	1 m – 10^4 m	10^{-2} m	10^{-5} m	10^{-7} m	10^{-8} m	10^{-10} m	10^{-15} m

long wavelength, low frequency → short wavelength, high frequency

6) All EM waves transfer energy from a source to an absorber. For example, when you warm yourself by an electric heater, infra-red waves transfer energy from the thermal energy store of the heater (the source) to your thermal energy store (the absorber).
7) The higher the frequency of the EM wave, the more energy it transfers.

Different EM Waves Have Different Properties

As you saw on page 61, when EM waves meet a boundary they can be absorbed, transmitted, refracted or reflected. What happens depends on the materials at the boundary and the wavelength of the EM wave:

- Some materials absorb some wavelengths of light but reflect others. This is what causes things to be a certain colour).
- Radio waves are refracted by some layers of the atmosphere but microwaves aren't, making them better for satellite communications.

blue light will not be transmitted

Differences in how EM waves are transmitted, reflected and absorbed have implications for human health:

1) Radio waves are transmitted through the body without being absorbed.
2) Some wavelengths of microwaves can be absorbed, causing heating of cells, which may be dangerous.
3) Infra-red (IR) and visible light are mostly reflected or absorbed by the skin, causing some heating too. IR can cause burns if the skin gets too hot.
4) Ultra-violet (UV) is also absorbed by the skin. But it has a higher frequency, so it transfers more energy, causing more damage. When it enters living cells, it collides with atoms in molecules, which may knock electrons off and cause ionisation — it's ionising radiation. This damages cells which may cause genetic mutation and cancer, and can lead to tissue damage or radiation sickness.
5) X-rays and gamma rays are also ionising, so they can cause tissue damage and cancer too. But they have even higher frequencies, so transfer even more energy, causing even more damage. They can also pass through the skin and be absorbed by deeper tissues.

The Sun produces a lot of UV radiation, but fortunately most of this is absorbed by the Earth's atmosphere.

Learn about the EM spectrum and wave goodbye to exam woe...

Here's a handy mnemonic for the order of EM waves: 'Rock Music Is Very Useful for eXperiments with Goats'.

Q1 Explain why gamma rays are more dangerous to humans than visible light. [2 marks]

Uses of EM Waves

Different EM waves have different properties, which make them useful to us in different ways.

Radio Waves are used for Communications

We use radio waves to transmit information like television and radio shows from one place to another:

1) Radio waves and all EM waves are just oscillating electric and magnetic fields.
2) Alternating currents (a.c.) in electrical circuits cause charges to oscillate. This creates an oscillating electric and magnetic field — an EM wave.
3) This EM wave will have the same frequency as the current that created it, so it can create a radio wave.
4) EM waves also cause charged particles to oscillate. If the charged particles are part of a circuit, this induces an alternating current of the same frequency as the EM wave that induced it.
5) So if you've got a transmitter and a receiver, you can encode information (e.g. a TV show) in an a.c. and then transmit it as a radio wave. The wave induces an a.c. in the receiver (e.g. the aerial) and bam, you've got your information.

There's more on a.c. on p.95.

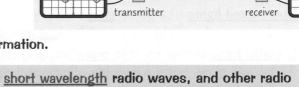

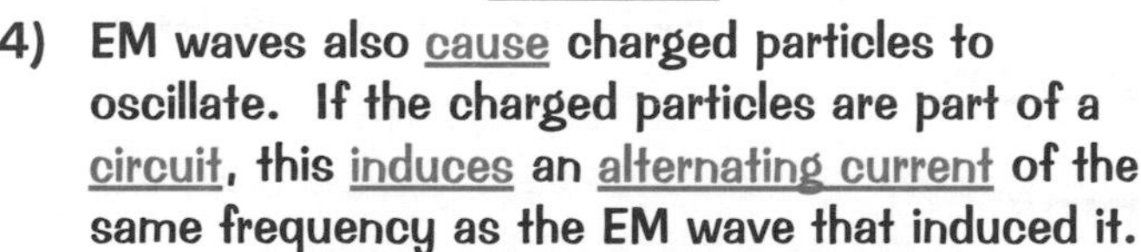

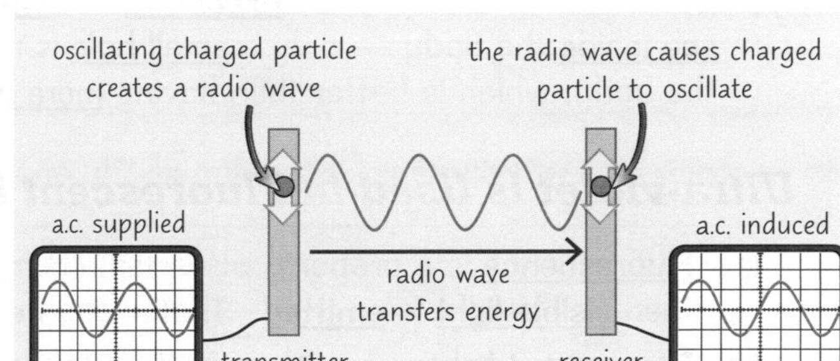

TV and FM radio transmissions use very short wavelength radio waves, and other radio transmissions (MW and LW) use medium and long-wave (funnily enough). Bluetooth® uses short radio waves to send data over short distances between devices.

Microwaves are Used for Communications and Cooking

1) Communication to and from satellites (including satellite TV signals and mobile phones) uses microwaves with a wavelength that can pass easily through the Earth's watery atmosphere.
2) We also use microwaves of a slightly different wavelength to cook food. These microwaves penetrate up to a few centimetres into the food before being absorbed and transferring energy to water molecules in the food, causing the water to heat up. The water molecules then transfer this energy to the rest of the molecules in the food by heating — which quickly cooks the food.

Infra-red Radiation Can be Used to Increase or Monitor Temperature

1) Infra-red (IR) radiation is given off by all objects. The hotter the object, the more it gives off.
2) Infra-red cameras can detect IR radiation and monitor temperature. They detect the IR and turn it into an electrical signal, which is displayed on a screen as a picture. The hotter an object is, the brighter it appears. E.g. IR is used in night-vision cameras.

3) IR radiation is also used in medical imaging (see page 69). IR cameras can detect increases in temperature caused by infections in a small area (e.g. at an infected wound) or in the whole body.
4) Absorbing IR radiation also causes objects to get hotter. Food can be cooked using IR radiation — the temperature of the food increases when it absorbs IR radiation, e.g. from a toaster's heating element.

Or you could just stream the radio over the Internet...

Microwaves are ace — without them I'd have nothing to eat and no one to talk to. Sad times.

Q1 Explain how an alternating current in a transmitter produces a radio wave. [2 marks]

Q2 Give one use of infra-red radiation. [1 mark]

More Uses of EM Waves

If you enjoyed the last page, you're in for a real treat. If not, I guess it sucks to be you...

Light Signals Can Travel Through Optical Fibres

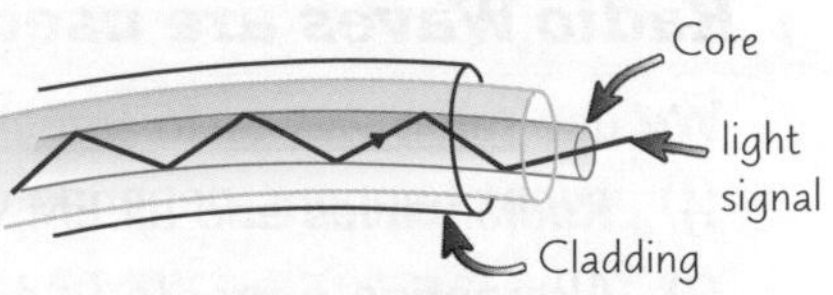

1) Light is used to look at things (and to take endless selfies and holiday snaps). But it's also used for communication using optical fibres, which carry data over long distances as pulses of light.
2) Optical fibres work by bouncing light off the sides of a very narrow core. The pulse of light enters the core at a certain angle at one end and is reflected again and again until it emerges at the other end.
3) Optical fibres are used for telephone and internet cables. They're also used for medical purposes to see inside the body — only a small hole is needed for the optical fibre (and any instruments) to enter the body, which is better than having more major surgery.

Ultra-violet is Used in Fluorescent Lamps

1) Fluorescence is a property of certain chemicals, where ultra-violet (UV) radiation is absorbed and then visible light is emitted. That's why fluorescent colours look so bright — they actually emit light.
2) Fluorescent lights use UV to emit visible light. They're energy-efficient so they're good to use when light is needed for long periods (like in your classroom).
3) Security pens can be used to mark property (e.g. laptops). Under UV light the ink will glow, but it's invisible otherwise, helping to identify stolen property.
4) UV rays can cause damage to the DNA in skin cells, so it's important to wear sunscreen if you're outside in strong sunlight.

Take that, ultrasound.

X-rays Let Us See Inside Things

1) X-rays can be used to view the internal structure of objects and materials, including our bodies.
2) They affect photographic film in the same way as light, meaning you can take X-ray photographs. But X-ray images are usually formed electronically these days.
3) Radiographers in hospitals take X-ray images to help doctors diagnose broken bones — X-rays are transmitted by flesh but are absorbed by denser material like bones or metal.
4) To produce an X-ray image, X-ray radiation is directed through the object or body onto a detector plate. The brighter bits of the image are where fewer X-rays get through, producing a negative image (the plate starts off all white).
5) Exposure to X-rays can cause cell damage, so radiographers and patients are protected as much as possible, e.g. by lead aprons and shields, and exposure to the radiation is kept to a minimum.

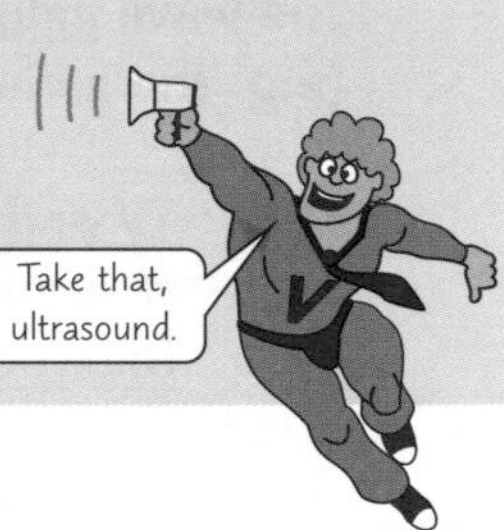

Gamma Rays are Used for Sterilising Things

1) Gamma rays are used to sterilise medical instruments — they kill microbes (e.g. bacteria).
2) This is better than trying to boil plastic instruments, which might be damaged by high temperatures.
3) Food can be sterilised in the same way — again killing microbes. This keeps the food fresh for longer, without having to freeze it, cook it or preserve it some other way, and it's perfectly safe to eat.
4) Gamma radiation is also used in cancer treatments — radiation is targeted at cancer cells to kill them. Doctors have to be careful to minimise the damage to healthy cells when treating cancer like this.
5) We also use gamma radiation in medical imaging (see page 69).

Phones, lights, medical images — what can't EM do?...

You've probably got the idea now that we use EM waves an awful lot. If you get asked about an example you haven't come across before, don't panic — just apply what you know about the EM spectrum and you'll be fine.

Q1 Give two uses of gamma rays. [2 marks]

Waves in Medical Imaging

And we're still not finished with uses of waves — is there no end to their talent...

Waves can be Used for Medical Imaging

1) As you know, when waves meet a boundary they can be absorbed, transmitted, refracted or reflected.
2) What happens depends on the type of wave and the media that make up the boundary.
3) This means that waves can be used to study things hidden from view, e.g. organs inside our body.
4) Different waves behave differently inside the body, so are useful for imaging different things. You need to know about ultrasound (see page 65), X-rays, gamma rays and infra-red.

X-rays Can Be used for Imaging Bones

1) X-rays are mostly transmitted by soft tissue, but absorbed by denser materials like bones and metal. So they can be used to diagnose conditions like bone fractures or dental problems.
2) Although X-rays are mostly transmitted by soft tissues, a little bit of absorption happens too. How much of the X-rays soft tissues absorb varies between tissues (e.g. muscles and organs).
3) This means, if you use a lot of X-rays you can produce high resolution images in 2D and 3D of soft and hard tissues in the body. These are called computerised tomography (CT) scans.

Gamma Rays are Used to See How Things Move Through the Body

Gamma rays are transmitted by skin, soft tissue and bone.
So if gamma rays are produced inside a patient, they can be detected outside the body:

1) Radiotracers are radioactive isotopes that patients either swallow or are injected with. As they move round the body, they emit gamma rays.
2) The gamma rays are detected by a gamma camera outside the patient and used to form an image.
3) The tracer is often part of a molecule that the body uses, e.g. glucose containing radioactive carbon-14. By looking at where the tracer ends up, doctors can see how the body is working. For example, cancerous tumours use more energy than healthy tissue, so they'll absorb more glucose containing the radioactive carbon and show up as bright spots on the image.

Infra-red Waves can tell You about Injuries and Infections

1) Infected or injured areas are usually hotter than other areas, so they give off more infra-red (IR). IR cameras can detect these differences in temperature and use them to create an image (see p.67).
2) This can be useful if you need to take lots of temperatures quickly (so can't use thermometers). For example, IR cameras have been used to check people at airports for signs of infection (fevers).

Medical Imaging is Full of Compromises

Some waves are dangerous, so doctors have to make compromises — they need a good enough image to diagnose problems, whilst putting the patient at as low a risk as possible:

1) Ultrasound waves are completely safe as far as we can tell. But they give a fairly fuzzy image and can only be used to make images of soft tissue (not bones).
2) X-rays are ionising, so they can cause damage to cells. But they give clear images of bones, and CT scans give useful high resolution images that you can't get from ultrasound.
3) Gamma rays are also ionising, but they can be used to get information on how the body's working.
4) Imaging with IR radiation is completely safe, but it can't tell us about very much — just temperature.

Gamma camera — sounds like an indie band from the '90s...

So many different ways of looking inside people — great for keeping you well, bad for physics revision.

Q1 Describe two ways in which X-rays are used in medical imaging. [2 marks]

Visible Light and Colour

The colour something appears to be is all about what wavelengths of light we're seeing when we look at it.

Colour and Transparency Depend on Absorbed Wavelengths

1) Colour is about differences in absorption, transmission and reflection of different wavelengths by different materials.
2) White light is a mixture of all the different colours of light, which all have different wavelengths.

3) Different objects absorb, transmit and reflect different wavelengths of light in different ways.
4) Opaque objects are objects that do not transmit light. When visible light waves hit them, they absorb some wavelengths of light and reflect others.
5) The colour of an opaque object depends on which wavelengths of light are reflected. E.g. a red apple appears to be red because the wavelengths corresponding to the red part of the visible spectrum are reflected.
6) Colours can also mix together to make other colours. The only colours you can't make by mixing are the primary colours: pure red, green and blue. So a banana may look yellow because it's reflecting yellow light OR because it's reflecting both red and green light.
7) White objects reflect all of the wavelengths of visible light equally.
8) Black objects absorb all wavelengths of visible light. Your eyes see black as the lack of any visible light (i.e. the lack of any colour).
9) Transparent (see-through) and translucent (partially see-through) objects transmit light, i.e. not all light that hits the surface of the object is absorbed or reflected — some (or most for transparent objects) can pass through.
10) Some wavelengths of light may be absorbed or reflected by translucent and (to a lesser extent) transparent objects. These objects will appear to be the colour of light that corresponds to the wavelengths most strongly transmitted by the object.

How I love my coat that reflects different wavelengths of li-ight!!!

Colour Filters Only Let Through Particular Wavelengths

white light

BLUE FILTER

All other colours are absorbed by the filter.

Blue light is transmitted.

1) Colour filters are used to filter out different wavelengths of light, so that only certain colours (wavelengths) are transmitted — the rest are absorbed.
2) A primary colour filter only transmits that colour, e.g. if white light is shone at a blue colour filter, only blue light will be let through. The rest of the light will be absorbed.
3) If you look at a blue object through a blue colour filter, it would still look blue. Blue light is reflected from the object's surface and is transmitted by the filter.
4) However, if the object was e.g. red (or any colour not made from blue light), the object would appear black when viewed through a blue filter. All of the light reflected by the object will be absorbed by the filter.
5) Filters that aren't for primary colours let through both the wavelengths of light corresponding to that colour and the wavelengths of the primary colours that can be added together to make that colour. E.g. cyan can be made from blue and green light mixed together. So a cyan colour filter will let through the wavelengths of light that correspond to cyan, blue and green.

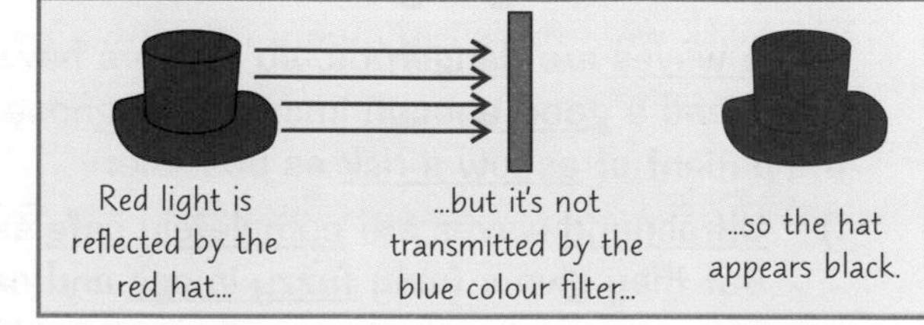

Red light is reflected by the red hat... ...but it's not transmitted by the blue colour filter... ...so the hat appears black.

Have you seen my white shirt? It's red and yellow and green and...

Hopefully you now know enough about absorption and reflection that you're feeling pretty confident. Once you've got them down, this page is pretty easy — red objects reflect red light and red filters let red light through. Simple.

Q1 a) Explain why a cucumber looks green. [2 marks]

b) State the colour a cucumber would look if you looked at it through a red filter. [1 mark]

Lenses and Images

Lenses bring light rays to a focus or spread them out. Which is pretty darn useful, I can tell you.

You Need to Know About Concave and Convex Lenses

Lenses form images by refracting light, which changes its direction. There are two main types of lens — convex and concave. They have different shapes and have opposite effects on light rays:

1) A concave (diverging) lens caves inwards. It causes parallel rays of light to diverge (spread out).
2) The axis of a lens is a line passing through the middle of the lens.
3) The principal focus (focal point) of a concave lens is the point where rays hitting the lens parallel to the axis appear to come from — trace them back until they all appear to meet up at a point behind the lens.

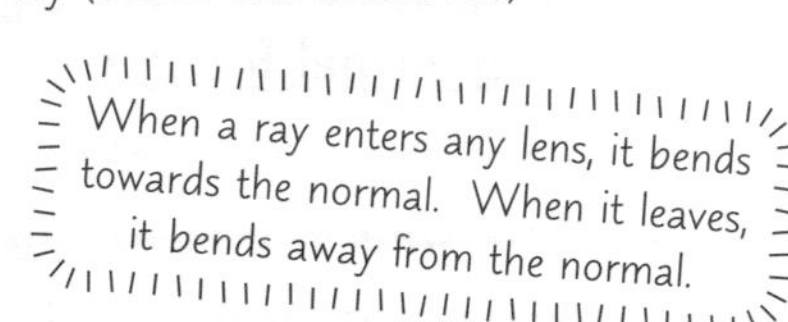

When a ray enters any lens, it bends towards the normal. When it leaves, it bends away from the normal.

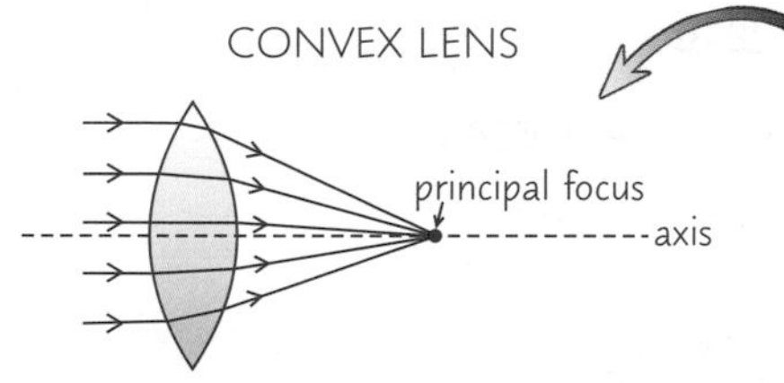

4) A convex (converging) lens bulges outwards. It causes parallel rays of light to converge (move together).
5) The principal focus of a convex lens is where rays hitting the lens parallel to the axis all meet.
6) For any lens, the distance from the centre of the lens to the principal focus is called the focal length. There's a principal focus on each side of any lens.

There are two types of image that lenses can form:

1) A **REAL image** is where the light from an object comes together to form an image on a 'screen'. E.g. the image formed on an eye's retina.
2) A **VIRTUAL image** is when the rays are diverging, so the light from the object appears to be coming from a completely different place. E.g. the image in a mirror is a virtual image.

Draw a Ray Diagram for an Image Through a Concave Lens

1) Pick a point on the top of the object. Draw a ray going from the object to the lens parallel to the axis of the lens.
2) Draw another ray from the top of the object going right through the middle of the lens.
3) The incident ray that's parallel to the axis is refracted so it appears to have come from the principal focus (F). Draw a ray from the principal focus. Make it dotted before it reaches the lens (as it's virtual here).
4) The ray passing through the middle of the lens doesn't bend.
5) Mark where this ray meets the virtual ray. That's the top of the image.
6) Repeat the process for a point on the bottom of the object. When the bottom of the object is on the axis, the bottom of the image is also on the axis.

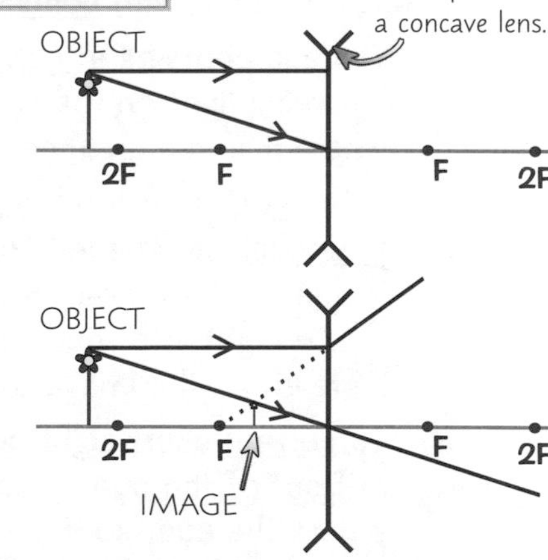

A concave lens always produces a virtual image. The image is the right way up, smaller than the object and on the same side of the lens as the object — no matter where the object is.

If the diagram shows the lens as a line, you don't need to show how the light refracts inside it. If it shows a picture of the lens (like the ones at the top of the page), then you do.

Lenses — there's absolutely nothing funny to say about them ...

...and we're not done with them yet. There's more about convex and concave lenses on the next page.

Q1 Copy and complete this diagram to show the path taken by the light rays as they pass through the lens, and after they emerge from the other side. [3 marks]

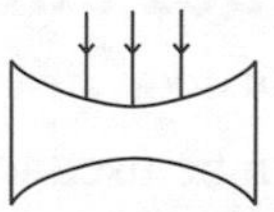

More on Lenses

You need to be able to draw ray diagrams for convex lenses too.

Draw a Ray Diagram for an Image Through a Convex Lens

In ray diagrams, this represents a convex lens.

1) Pick a point on the top of the object. Draw a ray going from the object to the lens parallel to the axis of the lens.
2) Draw another ray from the top of the object going right through the middle of the lens.
3) The incident ray that's parallel to the axis is refracted through the principal focus (F). Draw a refracted ray passing through F.
4) The ray passing through the middle of the lens doesn't bend.
5) Mark where the rays meet. That's the top of the image.
6) Repeat the process for a point on the bottom of the object. When the bottom of the object is on the axis, the bottom of the image is also on the axis.

The distance from the lens to the object affects the size and position of the image:

1) An object 2F (two focal lengths) from the lens produces a real, inverted (upside down) image the same size as the object and at 2F on the other side of the lens.
2) An object between F and 2F will make a real, inverted image bigger than the object and beyond 2F.
3) An object nearer than F will make a virtual image the right way up, bigger than the object and on the same side of the lens.

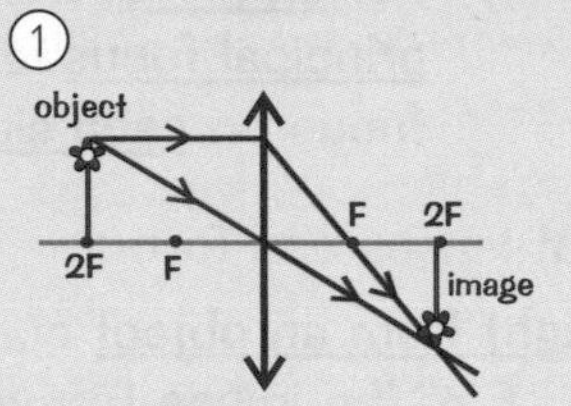

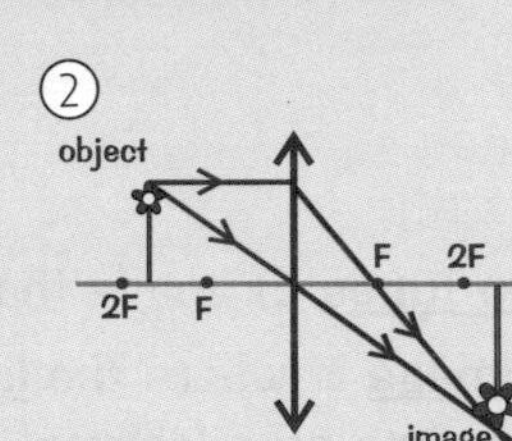

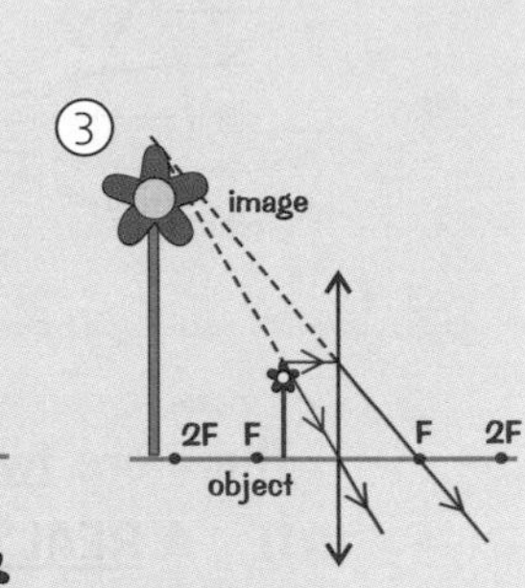

Lenses Can Correct Problems With Vision

Short-sighted people can't focus on distant objects. This is corrected with concave lenses:

1) The eye contains a convex lens to focus incoming light on the back of the eye (the retina), where it forms an image.
2) If the eyeball is too long or the lens is too powerful, the eye lens can't produce a focused image on the retina. Images of distant objects are brought into focus in front of the retina instead, so the image on the retina is blurry.
3) To correct short sight you put a concave lens in front of the eye. This diverges light before it enters the eye, so it can then be focused on the retina producing a sharp, clear image.

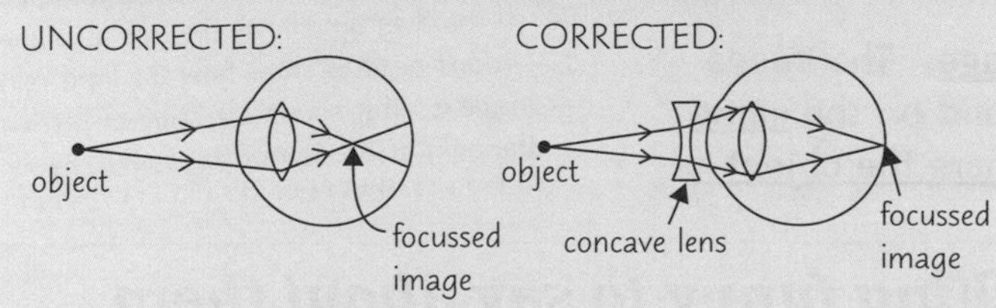

Long-sighted people can't focus on near objects. This is corrected with convex lenses:

1) Long sight happens if the lens is too weak or the eyeball is too short.
2) This means that images of near objects are brought into focus behind the back of the eye, so the image on the retina is blurry.
3) To correct long sight a convex lens is put in front of the eye. This means the light starts to converge before it enters the eye, so it can then be focused on the retina.

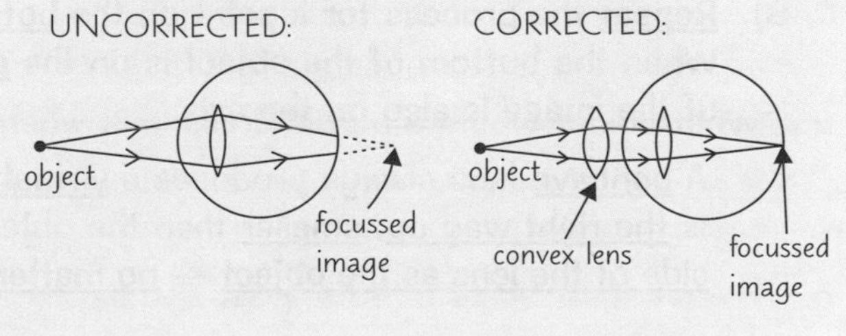

And not looking cool enough is corrected with sunglasses...

Phew, that's waves done and dusted. Just make sure you've got your head round all those diagrams.

Q1 Explain how lenses can be used to correct the vision of a short-sighted person. [3 marks]

Revision Questions for Topic P5

It's not quite time to wave goodbye to those pesky waves yet — have a go at these revision questions.

- Try these questions and tick off each one when you get it right.
- When you've done all the questions under a heading and are completely happy with it, tick it off.

Wave Basics (p.59-60)

1) Sketch a diagram of a wave. Label the amplitude, wavelength and rest position, and a crest and a trough.
2) What is the difference between a transverse wave and a longitudinal wave? Give one example of each.
3) Describe an experiment to measure the speed of sound.
4) Describe an experiment to measure the wavelength of a water wave.

Reflection and Refraction (p.61-63)

5) What three things can happen to a wave at a boundary between materials?
6) What is the one simple rule for all reflected waves?
7) What is the normal?
8) What causes waves to refract?
9) Draw a diagram showing specular reflection.
10) Why don't you get a clear reflection from a rough surface?
11) Describe an experiment for investigating the refraction of light by a prism.
12) Does light bend towards or away from the normal when entering air from glass?

Sound Waves (p.64-65)

13) What type of wave is a sound wave?
14) Which part of the ear converts vibrations into electrical signals?
15) What is ultrasound? Explain how it is used in medical imaging.

E.M. Waves (p.66-69)

16) What type of wave are EM waves?
17) List the waves in the EM spectrum, in order of increasing wavelength.
18) Explain why ultra-violet waves are dangerous.
19) Give one use of each type of EM wave.
20) Give one use of infra-red in medical imaging.

Light and Lenses (p.70-72)

21) Explain why the writing on the line above looks blue.
22) What colour would a purple dress look when viewed in yellow light?
23) Sketch a ray diagram of two parallel light rays, that are also parallel to the lens axis, passing through a convex lens. Label the principal focus.
24) Sketch a ray diagram of two parallel light rays, that are also parallel to the lens axis, passing through a concave lens. Label the principal focus.
25) Sketch a ray diagram showing the path of light through the eye of:
    a) a person with long sight without a correcting lens.
    b) a person with long sight with a correcting lens.

Isotopes and Radioactive Decay

Understanding what isotopes are is important for learning about radioactive decay. So let's get cracking.

Isotopes are Different Forms of the Same Element

1) Atoms consist of a nucleus (made up of protons and neutrons), surrounded by electrons.
2) The atomic/proton number is the number of protons in an atom. The number of protons defines what the element is (e.g. a carbon atom always has 6 protons).
3) Since protons are positively charged and neutrons are neutral, the nucleus of each element has a particular overall positive charge.
4) The mass number is the number of protons plus the number of neutrons in an atom — it tells you the mass of the nucleus.
5) You can represent atoms using this notation: Mass number — A, Atomic number — Z, X — Chemical symbol ($^{A}_{Z}X$)
6) Isotopes are atoms of the same element — they have the same number of protons but a different number of neutrons. So isotopes have a different nuclear mass but the same nuclear charge.

So isotopes have the same atomic number, but different mass numbers.

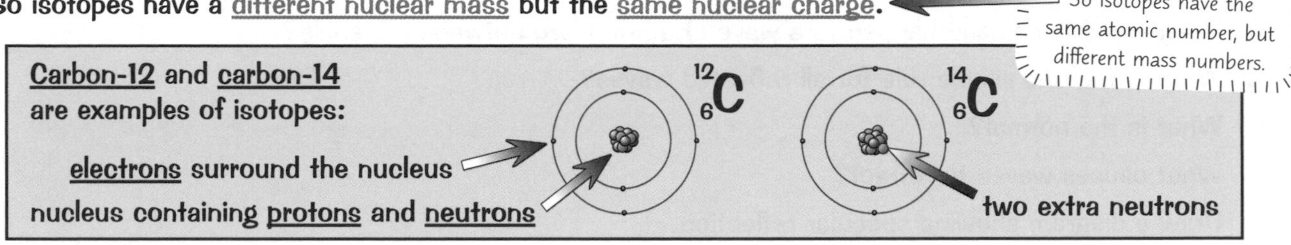

7) Most elements have different isotopes, but there are usually only one or two stable ones.
8) The other isotopes tend to be unstable and radioactive, which means they give out nuclear radiation and may decay into other elements (see below).

There are Different Ways that Nuclei can Decay

When a nucleus decays, it will spit out one or more of four types of radiation — alpha, beta, gamma or neutron. In the process, the nucleus will often change into a new element, as the nucleus changes its charge, its mass or both (see page 75).

- An alpha particle (α) is two neutrons and two protons — the same as a helium nucleus. They have a relative mass of 4 and a charge of +2.
- They are relatively big and heavy and slow moving.

- A beta particle (β) is simply an electron, with virtually no mass and a charge of −1.
- Beta particles move quite fast and are quite small.
- For every beta particle emitted, a neutron turns to a proton in the nucleus.

- After spitting out an alpha or beta particle, the nucleus might need to get rid of some extra energy. It does this by emitting a gamma ray — a type of electromagnetic wave.
- Gamma rays (γ) have no mass and no charge. They are just energy, so they don't change the element of the nucleus that emits them.

- If a nucleus contains a lot of neutrons, it may just throw out a neutron.
- The number of protons stays the same, but it now has a different nuclear mass, so it becomes an isotope of the same element.

Isotopes of an outfit — same dress, different accessories...

I'd learn those alpha, beta, gamma and neutron radiations if I were you. They'll be coming up again, mark my words.

Q1 Isotope A of an element has a mass number of 15 and an atomic number of 7.
Isotope B of the same element has 7 neutrons. What is the mass number of isotope B? [1 mark]

Radiation Properties and Decay Equations

Time to learn a bit more about some of the types of radiation before putting them in equations. How thrilling.

Different Types of Radiation Have Different Penetration Properties

1) When radiation travels through a material, it can collide with the material's atoms, which slows down or stops the radiation. This means the radiation can only penetrate so far into a material before it's absorbed. The range of the radiation depends on the type of radiation and material it's travelling through.

   Alpha particles don't get very far before they start hitting atoms — they have the shortest range in a material. Beta particles can travel quite far before hitting an atom. Gamma radiation travels a long way before hitting an atom — so gamma radiation has the longest range in a material.

2) Count rate is the number of radioactive particles that reach a detector in a given time. The further the radiation has to travel, the higher the chance it will be absorbed by the material it is travelling through. This means the count rate decreases the further the detector is from a radioactive source.

3) The different penetration properties means each nuclear radiation can be stopped by different materials:

   - Alpha particles are blocked by e.g. paper.
   - Beta particles are blocked by e.g. thin aluminium.
   - Gamma rays are blocked by e.g. thick lead.

   The alpha and beta particles would also be blocked by the lead, and the alpha particles would also be blocked by the aluminium.

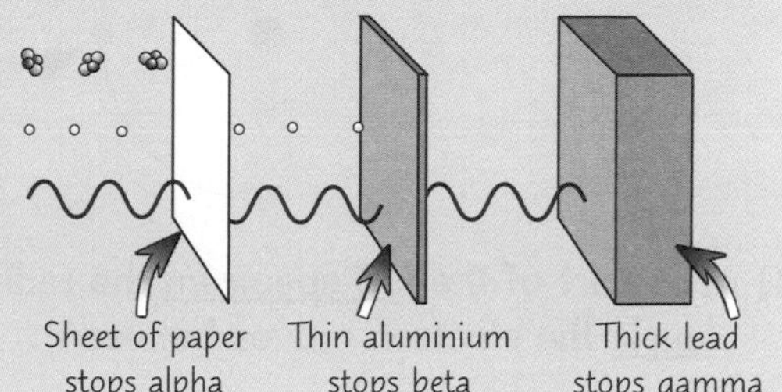
Sheet of paper stops alpha
Thin aluminium stops beta
Thick lead stops gamma

You Need to be Able to Balance Nuclear Equations

You can write nuclear decays as nuclear equations. You need to be able to balance these equations for alpha, beta and gamma decays by balancing the total masses and charges on each side.

Alpha Radiation

When a nucleus emits an alpha particle:

- the mass number decreases by 4 — as it loses two protons and two neutrons.
- the atomic number decreases by 2 — because it has two less protons.

$$^{226}_{88}\text{Ra} \rightarrow {}^{222}_{86}\text{Rn} + {}^{4}_{2}\alpha$$

mass number:	226	→	222	+	4 (= 226)
atomic number:	88	→	86	+	2 (= 88)

In both alpha and beta emissions, a new element will be formed, as the number of protons changes.

Beta Radiation

When a nucleus emits a beta particle, a neutron changes into a proton, so:

- The mass number doesn't change — as it has lost a neutron but gained a proton.
- The atomic number increases by 1 — because it has one more proton.

$$^{14}_{6}\text{C} \rightarrow {}^{14}_{7}\text{N} + {}^{0}_{-1}\beta$$

mass number:	14	→	14	+	0	(= 14)
atomic number:	6	→	7	+	(–1)	(= 6)

You can also write the beta particle as ${}^{0}_{-1}e^{-}$ in equations.

Gamma Radiation

When a nucleus emits a gamma ray:

- The mass number and the atomic number don't change.
- You might see gamma rays written as γ in balanced equations.

$$^{234}_{91}\text{Pa} \rightarrow {}^{234}_{91}\text{Pa} + \gamma$$

I think balancing equations is more fun than anything ever...

Right? Right?? *cough* I can't see your face, but I'm going to take a wild guess and say you don't believe me.

Q1 A uranium (U) atom with 92 protons and 146 neutrons decays into a thorium (Th) atom by emitting an alpha particle. Write a balanced equation to show this decay. [3 marks]

Electron Energy Levels

There's some quirky stuff on this page — and the best part is that you can tell everyone you've been doing a little quantum physics today. Honestly. And if you study physics to a higher level, things get even quirkier.

Electrons Can be Excited to Higher Energy Levels

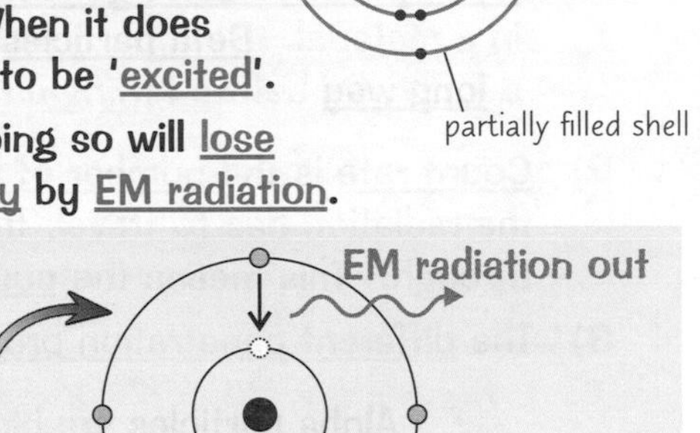

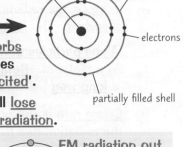

1) Electrons in an atom sit in different energy levels or shells. Each energy level is a different distance from the nucleus.
2) An inner electron can move up one or more energy levels in one go if it absorbs electromagnetic (EM) radiation with the right amount of energy. When it does move up, it moves to an partially filled (or empty) shell and is said to be 'excited'.
3) The electron will then fall back to its original energy level, and in doing so will lose the same amount of energy it absorbed. The energy is carried away by EM radiation.

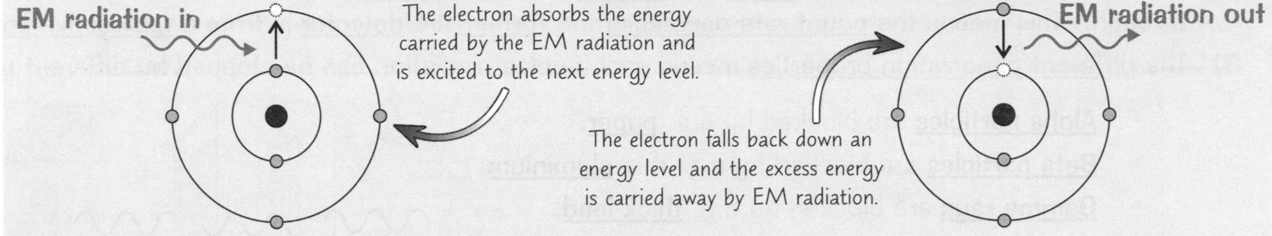

EM radiation in
The electron absorbs the energy carried by the EM radiation and is excited to the next energy level.
The electron falls back down an energy level and the excess energy is carried away by EM radiation.
EM radiation out

4) The part of the EM spectrum the radiation is from depends on its energy (which depends on the energy levels the electron moves between). A higher energy means a higher frequency of EM radiation.

An Atom is Ionised if it Loses an Electron

1) If an outer electron absorbs radiation with enough energy, it can move so far that it leaves the atom. It is now a free electron and the atom is said to have been ionised.
2) The atom is now a positive ion. It's positive because there are now more protons than electrons.
3) An atom can lose more than one electron. The more electrons it loses, the greater its positive charge.

Nuclear Radiation Ionises Atoms

1) Alpha, beta and gamma radiation can ionise atoms, and so can also be called ionising radiation.
2) The ionisation power is different for different ionising radiations — this is a measure of how likely it is that the radiation will ionise an atom.
3) Alpha particles have the highest ionisation power — this means that they can't travel very far through a substance without hitting an atom and ionising it. Gamma radiation has the lowest ionisation power.

Fluorescent Tubes use Excited Electrons to Produce Light

1) Fluorescent tubes contain mercury vapour. Electrons are accelerated through the mercury vapour, which ionises some of the mercury atoms, producing more free electrons.
2) When this flow of free electrons collides with electrons in other mercury atoms, the electrons in the mercury atoms are excited to higher energy levels.
3) When these excited electrons return to their original energy levels, they emit radiation in the ultraviolet range of the electromagnetic spectrum (see page 66).
4) A phosphorus coating on the inside of the tube absorbs this radiation, exciting its electrons to higher energy levels. These electrons then cascade down the energy levels, emitting many different frequencies of radiation, all in the visible part of the electromagnetic spectrum.

What's an atom's favourite chore? Ioning...

So, an electron absorbs EM radiation and moves up one or more energy levels, then falls back to its original energy level and loses the same amount of energy it absorbed, which is carried away by EM radiation. Simple...

Q1 What is a positive ion and how is one formed? [2 marks]

Half-Life

Radioactive decay is totally random, so how can we know how an isotope will decay? I give you, half-lives.

The Radioactivity of a Sample Always Decreases Over Time

1) Radioactive decay is a random process, so you can't predict when a particular nucleus is going to decay.
2) Instead, you can make predictions about large numbers of nuclei of an isotope.
3) Radioactive isotopes decay at different rates. The number of unstable nuclei that decay in a given time is called the activity and is measured in becquerels (Bq) — the number of nuclei that decay each second.
4) The radiation emitted from a decaying nucleus can be detected using a Geiger Muller tube, which measures the count rate (see page 75) in counts per minute (or per second).
5) As more unstable nuclei decay, the activity of the source as a whole decreases.
6) How quickly the activity decreases is given by the half-life:

The half-life of a source is the average time taken for its activity (or count rate) to halve.

If the activity of a source decreases, the count rate (at a fixed distance) also decreases.

7) It can also be thought of as the average time taken for half of the remaining unstable nuclei to decay.
8) A short half-life means the activity falls quickly, because lots of the nuclei decay in a short time.
9) A long half-life means the activity falls more slowly because most of the nuclei don't decay for a long time — they just sit there, basically unstable, but kind of biding their time.

When the activity's really low, the randomness of radioactive decay becomes more noticeable.

Half-Life can be Calculated from Numbers or from a Graph

You could be asked to calculate how you'd expect the activity of a source to change over time:

A sample of a radioactive isotope has an activity of 1000 Bq and a half-life of 5 years:

- After 1 half-life (5 years) the activity will be 1000 ÷ 2 = 500 Bq.
- After 2 half-lives (10 years) the activity will be 500 ÷ 2 = 250 Bq.

You can also find the net decline of a sample — how much the activity (or the number of undecayed nuclei) decreases by over a period of time — normally a ratio.

For this example, the net decline of the sample after 2 half-lives (10 years) is 1000 – 250 = 750 Bq. Or as a ratio: decrease in activity/original activity = 750/1000 = 3/4.

You also need to be able to find the half-life of a sample from a graph...

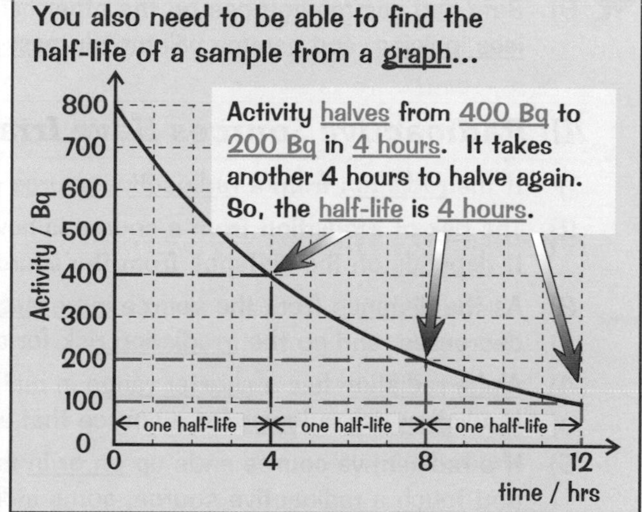

If you're given count rates rather then activity, you can find the half-life in exactly the same way.

EXAMPLE: The count rate of a radioactive sample is measured as 640 counts per minute. Two hours later it has fallen to 40 counts per minute. Find its half-life.

1) Count how many half-lives it took to fall to 40 counts per minute.

Initial count:		after 1 half-life:		after 2 half-lives:		after 3 half-lives:		after 4 half-lives:
640	(÷2) →	320	(÷2) →	160	(÷2) →	80	(÷2) →	40

2) Calculate the half-life of the sample. Two hours is four half-lives — so the half-life is 2 hours ÷ 4 = 30 min

Half-life of a box of chocolates — about five minutes...

To measure half-life, you time how long it takes for the counts per minute (or second) to halve.

Q1 The half-life of a radioactive source is 60 hr. Find its activity after 240 hr, if it is initially 480 Bq. [2 marks]

Dangers of Radioactivity

Time to find out about the hazards of ionising radiation — it damages living cells when it ionises atoms.

Ionising Radiation Harms Living Cells

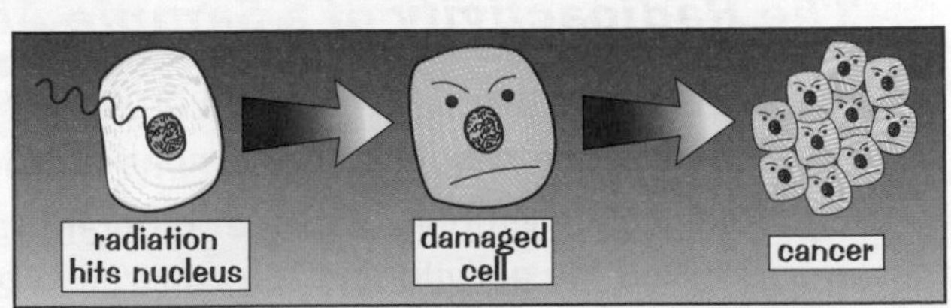

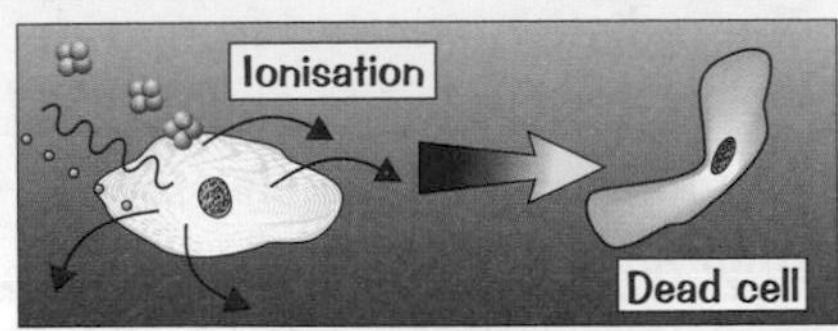

1) Some materials absorb ionising radiation — it can enter living cells and interact with molecules.
2) These interactions cause ionisation (they produce charged particles called ions).
3) Lower doses of ionising radiation damage living cells by causing mutations in the DNA. This can cause the cell to divide uncontrollably — which is cancer.
4) Higher doses tend to kill cells completely, which causes radiation sickness if a lot of cells all get blasted at once.

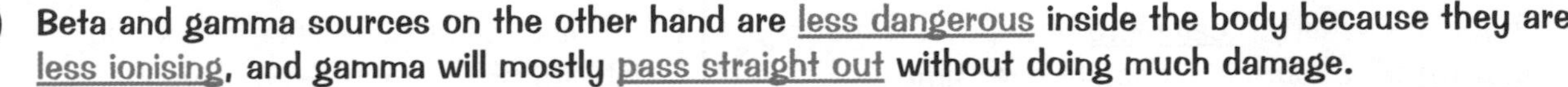

Which Radiation is the Most Dangerous Depends on Where it is

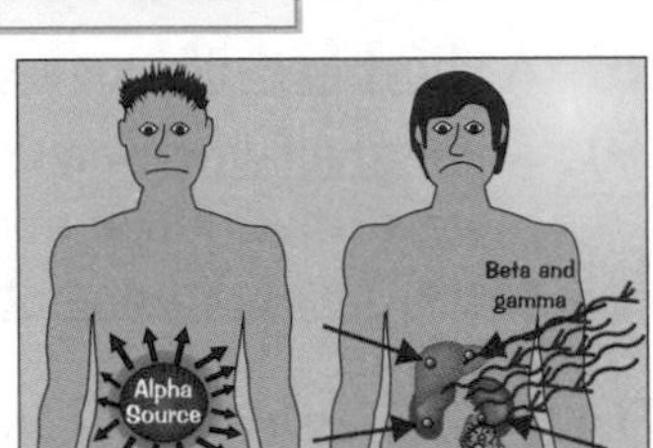

1) OUTSIDE the body, beta and gamma sources are the most dangerous.
2) This is because beta and gamma can still get inside to the delicate organs — they can pass through skin.
3) Alpha is much less dangerous because it can't penetrate the skin.
4) INSIDE the body, an alpha source is the most dangerous because they're the most ionising and they do all their damage in a very localised area.
5) Beta and gamma sources on the other hand are less dangerous inside the body because they are less ionising, and gamma will mostly pass straight out without doing much damage.

All Radioactive Sources Have Irradiation and Contamination Risks

1) If the radiation from a radioactive source reaches an object, the object is said to be irradiated.
2) The risk of irradiation from a source is how likely it is that an object will be irradiated by the source. It depends on the distance from the source and the type of radiation that the source emits.
3) As the distance from the source increases, the amount of radiation reaching that point decreases, and so the irradiation risk for any source is lower at larger distances.
4) Alpha radiation has a shorter range in materials compared to gamma radiation, so the irradiation risk is lower for a source that emits alpha radiation (at a given distance).
5) If a radioactive source ends up on or in the object, we say the object is contaminated — e.g. if you touch a radioactive source, some atoms of it might rub off onto your hand, contaminating you.
6) The contamination risk is how likely it is that an object could get contaminated. If a radioactive source is a solid, then there's no contamination risk for an object that doesn't touch the source. But if the source is a gas, then it could move and come into contact with the object, increasing the contamination risk. Gases are particularly dangerous for people as they can be inhaled, contaminating you from the inside.
7) If an object becomes contaminated, then the irradiation risk due to the source is very high as the distance between the source and object is so small.
8) Irradiation is temporary — if the source is taken away, any irradiation it's causing stops. Contamination lasts longer — if the original source is taken away, the atoms causing the contamination are left behind, potentially causing more harm.

Top tip number 364 — if something is radioactive, don't lick it...

If you're working with radioactive sources, read about the safety risks and make experiments as safe as possible.

Q1 Give two effects that ionising radiation can have on living cells. [2 marks]

Q2 Compare the irradiation risks and the contamination risks of a radioactive solid that emits alpha radiation and a radioactive solid that emits beta radiation when they are the same distance from a person. [4 marks]

Half-Life and Uses of Radiation

Ionising radiation is very dangerous stuff, but used in the right way it can be so useful that it saves lives.

The Hazards Associated with a Radioactive Source Depend on its Half-Life

1) The lower the activity of a radioactive source, the safer it is to be around.
2) If two sources with different half-lives contain the same number of radioactive nuclei, the source with the longer half-life will have a lower activity (since its atoms are less likely to decay).
3) If two sources with different half-lives start off with the same activity, the activity of the sample with the shorter half-life will fall faster than the activity of the sample with the longer-half life (assuming they both produce the same kind of radiation). So, after a while, the source with the longer half-life will have a higher activity and will be more dangerous to be around.
4) When choosing a radioactive source for an application, it's sometimes important to find a balance between a source that has a high enough activity to be useful but that won't be dangerous for too long.

Tracers in Medicine — Short Half-life Gamma Emitters

1) Certain radioactive isotopes that emit gamma radiation are used as tracers in the body.
2) They can be injected or ingested (drunk or eaten) to see how parts of the body are working, e.g. organs.
3) They spread through the body and their progress is followed on the outside using a radiation detector.
4) They need a relatively short half-life — i.e. a few hours, so that the radioactivity in the patient quickly disappears, but long enough that it still emits enough radiation by the time it reaches the correct place.
5) All medical tracers are usually GAMMA (never alpha) sources — gamma radiation can penetrate tissue, so pass out of the body and are detected. Alpha can't, and is more dangerous inside the body.

Radiotherapy — the Treatment of Cancer Using Radiation

1) Since high doses of radiation will kill living cells, they can be used to treat cancers.
2) The radiation is directed carefully and at a specific dosage (depending on the size and type of tumour, and size and age of patient), so it kills the cancer cells without damaging too many normal cells.
3) However, a fair bit of damage is often done to normal cells, which makes the patient feel very ill. But if the cancer is successfully killed off in the end, then it's worth it.

To treat cancer externally (using gamma rays):

- The gamma rays are focused on the tumour using a wide beam.
- The patient stays still and the beam is rotated round them with the tumour at the centre.

γ rays focused on tumour

Source rotated outside the body.

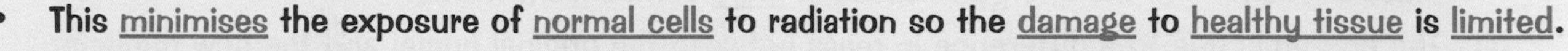

- This minimises the exposure of normal cells to radiation so the damage to healthy tissue is limited.
- The treatment is given in doses with time between for the healthy cells to be repaired or replaced.

To treat cancer internally:

- Implants containing beta-emitters are placed next to or inside the tumour. The beta particles damage the cells in the tumour, but have a short enough range that the damage to healthy tissue is limited.

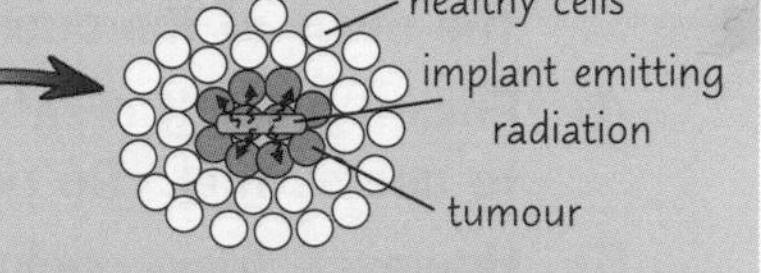

- An implant with a long half-life should be removed to stop the radiation killing healthy cells once the cancerous cells have been killed. If the half-life is short enough, the implant can be left in.
- Alpha-emitters can be injected into a tumour. Alpha particles are strongly ionising, so they do lots of damage to the cancer cells. But as they have a short range, damage to normal tissue is limited.

So radiation is pretty handy in medicine...

Try making lists of when and why the different types of radiation are used in medicine to see what you've learnt.

Q1 Explain why radioactive sources that emit alpha radiation are not used as medical tracers. [2 marks]

Fission and Fusion

Splitting up and squishing together nuclei can release some serious energy. Read on to find out how...

Nuclear Fission — the Splitting Up of Big Atomic Nuclei

Nuclear fission is a type of nuclear reaction that is used to release energy from large and unstable nuclei (e.g. uranium or plutonium) by splitting them into smaller nuclei.
Nuclear fission can occur in two ways:

- Spontaneously — the fission is unforced and happens by itself.
- By absorbing a neutron — if a nucleus absorbs a neutron then it becomes unstable and splits.

When a large nucleus splits it forms two new smaller nuclei (usually radioactive), and possibly a few neutrons. A nucleus splitting gives out a lot of energy — some of this energy is transferred to the kinetic energy stores of the fission products. There is also a lot of extra energy which is carried away by gamma radiation.

Nuclear Fission can Lead to a Chain Reaction

1) Nuclear fission of uranium can happen if a slow moving neutron is absorbed into a uranium nucleus. This addition of a neutron makes the nucleus unstable, which causes it to split.

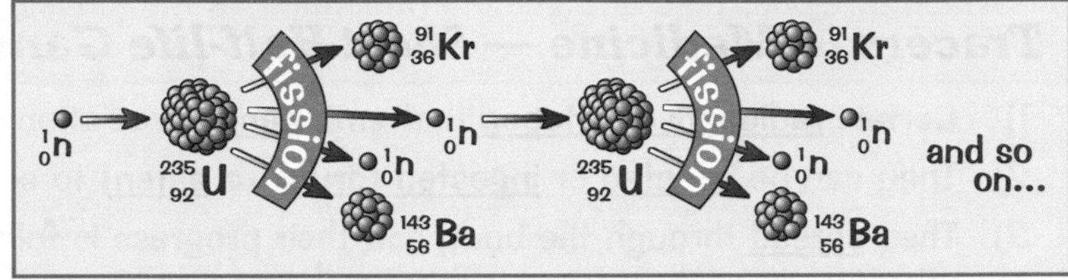

2) Each time a uranium nucleus splits up, it spits out two or three neutrons, some of which might be absorbed by other nuclei, causing them to split too, and thus causing a chain reaction.
3) Nuclear power stations generate electricity from chain reactions, using uranium or plutonium as fuel.
4) The energy which is released in the chain reaction is used to heat water to make steam, which is used to drive a steam turbine connected to an electricity generator.
5) The main problem with nuclear power is the disposal of waste. The products left over after fission are highly radioactive and have long half-lives. They're difficult and expensive to dispose of safely.
6) Nuclear fuel is cheap but the overall cost of nuclear power is high due to the cost of the power plant and final decommissioning. Dismantling a nuclear plant safely takes decades.
7) Nuclear power carries the risk of radiation leaks from the plant or major catastrophes like Chernobyl.

Nuclear Fusion — the Joining of Small Atomic Nuclei

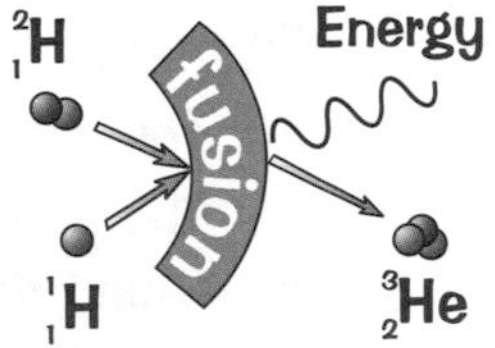

1) Two light nuclei can join to create a larger nucleus — this is called nuclear fusion. For example, two hydrogen nuclei can fuse to form a helium nucleus.
2) Fusion releases a lot of energy (more than fission for a given mass of fuel) — all the energy released in stars comes from fusion.
3) The energy is due to a difference in mass between the original nuclei and the new nucleus. For example, in the diagram on the right, the total mass of the hydrogen nuclei is larger than the mass of the helium nucleus. This extra mass is converted into energy and carried away by radiation. The mass of the nuclei before fusion will always be larger than the mass of the nucleus after fusion.
4) Fusion doesn't create radioactive waste, and there's plenty of hydrogen knocking about to use as fuel. So people are trying to develop fusion reactors to generate electricity.
5) However, fusion only happens at really high temperatures, about 10 000 000 °C, and high pressures. To keep the hydrogen in these conditions, you need an extremely strong magnetic field.
6) There are a few experimental reactors around, but none of them are generating electricity yet.

Ten million degrees — that's hot...

Fission — splitting up big nuclei for energy. Fusion — combining small nuclei for energy. Nowt else to it. Well...

Q1 In nuclear fission, what happens to the excess energy that isn't transferred to the kinetic energy stores of the smaller nuclei and neutrons produced? [1 mark]

Q2 When two nuclei fuse together, energy is released. Where does this energy come from? [1 mark]

Revision Questions for Topic P6

Well, that wraps up Topic P6 — so have a go at these questions to see what needs a bit more practice.

- Try these questions and tick off each one when you get it right.
- When you've done all the questions under a heading and are completely happy with it, tick it off.

Types of Radiation (p.74-76)

1) What is the atomic number of an atom?
2) What is the mass number of an atom?
3) Define an isotope.
4) When is nuclear radiation produced?
5) What is an alpha particle?
6) What is a beta particle?
7) Which of alpha, beta and gamma radiation has the longest range in air?
8) What happens to the count rate of radiation with an increasing distance from the source of radiation?
9) Which types of radiation are stopped by: a) paper, b) thin aluminium, c) thick lead?
10) State what happens to the mass number and atomic number of a nucleus that undergoes alpha decay.
11) State what happens to the mass number and atomic number of a nucleus that undergoes beta decay.
12) What is electron excitation and when does it occur?
13) List alpha, beta and gamma radiation in the order of how strongly ionising they are.

Applications of Radioactive Sources (p.77-78)

14) What is meant by the activity of a radioactive source and what are its units?
15) Define the half-life of a radioactive source.
16) What is meant by the net decline in activity for a radioactive source?
17) Explain how radiation can lead to cancer.
18) What is the irradiation risk of a radioactive source?
19) What is the contamination risk of a radioactive source?

Uses of Unstable Nuclei (p.79-80)

20) What types of radiation could be produced by a radioactive source that's used as a medical tracer?
21) Explain how radioactive sources are used as medical tracers.
22) Describe how gamma sources are used to treat a tumour in the body.
23) Explain how implants can be used to treat tumours.
24) What is nuclear fission?
25) How can nuclear fission lead to a chain reaction?
26) What is nuclear fusion?

Conservation of Energy

Energy. Might seem a tricky little beast, but know this — it can be transferred and stored in different ways.

Energy is Transferred Between Energy Stores

Energy can be held in different stores. Here are the stores you need to learn, plus examples of objects with energy in each of these stores:

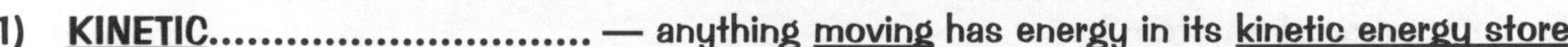

1) **KINETIC**............................ — anything moving has energy in its kinetic energy store.
2) **THERMAL**............................ — any object — the hotter it is, the more energy it has in this store.
3) **CHEMICAL**.......................... — anything that can release energy by a chemical reaction, e.g. food, fuels.
4) **GRAVITATIONAL POTENTIAL**... — anything in a gravitational field (i.e. anything which can fall).
5) **ELASTIC POTENTIAL**............. — anything stretched, like springs and rubber bands.
6) **ELECTROSTATIC**.................. — e.g. two charges that attract or repel each other.
7) **MAGNETIC**.......................... — e.g. two magnets that attract or repel each other.
8) **NUCLEAR**............................ — atomic nuclei release energy from this store in nuclear reactions.

Energy can be transferred between stores in four main ways:

Mechanically — an object moving due to a force acting on it, e.g. pushing, pulling, stretching or squashing.
Electrically — a charge moving through a potential difference, e.g. charges moving round a circuit.
By heating — energy transferred from a hotter object to a colder object, e.g. heating a pan of water on a hob.
By radiation — energy transferred e.g. by light/sound waves, e.g. energy from the Sun reaching Earth by light.

There is a Law of Conservation of Energy

There are plenty of different stores of energy, but energy always obeys the law below:

> Energy can be stored, transferred between stores, and dissipated — but it can never be created or destroyed. The total energy of a closed system has no net change.

Dissipated is a fancy way of saying the energy is spread out and lost.

A closed system is just a system (a collection of objects) that can be treated completely on its own, without any matter being exchanged with the surroundings.

Energy Transfers Show... well... the Transfer of Energy

In the exam, they might ask you about any situation where energy is transferred. If you understand a few different examples, it'll be easier to think through whatever they ask you about in the exam.

A BALL ROLLING UP A SLOPE: energy is transferred mechanically from the kinetic energy store of the ball to its gravitational potential energy store.

A BAT HITTING A BALL: some energy in the kinetic energy store of the bat is transferred mechanically to the thermal energy stores of the bat, the ball and their surroundings. Some energy is transferred mechanically from the kinetic energy store of the bat to the kinetic energy store of the ball. The rest of the energy is carried away by sound.

A CAR SLOWING DOWN (without braking): energy in the kinetic energy store of the car is transferred mechanically (due to friction between the tyres and road) and then by heating to the thermal energy stores of the car and road.

AN ELECTRIC KETTLE BOILING WATER: energy is transferred electrically from the mains to the thermal energy store of the kettle's heating element. It is then transferred by heating to the thermal energy store of the water.

Energy can't be created or destroyed — only talked about a lot...

This is important, so remember it. Energy can only be transferred to a different store, never destroyed.

Q1 Describe the energy transfers for a falling ball landing on the ground without bouncing. [3 marks]

Q2 Describe the energy transfers that occur when a piece of wood is burning. [2 marks]

Efficiency

So energy is transferred between different stores. But not all of the energy is transferred to useful stores.

Most Energy Transfers Involve Some Losses, Often by Heating

1) You've already met the law of conservation of energy on the previous page, but another important principle you need to know is:

Energy is only useful when it is transferred from one store to a useful store.

2) Useful devices can transfer energy from one store to a useful store.
3) However, some of the input energy is always lost or wasted, often to thermal energy stores by heating. For example, a motor will transfer energy to its kinetic energy store (useful), but will also transfer energy to the thermal energy stores of the motor and the surroundings (wasted).

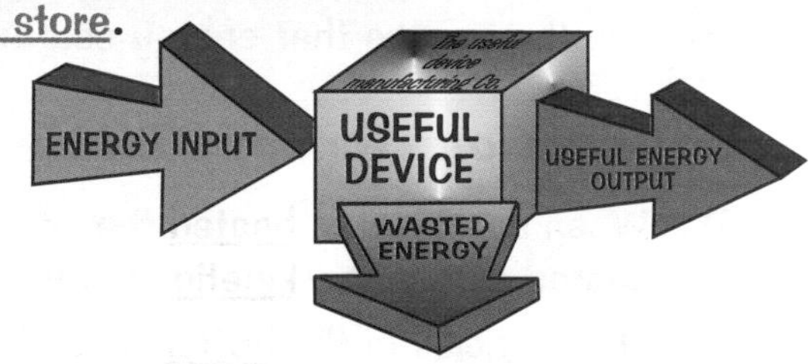

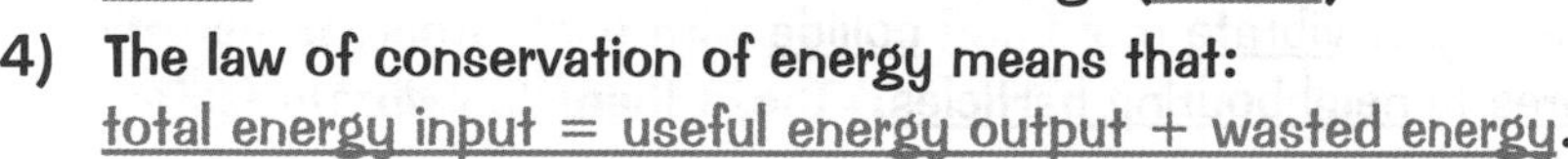

4) The law of conservation of energy means that:
total energy input = useful energy output + wasted energy.
5) The less energy that's wasted, the more efficient the device is said to be.

The amount of energy wasted can often be reduced — see page 85.

You can Calculate the Efficiency of an Energy Transfer

The efficiency of any device is defined as:

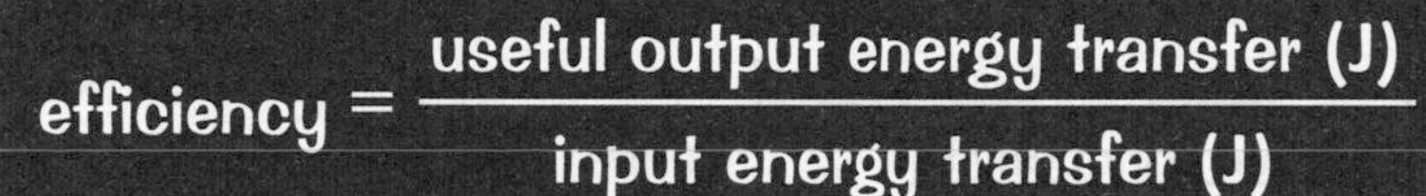

$$\text{efficiency} = \frac{\text{useful output energy transfer (J)}}{\text{input energy transfer (J)}}$$

This will give the efficiency as a decimal. To give it as a percentage, you need to multiply the answer by 100, e.g. 0.75 = 75%.

EXAMPLE:

A toaster transfers 216 000 J of energy electrically from the mains. 84 000 J of energy is transferred to the bread's thermal energy store. Calculate the efficiency of the toaster.

$$\text{efficiency} = \frac{\text{useful output energy transfer}}{\text{input energy transfer}} = \frac{84\,000}{216\,000} = 0.38888... = 0.39 \text{ (to 2 s.f.)}$$

This could also be written as 39% (to 2 s.f.).

Phew!

All devices have an efficiency, but because some energy is always wasted, the efficiency can never be equal to or higher than 1 (or 100%).

We Generally Can't Do Anything Useful with Wasted Energy

1) The wasted energy that's output by a device is transferred to less useful stores — normally by heating, or by light or sound. As the energy is transferred away from the device to its surroundings, the energy often spreads out and becomes less concentrated — we say it dissipates.

For example, a pan of water on a hob — the hob will transfer energy to the water, but some energy will be dissipated to the surrounding air by heating.

2) According to the law of conservation of energy (see page 82), the total amount of energy stays the same. So the energy is still there, but it can't be easily used or collected back in again.

Make sure your revising efficiency is high...

So one really important thing to take from here — devices that transfer energy from one store to other stores will always transfer energy to stores that aren't useful. And when I say always, I mean always. Always. (Always.)

Q1 An electrical device wastes 420 J of energy when it has an input energy of 500 J. Calculate the efficiency of the device as a percentage. [3 marks]

Energy Transfer by Heating

So you know energy can be transferred by heating, but what does that actually mean? I'm glad you asked...

Energy is Transferred by Heating in Three Different Ways

1) When an object is heated, energy is transferred to its thermal energy store and its temperature increases. The energy transferred is equal to: $m \times$ specific heat capacity $\times$ temperature change.
2) If energy is transferred by heating from a hotter object to a cooler object, the hotter object's temperature will decrease and the cooler object's temperature will increase.
3) The three ways that energy can be transferred by heating are: conduction, convection or radiation.

Conduction Occurs Mainly in Solids

1) When an object is heated the energy transferred to the object is shared across the kinetic energy stores of the particles in the object.
2) The particles in the hotter part of the object vibrate more and collide with each other, transferring energy from their kinetic energy stores to neighbouring particles. These then also vibrate faster, increasing the temperature of that part of the object. This continues until the extra energy is spread out evenly across all the particles, and the temperature of the object is the same everywhere.

CONDUCTION is the process where vibrating particles pass extra energy in their kinetic energy stores to the kinetic energy stores of neighbouring particles.

3) Generally conduction occurs mainly in solids, as particles are held tightly together. Particles in liquids and gases are further apart, so conduction of energy is a lot slower.
4) All objects have a thermal conductivity — it describes how well an object transfers energy by conduction. Metal has a high thermal conductivity, and liquids and gases have a low thermal conductivity.

Air is a good insulator.

Convection Occurs in Fluids (Liquids and Gases)

1) When you heat up a liquid or gas, the particles move faster, and the fluid expands, becoming less dense.
2) The warmer, less dense fluid rises above its colder, denser surroundings.
3) As the warm fluid rises, cooler fluid takes its place. The process continues until you end up with a circulation of fluid (convection currents).

Convection can't happen in solids because the particles can't move (just vibrate on the spot).

CONVECTION occurs when the particles with more energy in their kinetic energy stores move from the hotter region to the cooler region — and take their kinetic energy stores with them.

4) Radiators in buildings rely on convection to make the warm air circulate round the room.
5) To reduce convection, you need to stop the fluid moving. Clothes, blankets and foam cavity wall insulation all work by trapping pockets of air. The air can't move so the energy has to conduct very slowly through the pockets of air, as well as the material in between.

Radiation can Travel Through a Vacuum

1) For energy to be transferred by conduction or convection, you need particles. But energy can also be transferred by radiation, which can travel through a vacuum. When energy is transferred by heating by radiation, the energy is carried by infra-red waves (see page 67).
2) All objects continually emit and absorb radiation — the hotter an object gets, the more radiation it emits.
3) Cooler objects will absorb the radiation emitted by hotter things, so their temperature increases.
4) Matt black surfaces are very good absorbers and emitters of radiation.
5) Light-coloured, smooth and shiny objects are very poor absorbers and emitters of radiation.

Conduction — nothing to do with organising an orchestra...

Sometimes I'm just too funny for my own good. Pure gold this stuff.

Q1 Why would hot water in a black mug cool down faster than if the mug was white? [2 marks]

Reducing Unwanted Energy Transfers

It's always best not to throw energy away willy-nilly, so we try to increase the efficiency of everything.

Insulating Your House Reduces Energy Loss

1) Energy in the home can be transferred usefully (e.g. by radiators) and wasted (e.g. by windows).
2) To save energy, a house can be designed to lose less energy (see below). You can also make things more efficient, so they waste less energy, e.g. use energy-saving light bulbs instead of normal ones.

Loft Insulation

Fibreglass 'wool' laid on the loft floor and ceiling reduces energy loss from the house by conduction and convection.

Hot Water Tank Jacket

Reduces conduction, keeping the water hot.

Cavity Walls & Cavity Wall Insulation

Two layers of bricks with a gap between them reduce conduction, but energy is also transferred across the gap by convection. Squirting insulating foam into the gap traps pockets of air to minimise this convection.

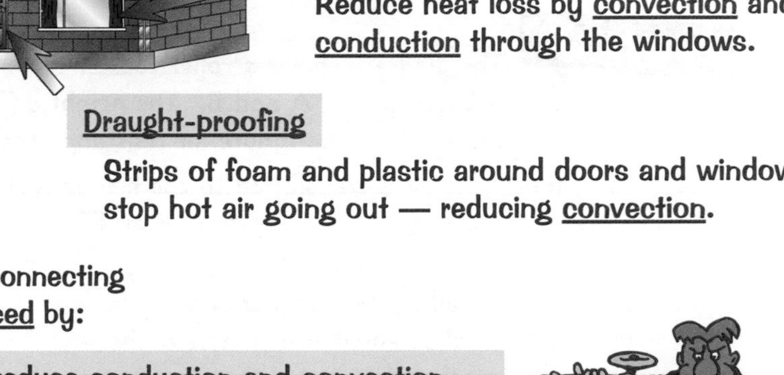

Double Glazing

Two layers of glass with an air gap between reduce conduction.

Thick Curtains

Reduce heat loss by convection and conduction through the windows.

Energy is still lost from the walls by radiation though. Also, if there are any spaces where air is not trapped there'll still be some convection too.

Draught-proofing

Strips of foam and plastic around doors and windows stop hot air going out — reducing convection.

3) The energy loss from hot water pipes (e.g. connecting the boiler to the radiators) can also be reduced by:

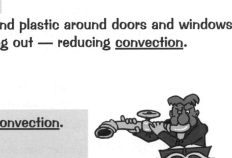

- Covering the pipes with insulation to reduce conduction and convection.
- Painting the pipes white to reduce energy loss by radiation.
- Making the pipes as short as possible, so the water spends less time in the pipes.
- Making the pipes as wide as possible, so they have a smaller surface area to volume ratio. This means a smaller fraction of the water in the pipes is next to the surface of the pipe, and so less energy is lost by conduction.

4) The thickness of walls affects how quickly energy is transferred out of a building. The thicker the walls, the lower the rate of energy transfer. The thermal conductivity of the material the walls are made from also affects the rate of energy transfer. A high thermal conductivity means a high rate of energy transfer.

Reducing Friction Reduces Energy Loss

1) Friction within a system also leads to energy being lost through heating.
2) This can be reduced with lubrication, for example, using oil on a bike chain.
3) Changing the shape of an object, e.g. making a car more streamlined, reduces friction from air resistance.

Now I just need to buy a hot water tank shirt, socks and trousers...

I know what you're thinking — what about underwear for the hot water tank? Don't be so ridiculous.

Q1 State three ways that you could reduce the amount of energy loss from a house. [3 marks]

Q2 State two properties that affect how quickly energy is transferred through a wall. [2 marks]

Mechanical Energy Transfers

Cast your mind back to p.35 — when a force is applied to an object, work is done and energy is transferred.

Falling Objects Transfer Energy Between Stores

1) When an object falls, work is done on the object by the force due to gravity (this is weight, see p.33). Some of the energy in its gravitational potential energy store is transferred to its kinetic energy store.
2) If something is thrown upwards by applying a force to it, the work done by the force causes it to gain height, and energy in its kinetic energy store is transferred to its gravitational potential energy store.
3) In practice, some of the energy will be dissipated through heating due to air resistance, but in the exam they'll likely say you can ignore air resistance, in which case you'll just need to remember this really quite obvious formula:

Energy transferred to/from an object's kinetic energy store = Energy transferred from/to the object's gravitational potential energy store

This is because of the law of conservation of energy (p.82).

4) The equation for calculating the energy in the kinetic energy store of an object is: kinetic energy = ½ × mass × (speed)² = $\frac{1}{2} \times mv^2$.
5) The equation for calculating the energy in the gravitational potential energy store of an object is: gravitational potential energy = mass × height × gravitational field strength = $m \times h \times g$. If an object moves, you can use its change in height for h to calculate the energy transferred to or from this store.

EXAMPLE:

The diagram shows a roller coaster carriage with mass 500 kg falling between points A and B. The height difference between A and B is 20 m. You can ignore air resistance and friction for this question.

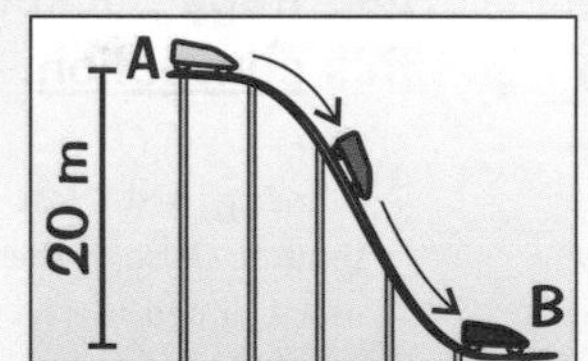

a) How much energy is transferred to the kinetic energy store of the carriage in moving from A to B?

As you're ignoring friction and air resistance, you know that all of the energy transferred from the gravitational potential energy store of the carriage is transferred to its kinetic energy store.

So kinetic energy = gravitational potential energy
$= m \times h \times g$
$= 500 \times 20 \times 10$
$= 100\ 000$ J

You should know that $g = 10$ N/kg for the exam.

b) The roller coaster was stationary at the top of the track. Calculate its speed at the bottom.

1) 100 000 J is the energy in the carriage's kinetic energy store at the bottom of the track, so rearrange the kinetic energy equation to find v^2.

v^2 = kinetic energy ÷ (½ × m)
= 100 000 ÷ (½ × 500) = 400

2) Take the square root of the answer to find v.

$v = \sqrt{400} = 20$ m/s

If you know the mass of an object and how much energy is in its kinetic energy store, you can calculate its speed. Handy.

Elastic Objects Have Elastic Potential Energy Stores

1) When an elastic object, e.g. a spring, is squashed by a moving object, work is done on the spring and energy is transferred from the object's kinetic energy store to the spring's elastic potential energy store.
2) As the spring pushes the object back out, the spring transfers the energy back to the kinetic energy store of the object.
3) The same energy transfers would take place if the object was stretching the spring and then the spring pulled the object back in.
4) The energy transferred to the elastic potential energy store of a stretched or squashed spring is equal to 0.5 × spring constant × (extension)².

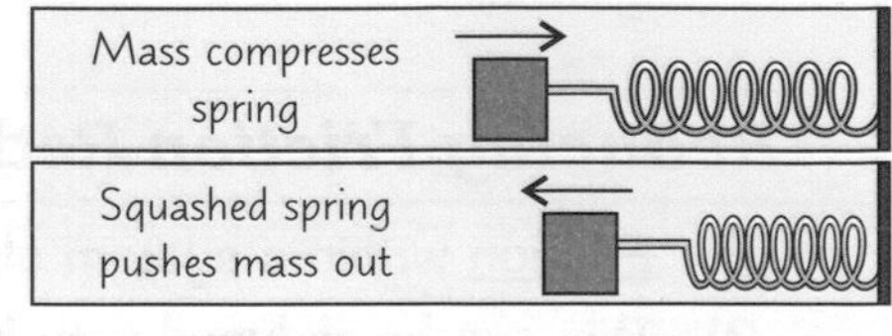

When an elastic object is stretched or compressed, energy can be lost as some energy is transferred to the thermal energy store of the object, causing it to heat up.

Transfer this information to your exam knowledge stores...

So, down to the real important stuff. Make sure you know the equations here, or this will be a bit of a struggle.

Q1 A spring with spring constant 6.50 N/m is squashed by 0.120 m. Calculate the energy transferred to the elastic potential energy store of the spring. [2 marks]

Electrical Energy Transfers

More energy transfers eh? Well, you know the saying — practice makes perhaps the most prepared student.

Electrical Circuits Transfer Energy Electrically

1) When a device is plugged into a socket in the wall, it's connected to the mains (i.e. the national grid). Energy is transferred electrically from the mains to the device.
2) A battery has energy in its chemical energy store — this energy can be transferred electrically to devices in a circuit. Here are some examples of electrical devices and how they transfer the energy supplied:

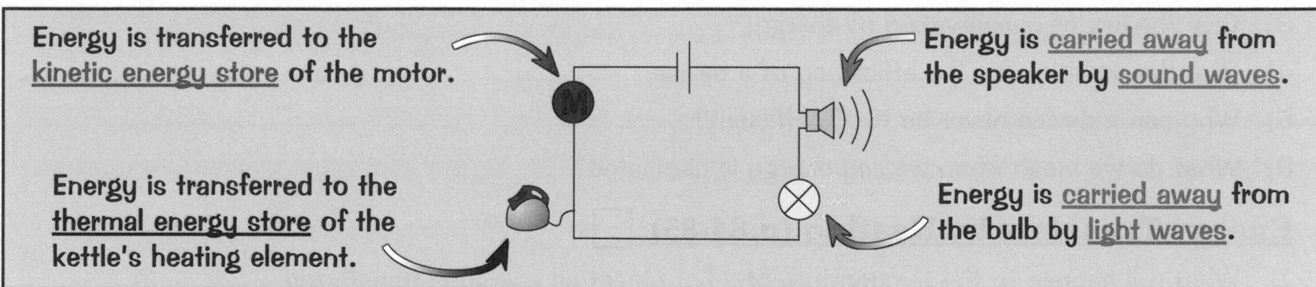

Energy is transferred to the kinetic energy store of the motor.
M
Energy is carried away from the speaker by sound waves.
Energy is transferred to the thermal energy store of the kettle's heating element.
Energy is carried away from the bulb by light waves.

4) Not all of the energy transferred by the battery will be transferred usefully — some is wasted .
5) Some energy is lost as it's transferred to the device — e.g. energy is transferred to the thermal energy stores of the wires by heating.
6) Some energy is also lost in the device itself, for example:
   - a motor heats up as energy is transferred to its thermal energy store due to friction),
   - a heating element within a kettle will also transfer energy to the thermal energy stores of the kettle and the surroundings.

Electrical Appliances Have Power Ratings

1) The amount of energy transferred to a device is the same as the work done by the battery or mains when a current flows (minus any energy lost to the wires, see above).

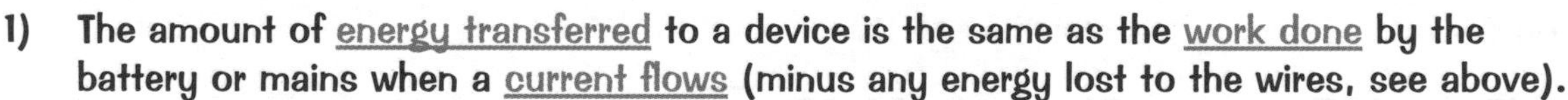

2) The energy transferred to a device is equal to energy transferred = power × time (where power = current × potential difference). Remember — power is measured in watts, W.

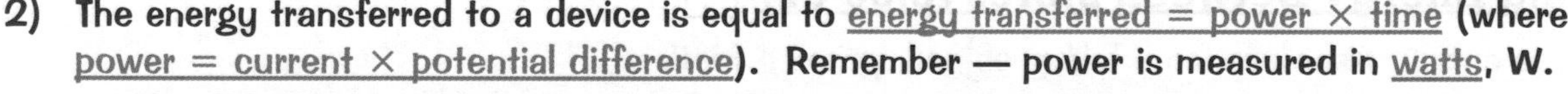

3) The power rating of electrical appliances (bulbs, kettles, hair dryers etc.) is often written on the appliance — it tells you how much energy is transferred to the appliance per second (the rate of energy transfer):

A 850 W microwave will transfer 850 J of energy from the mains per second. But this doesn't mean 850 J of energy is transferred to the food by heating every second, because no device is 100% efficient and some energy is wasted by the device (see above).

The energy transferred to a device can also be measured in kilowatt-hours, kWh — the amount of energy transferred to a 1000 W device in 1 hour.

EXAMPLE: A kettle has a current of 12.5 A when a voltage of 230 V is applied across it.

a) Calculate the power rating of the kettle. power = current × potential difference = 12.5 × 230 = 2875 W

b) How much energy is transferred to the kettle from the mains in 4.0 minutes? Give your answer in standard form.

Standard form is on p.12.

4 min in seconds is 4 × 60 = 240 s, so energy transferred = power × time = 2875 × 240 = 690 000 J

690 000 = 6.9 0 0 0 0 × 10^5 = 6.9 × 10^5 J

Go and put the kettle on, you deserve a brew...

The power rating tells you how much energy is transferred to a device per second, and the efficiency tells you what fraction of this energy is usefully transferred by the device. Remember — no device is 100% efficient.

Q1 A light bulb with a power rating of 35 W is connected to a battery for 2.0 minutes. Calculate the energy transferred to the bulb during this time, and explain why the energy transferred from the bulb by light waves will be less than your calculated value. [3 marks]

Revision Questions for Topic P7

Well, that wraps up Topic P7 — but now to find out how much has sunk in, and how much is left to learn...

- Try these questions and tick off each one when you get it right.
- When you've done all the questions under a heading and are completely happy with it, tick it off.

Energy Stores and Efficiency (p.82-83)

1) State the eight types of energy stores.
2) State the four ways of transferring energy between energy stores.
3) Give the law of conservation of energy.
4) Give the equation for the efficiency of a device.
5) Why can a device never be 100% efficient?
6) What do we mean when we say energy is dissipated?

Energy Transfers by Heating (p.84-85)

7) What will happen to the temperature of a hot object as energy is transferred from its thermal energy store to the thermal energy store of a cooler object?
8) Give the three ways that energy could be transferred by heating.
9) Explain how energy is transferred by conduction.
10) Explain how energy is transferred by convection.
11) Will a black surface absorb radiation more or less quickly than a white surface?
12) Explain how cavity walls and cavity wall insulation reduce energy loss from buildings.
13) Give two ways that energy loss through windows can be reduced.
14) What effect does increasing the thermal conductivity of a wall have on the rate of energy transfer through it?

Transferring Energy Between Stores (p.86-87)

15) Describe the energy transfers for a falling object, ignoring friction.
16) Describe the energy transfers for an object thrown in the air, ignoring friction.
17) Give the equation for the energy in the kinetic energy store of a moving object.
18) Give the equation for the energy transferred to the gravitational potential energy store of an object that is lifted a height, h, above the ground.
19) Give the equation for the energy in the elastic potential energy store of a stretched spring.
20) Describe the energy transfers for a squashed spring being released and moving a mass.
21) Describe how energy is usefully transferred when a motor is connected to a battery.
22) Describe how energy is usefully transferred when a loudspeaker is connected to a battery.
23) How is energy lost in a motor?
24) How is energy lost in a heating device?
25) Give an equation in terms of power and time for the energy transferred by a component in a circuit.
26) Give an equation in terms of current and potential difference for the energy transferred by a circuit.
27) What is the power rating of an electrical appliance?

Everyday Speeds and Accelerations

Are you ready for a super speedy page? Get set... gooooooooooo!!

Speeds can be Given in Different Units

The unit for speed you'll mainly use in science is metres per second, m/s. In the real world speeds are often measured in miles per hour, mph or kilometres per hour, km/hr. Make sure you can convert between them.

Convert mph to km/hr:
There are about 1.6 kilometres to every mile. So multiply by 1.6.
So 30 mph = 30 × 1.6 = 48 km/hr.

Convert km/hr into m/s:
Divide by 3600 (i.e. 60 × 60) to turn hr into s, then multiply by 1000 to change from km to m. Or just divide by 3.6.
So 48 km/hr = 48 ÷ 3.6 = 13.33... ≈ 13 m/s (to 2 s.f.).

Learn these Typical Speeds

1) Walking — 1.4 m/s (5 km/hr)
2) Running — 3 m/s (11 km/hr)
3) Cycling — 5.5 m/s (20 km/hr)
4) Cars in a built-up area — 13 m/s (47 km/hr or 30 mph)
5) Cars on a motorway — 31 m/s (112 km/hr or 70 mph)
6) Trains — up to 55 m/s (200 km/hr)
7) A breeze — 5 m/s
8) A gale — 20 m/s
9) The speed of sound in air is 340 m/s

You Need to be Able to Estimate Acceleration

To estimate an acceleration, you may need to estimate the time a change in speed takes, then use the equation: acceleration = change in velocity ÷ time taken.

EXAMPLE: A car starts from rest and accelerates up to 50 km/hr as quickly as possible. Estimate its acceleration in m/s^2.

First, change the speed to m/s: 50 km/hr = 50 ÷ 3.6 = 13.88... m/s.

This is a fairly typical speed for a car in town. From experience you'd guess it takes a few seconds for most cars to get up to this speed — say it takes 2 seconds.

Acceleration = change in velocity ÷ time taken = 13.88... ÷ 2 = 6.94... ≈ 7 m/s^2 (to 1 s.f.)

Give your answer to 1 s.f. for rough estimates like this.

Large Decelerations can be Dangerous

1) Large decelerations of objects and people (e.g. in car crashes), and the forces involved can cause injuries. This is because a large deceleration requires a large force (since $F = ma$).
2) The force on an object can be lowered by slowing the object down over a longer time, i.e. decreasing its deceleration (since a = change in speed ÷ t, and $F = ma$ again). You can also think of this in terms of momentum — the longer it takes for a change in momentum, the smaller the forces acting.
3) Safety features in cars are designed to increase collision times, which reduces the deceleration and forces, and so reduces the risk of injury. For example, seat belts stretch slightly and air bags slow you down gradually. Crumple zones are areas at the front and back of a car which crumple up easily in a collision, increasing the time taken to stop.
4) This stuff's not just about car collisions — for example bike helmets contain a crushable layer of foam which increases the time taken for your head to stop, reducing the deceleration and forces acting. Shin pads work this way too — if something hits a shin pad, the pad deforms, reducing deceleration and the force on your leg.

Some safety features also work by stopping you hitting hard surfaces like the dashboard or the road.

My acceleration towards the kettle is about 10 m/s^2...

This stuff is pretty dull, but it's important for the next few pages, so make sure you know it all.

Q1 A car pulls onto a motorway slip-road and accelerates from 50 mph to 70 mph as quickly as possible. Estimate its acceleration in m/s^2. [3 marks]

Stopping Distances and Reaction Times

The stopping distance of a vehicle is the distance covered between the driver first spotting a hazard and the vehicle coming to a complete stop. It's made up of the thinking distance and the braking distance.

Stopping Distance = Thinking Distance + Braking Distance

The longer it takes a car to stop after seeing a hazard, the higher the risk of crashing. The distance it takes to stop a car (stopping distance) is divided into the thinking distance and the braking distance:

The thinking distance is the distance the car travels in the driver's reaction time (the time between noticing the hazard and applying the brakes). It's affected by two main factors:

1) Your reaction time — this is affected by tiredness, alcohol, drugs and distractions.
2) Your speed — the faster you're going, the further you'll travel during your reaction time.

The braking distance is the distance taken to stop once the brakes have been applied. It's affected by:

1) Your speed — the faster you're going, the further it takes to stop (see next page).
2) The mass of the car — a car full of people and luggage won't stop as quickly as an empty car.
3) The condition of the brakes — worn or faulty brakes won't be able to brake with as much force.
4) How good the grip of your tyres is — you're more likely to skid when the road is dirty, if it's icy or wet and if the tyres are bald (tyres must have a minimum tread depth of 1.6 mm).

In the exam, you may need to spot the factors affecting thinking and braking distance in different situations. E.g. if a parent is driving her children to school early in the morning on an autumn day, her thinking distance could be affected by tiredness, or by her children distracting her. Her braking distance could be affected by ice, or by leaves on the road reducing the grip.

The Ruler Drop Experiment Measures Reaction Times

1) Stand with your hand open. Get someone else to hold a ruler so it hangs between your thumb and forefinger, and your forefinger's lined up with zero. You may need a third person to be at eye level with the ruler to check it's lined up.
2) Without giving any warning, the person holding the ruler drops it. Close your thumb and finger to try to catch the ruler as quickly as possible.
3) The measurement on the ruler at the point where it was caught is how far the ruler dropped in the time it took you to react.
4) The longer the distance, the longer the reaction time.
5) You can calculate how long the ruler was falling for (the reaction time) because its acceleration is constant (and equal to g, 10 m/s^2).

finger in line with zero

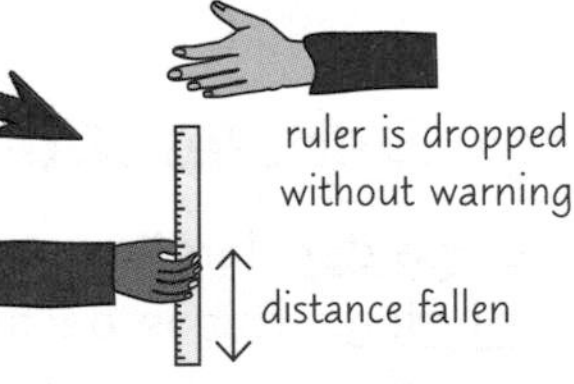

Say you caught the ruler at 20 cm. From page 22 you know: $v^2 - u^2 = 2ad$. $u = 0$, $a = 10$ m/s^2 and $d = 0.2$ m, so: $v = \sqrt{2 \times 10 \times 0.2} = 2$ m/s. v is equal to the change in speed of the ruler.

From page 22 you also know a = change in $v \div t$, so $t = 2 \div 10 = 0.2$ s — your reaction time.

6) It's hard to do this experiment accurately, so do a lot of repeats and find the mean distance that the ruler fell. Use this mean in the calculation above.
7) You could investigate some factors affecting reaction time, e.g. introduce distractions like music playing.
8) Make sure it's a fair test — keep the variables you aren't testing the same every time, e.g. use the same ruler for each repeat and have the same person dropping it.
9) For an experiment like this, a typical reaction time is 0.2-0.6 s.

There are lots of other ways to measure reaction times, e.g. pressing a button when a computer screen changes.

Stop right there — and learn this page...

Bad visibility also causes accidents — if it's foggy, it's harder to notice a hazard, so there's less room to stop.

Q1 Drivers on long journeys should take regular breaks. Explain why, in terms of stopping distance. [3 marks]

Stopping Safely

So now you know what affects a car's stopping distance, let's have a look at the facts and figures.

Drivers Need to Leave Enough Space to Stop

1) These typical stopping distances are from the Highway Code.
2) To avoid an accident, drivers must leave enough space in front so they could stop safely — at least equal to the stopping distance for their speed.
3) Speed limits are really important because speed affects stopping distances so much. (Remember, weather and road conditions can affect them too.)

hazard spotted

30 mph / 13 m/s — 9 m thinking, 14 m braking — Total 23 m, 6 car lengths

50 mph / 22 m/s — 15 m thinking, 38 m braking — Total 53 m, 13 car lengths

70 mph / 31 m/s — 21 m thinking, 75 m braking — Total 96 m, 24 car lengths

thinking distance | braking distance

4) As speeds increases, thinking distance increases at the same rate. This is because the driver's reaction time will stay fairly constant, but the higher the speed, the further you go in that time (since $d = st$).

Reaction time can be affected by factors like tiredness though..

5) However, braking distance and speed have a squared relationship — if speed doubles, braking distance increases 4-fold (2^2), and if speed trebles, braking distance increases 9-fold (3^2).

The brakes of a car do work on the car's wheels. This transfers energy from the car's kinetic energy store to the thermal energy store of the brakes. To stop a car, the brakes must transfer all of this energy, so:

Energy in the car's kinetic energy store = Work done by the brakes

$$\frac{1}{2} \times m \times v^2 = F \times d$$

m = mass of the car, v = speed of car, F = braking force, d = braking distance

This means that doubling the mass doubles the braking distance.

You can Estimate the Forces Involved in Acceleration

You might need to know some rough vehicle masses first though: Car — around 1000 kg. Single decker bus — around 10 000 kg. Loaded lorry — around 30 000 kg.

EXAMPLE: A car travelling at 25 m/s makes an emergency stop to avoid a hazard 50 m ahead. Estimate the braking force, F, needed to produce the required deceleration.

1) Assume the deceleration is uniform, and use $v^2 - u^2 = 2ad$ to find the deceleration. $a = (v^2 - u^2) \div 2d = (0^2 - 25^2) \div (2 \times 50) = -6.25$
2) Then use $F = ma$, assuming that $m \sim 1000$ kg. $F = 1000 \times 6.25 = 6250$ N, so F is ~ 6000 N

You could have used the equation above too.

Very large decelerations can be dangerous because they may cause the brakes to overheat (so they don't work as well) or they could cause the vehicle to skid. They can cause injuries too (see page 89).

Thinking and Braking Distance can be Seen on v-t Graphs

See p.25 for more on v-t graphs.

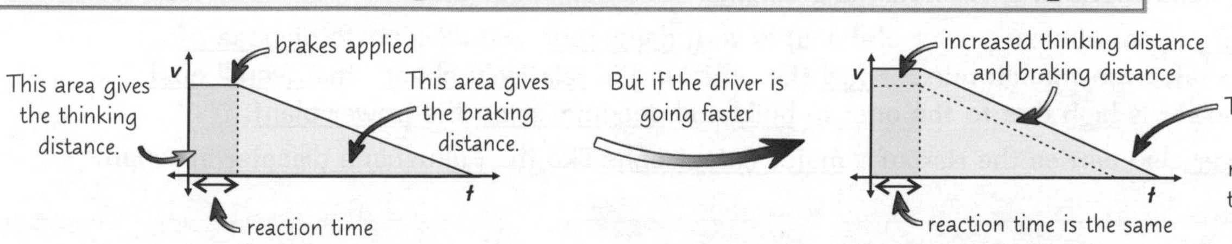

brakes applied
v
This area gives the thinking distance.
This area gives the braking distance.
t
reaction time
But if the driver is going faster
increased thinking distance and braking distance
v
t
reaction time is the same
The gradient (deceleration) is the same, as the maximum force applied to the brakes hasn't changed.

It's enough to put you off learning to drive, isn't it...

This is quite a tough page, but it's important, so head back to the top and read it again.

Q1 Estimate the force needed to stop a lorry travelling at 16 m/s within 50 m. [4 marks]

Non-Renewable Energy Sources

We use A LOT of electricity — I bet you're reading this in a room with an electric light, with your phone on in your pocket, and maybe the radio in the background. The energy to power it all has to come from somewhere.

Non-Renewable Energy Sources Will Run Out One Day

1) We get most of our energy from non-renewable sources.
2) These are sources that will run out one day and they damage the environment.
3) The main non-renewables are the three fossil fuels (coal, oil and natural gas) and nuclear fuels (uranium and plutonium).

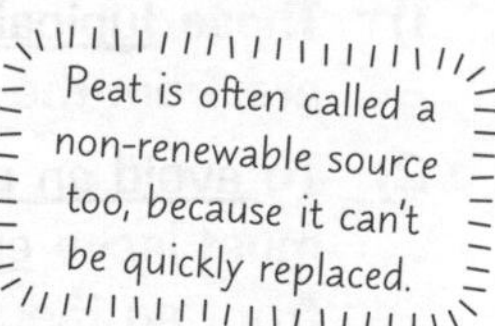

Peat is often called a non-renewable source too, because it can't be quickly replaced.

Most Power Stations Use Steam to Drive a Turbine

We currently generate most of our electricity from burning fossil fuels in power stations, like this:

1) As the fossil fuel burns (in oxygen) the energy in its chemical energy store is transferred to the thermal energy store of the water.
2) The water boils to form steam, which turns a turbine, transferring energy to the kinetic energy store of the turbine.

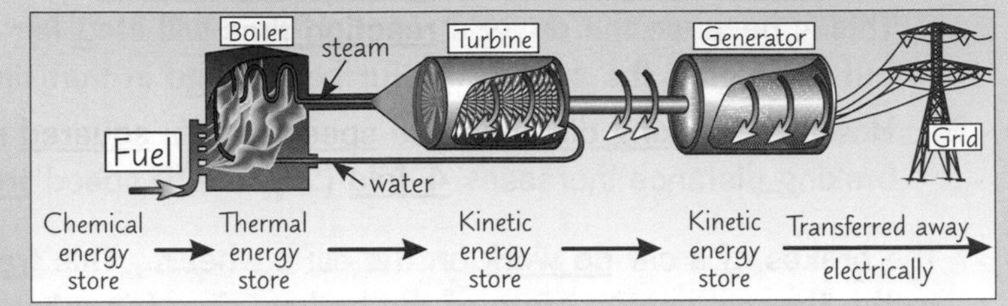

3) As the turbine revolves, so does the generator, which you can think of as a big alternator (see p.56).
4) The generator transfers the energy electrically away from the power station, via the national grid.

Nuclear Reactors Are Just Fancy Boilers

1) A nuclear power station is mostly the same as the one above, but the energy from nuclear fission is used to heat water to make steam to drive turbines, etc. The difference is in the boiler:
2) Nuclear power stations take the longest time of all the power stations to start up. Natural gas power stations take the shortest time.

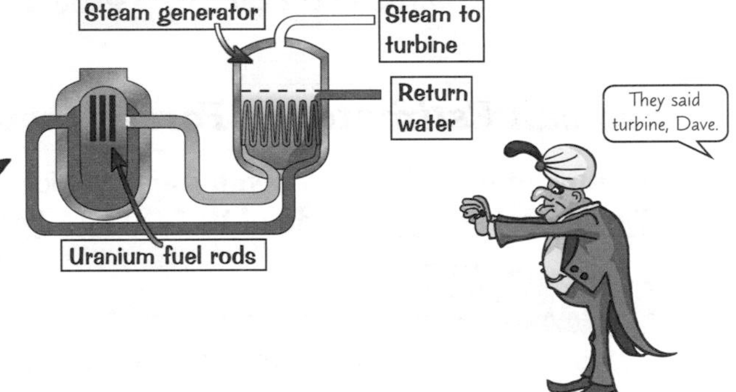

They said turbine, Dave.

Non-Renewable Sources Cause Environmental Problems

1) All three fossil fuels (coal, oil and natural gas) release CO_2 — coal releases the most, then oil, then natural gas. This CO_2 contributes to climate change and global warming.
2) Burning coal and oil releases sulfur dioxide, which causes acid rain. This is reduced by taking the sulfur out before it's burned, or cleaning up the emissions.
3) Coal mining makes a mess of the landscape, especially "open-cast mining".
4) Oil spillages cause serious environmental problems.
5) Nuclear waste (from nuclear power stations) is very dangerous and difficult to dispose of. This means that, even though nuclear fuel (i.e. uranium) is relatively cheap, the overall cost of nuclear power is high due to the cost to build and decommission the power plant.
6) Nuclear power also carries the risk of a major catastrophe like the Fukushima disaster in Japan.

It all boils down to steam...

Steam engines were invented as long ago as the 17th century, yet we're still using that idea to produce most of our electricity over 300 years later. Pretty impressive, eh?

Q1 Describe how a coal-fired power station works. [2 marks]

Renewable Energy Sources

Renewable energy sources, unlike non-renewables, don't run out (funny that).

Renewable Energy Sources Will Never Run Out

1) A renewable energy source is one that will never run out.
2) Most of them do some damage to the environment, but in less nasty ways than non-renewables.
3) They don't provide as much energy as non-renewables and the weather-dependent ones can be unreliable.
4) Renewable sources include bio-fuels, wind power, the Sun, hydro-electricity and the tides.

Bio-fuels are Made from Plants and Waste

1) Bio-fuels can be made from anything from farm waste, animal droppings and landfill rubbish to specially grown crops (e.g. sugar cane, vegetable oils or trees).
2) They're renewable because we can just grow more.
3) They can be burnt to produce electricity or used to run cars in the same way as fossil fuels.
4) They aren't meant to have any net effect on the level of CO_2 in the atmosphere (they're carbon neutral). But there is some debate about whether this is true, as this only really works if you keep growing plants (either to burn or as animal feed) at at least the rate that you're burning things.
5) Bio-fuels are fairly reliable as the crops grow fairly quickly. But it's harder to respond to immediate energy demands, as crops take time to grow (you can stockpile bio-fuels to combat this).
6) The cost to make bio-fuels is very high and some worry that growing crops specifically for bio-fuels will mean there isn't enough space or water to meet the demands for crops that are grown for food.
7) In some places, large areas of land have been cleared to grow bio-fuels, resulting in species losing their habitats. The decay and burning of this vegetation also increases CO_2 and methane emissions.

Wind Power — Lots of Little Wind Turbines

1) Each wind turbine has a generator inside it — the rotating blades turn the generator and produce electricity.
2) There's no pollution (except for a little bit when they're manufactured).
3) But some people think they spoil the view. And they can be very noisy, which can be annoying for people living nearby.
4) They only work when it's windy, so you can't always supply electricity, or respond to high demand.

Solar Cells — Expensive but No Environmental Damage

(well, there may be a bit caused by making the cells)

1) Solar cells are made from special materials that release electrons when light falls on them, generating an electric current.
2) Solar power is often used in remote places where there's not much choice (e.g. the Australian outback) and to power electric road signs and satellites.
3) There's no pollution. (Although they do use quite a lot of energy to make.)
4) Solar cells are mainly used to generate electricity on a relatively small scale, e.g. in homes.
5) Solar power is most suitable for sunny countries, but it can be used in cloudy countries like Britain.
6) And of course, you can't make solar power at night or increase production when there's extra demand.

Time to recharge.

Burning poo.... lovely...

Given our electricity-guzzling ways, it's pretty important we find ways to generate electricity without destroying the planet. Burning cow pats may not be the ultimate fix, but it's a start. See the next page for more ways.

Q1 State two renewable energy sources. [2 marks]

Q2 State two disadvantages of using wind power to generate electricity. [2 marks]

More On Energy Sources

Two more renewable energy sources to learn, then we'll look at trends in the crazy world of energy production.

Hydro-electricity — Building Dams and Flooding Valleys

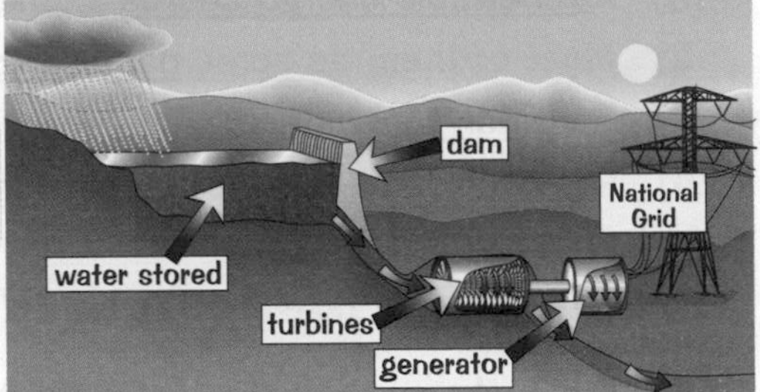

1) Producing hydro-electricity usually involves flooding a valley by building a big dam.
2) Rainwater is caught and allowed out through turbines.
3) There is a big impact on the environment due to the flooding of the valley and possible loss of habitat for some species.
4) A big advantage is immediate response to increased electricity demand — more water can be let out through the turbines to generate more electricity.
5) Initial costs are often high but there are minimal running costs and it's a reliable energy source.

Tidal Barrages — Using the Sun and Moon's Gravity

1) Tidal barrages are big dams built across river estuaries with turbines in them.
2) As the tide comes in it fills up the estuary. The water is then let out through turbines at a set speed.
3) There is no pollution but they affect boat access, can spoil the view and they alter the habitat for wildlife, e.g. wading birds.
4) Tides are pretty reliable (they always happen twice a day). But the height is variable and they don't work when the water level is the same either side.
5) Even though it can only be used in some estuaries, tidal barrages have great potential.

Renewables are Growing, but we Still Depend on Coal and Gas

1) Over the 20th century, the electricity use of the UK hugely increased, as the population got bigger and people began to use electricity for more and more things.
2) Most of this electricity was generated using fossil fuels (mostly coal and gas) and from nuclear power.
3) Over time, we've become more aware that these fuels will run out one day and that they cause environmental damage.
4) So we're investing time and money in developing renewable energy sources, but progress is slow.
5) In the UK, renewable sources still only account for generating around 20% of the electricity we use — most of our electricity still comes from burning coal and gas. This is partly because most renewable sources generate less electricity than a big coal-fired power station, and many renewable energy sources are weather-dependent (e.g. wind and solar) so the amount they supply fluctuates a lot.
6) It's not just about generating electricity renewably — we're also trying to use less. Since the beginning of the 21st century, our electricity use has been decreasing (slowly), as we get better at making appliances more efficient and people have become more aware of the need to save energy.
7) We don't just burn fossil fuels to generate electricity — we use oil (diesel and petrol) to fuel our cars, and gas to heat our homes and cook our food.
8) We're investigating other ways to power cars, e.g. electric cars, but none of these have taken off yet.

Nuclear power is another option for decreasing fossil fuels use and the UK is investing in nuclear power. But some people worry about the possibility of nuclear accidents and the dangers of nuclear waste.

Trends in energy use — light bulbs wearing sunglasses...

There are problems with every kind of electricity production, and no one wants any of them happening in their backyard. But if we want to carry on living the way we are, we're going to need to make some compromises.

Q1 Give one advantage and one disadvantage of producing hydro-electricity. [2 marks]

Q2 Many people want to replace non-renewable energy sources for generating electricity with renewable energy sources. Suggest why. [2 marks]

Electricity and the National Grid

There are two types of current — alternating and direct. The national grid supplies alternating current.

Alternating Voltage Keeps Changing Direction

1) An alternating current (a.c.) is produced by an alternating voltage (or alternating potential difference, p.d.) — the p.d. and current constantly change direction.
2) The UK mains electricity (in your home) is a.c. at 50 Hz and around 230 V.
3) Direct current (d.c.) is produced by a direct voltage — the current and the p.d. don't change direction.
4) You get d.c. from batteries and cells.
5) A cathode ray oscilloscope (CRO) trace can show how the p.d. of a supply changes with time.
6) If you connect an alternating voltage to the CRO, you see a wave — it goes up and down in a regular pattern.
7) Direct voltage gives a horizontal line — it doesn't vary.
8) The height at any point shows the input p.d. at that point.

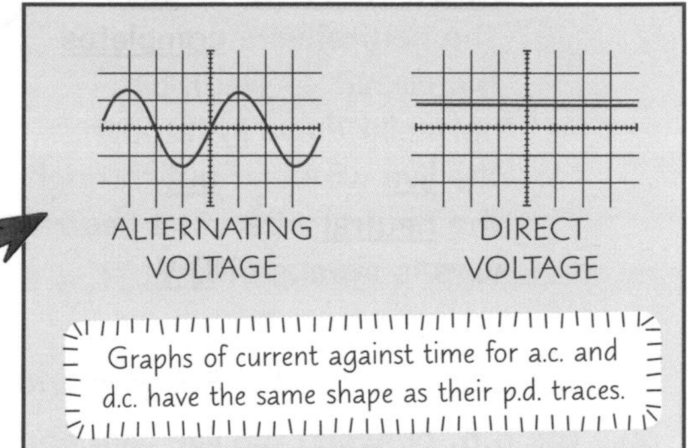
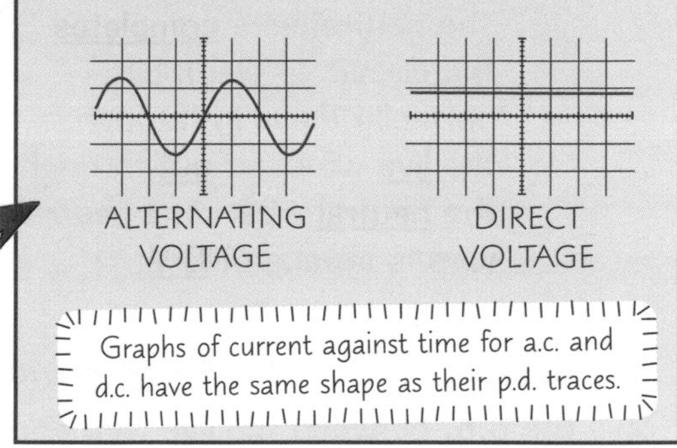

Graphs of current against time for a.c. and d.c. have the same shape as their p.d. traces.

Electricity Gets Around via the National Grid...

1) The national grid is a network of wires and transformers that connects UK power stations to consumers (anyone who uses electricity).
2) It transfers energy electrically from power stations (the supply) to where it's needed in homes and industry (the demand).
3) To transmit the huge amount of power needed, you need either a high p.d. or a high current (as $P = IV$).
4) The problem with a high current is that you lose loads of energy as the wires heat up and energy is transferred to the thermal energy store of the surroundings. The power lost is given by $P = I^2R$, where R is the resistance of the wires (so you can reduce losses by using wires of a lower resistance).
5) Wasted energy and power costs money, so it's cheaper to boost the p.d. up really high (to 400 000 V) and keep the current very low — this makes the national grid an efficient way of transferring energy.

Power is the energy transferred in a given time, so a higher power means more energy is transferred.

...With a Little Help from Transformers

Look at p.57 for more on how transformers work and to see a rather funky equation in action.

1) To get the voltage up to 400 000 V for efficient transmission we use transformers (and big pylons with huge insulators).
2) Transformers all have two coils, the primary and the secondary, joined with an iron core.
3) The potential difference is increased using a step-up transformer. They have more turns on the secondary coil than the primary coil.
4) It's then reduced again at the local consumer end using a step-down transformer. They have more turns on the primary coil than the secondary.
5) The power supplied to a primary coil is given by power (W) = p.d. (V) × current (A). As transformers are nearly 100% efficient then input power = output power, so:

p.d. across primary coil (V) × current in primary coil (A) = p.d. across secondary coil (V) × current in secondary coil (A)

Transformers — there's more than meets the eye...

Fun fact — the step-down transformers on power lines get a bit warm, so birds love to nest on them. In some places electricity companies have to go round moving nests to stop them from causing problems.

Q1 A transformer steps up a 42 V supply to 210 V. The current in the secondary coil is 0.20 A. Calculate the current in the primary coil. [2 marks]

Wiring in the Home

Now then, did you know... electricity is dangerous. It can kill you. Well just watch out for it, that's all.

Plugs Contain Three Wires

Appliances usually contain three wires.
You need to know what each of them is for:

1) **LIVE WIRE — brown.**
The live wire carries the voltage (potential difference, p.d.). It alternates between a high +ve and –ve voltage of about 230 V.

2) **NEUTRAL WIRE — blue.**
The neutral wire completes the circuit — electricity normally flows in through the live wire and out through the neutral wire. The neutral wire is always at 0 V.

FUSE (see below)

3) **EARTH WIRE — green and yellow.**
The earth wire is for safety. It carries the current away if something goes wrong. It's also at 0 V.

1) The p.d. between the live wire and the neutral wire equals the supply p.d. (230 V for the mains).
2) The p.d. between the live wire and the earth wire is also 230 V for a mains-connected appliance.
3) There is no p.d. between the neutral wire and the earth wire — they're both at 0 V.
4) Your body is also at 0 V. This means if you touched the live wire, there'd be a large p.d. across your body and a current would flow through you. This large electric shock could injure or even kill you.
5) Even if a plug socket is off (i.e. the switch is open) there is still a danger of an electric shock. A current isn't flowing, but there is still a p.d. in the live part of the socket, so your body could provide a link between the supply and the earth if you made contact with it.

Earthing and Fuses Prevent Fires and Shocks

1) Electricity will flow through anything that conducts. So if the live wire accidentally connects with something metal (e.g. the case of an appliance) current will flow. This could cause serious electric shocks and fires.
2) All appliances with metal cases must be "earthed" for safety. This means the case must be attached to an earth wire.
3) If a fault develops so the live wire touches the metal case, then a current will flow down the earth wire.
4) The earth wire is very thick, to give it a low resistance. This means the total resistance of the circuit decreases. Current = p.d. ÷ resistance, so this causes a big current to flow through the live wire, the case, and out down the earth wire.
5) This surge in current melts the fuse, breaking the circuit and cutting off the live supply. This isolates the appliance, so it's impossible to get an electric shock from the case. It also prevents fires caused by the heating effect of a large current.
6) Fuses and earthing also protect the circuits and wiring in your appliances from getting fried if there is a current surge.
7) If the appliance has a casing that's non-conductive (e.g. plastic) then it's double insulated. Anything with double insulation doesn't need an earth wire as it can't become live.

normal toaster — current flows from live to neutral

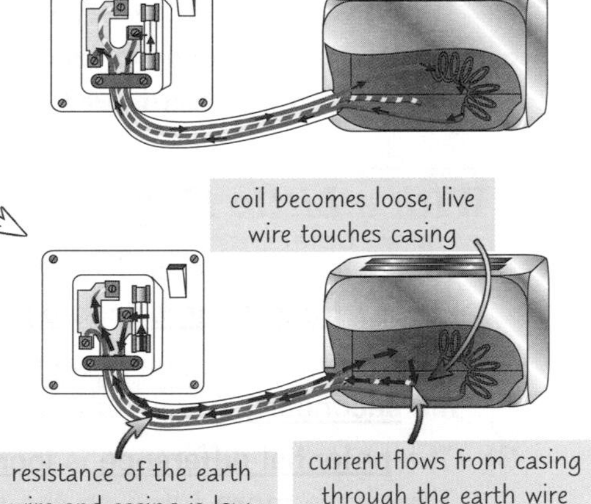
coil becomes loose, live wire touches casing
resistance of the earth wire and casing is low, so current increases
current flows from casing through the earth wire

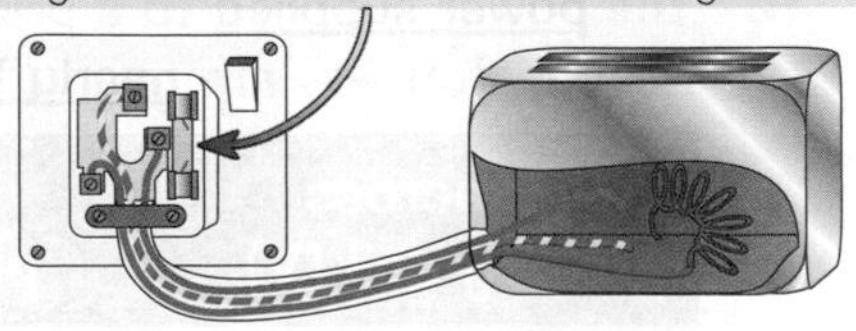
surge of current melts the fuse, breaking the circuit

Electricity rule number 1 — don't stick your fingers in the socket...

So wiring's fun isn't it? Unfortunately, it could be in your exams so you'd best get it learnt.

Q1 A metal kettle is plugged into the mains electricity supply (230 V, 50 Hz).
a) Explain why the kettle needs an earth wire and how it works. [3 marks]
b) State the potential difference between the kettle's earth and neutral wires. [1 mark]

The Solar System and Orbits

Ironically, for a page about space, there's not much of it left on this page...

Our Solar System has One Star — The Sun

The Solar System's made up of a star (the Sun) and the stuff orbiting it. This includes things like:

1) Planets — these are large objects that orbit a star. The planets of our Solar System in order from the Sun outwards — Mercury, Venus, Earth, Mars, Jupiter, Saturn, Uranus and Neptune.
2) Minor planets — planet-like objects that orbit stars, but don't meet the rules for a planet (e.g. Pluto).
3) Natural satellites like moons — smaller things orbiting planets. Jupiter has about 67, we've got THE Moon.
4) Artificial satellites — man-made objects with specially designed orbits. Most of them orbit the Earth:

Satellites in Geostationary Orbit

1) These have a high orbit over the Earth's equator and orbit once every 24 hours.
2) This means that they stay above the same point on the Earth's surface, because the Earth rotates with them. So they're called geostationary or geosynchronous satellites.
3) They're ideal for communications (e.g. telephone, TV and radio) because they stay at the same point above the Earth, so it's easy to point transmitters and receivers at them. That, and they can transfer signals from one side of the Earth to another in a fraction of a second.

Satellites in Polar Orbit

1) These satellites sweep low over both poles whilst the Earth rotates beneath them.
2) They're much closer to the Earth than geostationary satellites, so they move much faster (see below). This means they orbit really quickly, often taking less than 2 hours.
3) Because the orbits are short, they can scan the next bit of the globe each orbit, allowing the whole surface of the Earth to be monitored each day.
4) They're used for the weather, mapping and surveillance.

They said polar, Dave.

Gravity Provides the Force That Causes Orbits

1) The orbits of the planets around the Sun, and satellites around planets, are almost circular.
2) If an object is travelling in a circle it's constantly changing direction. This means its velocity is constantly changing, so it's accelerating. (Speed doesn't have direction though, so that's not changing.)
3) For an object to accelerate, there must be a force acting on it. For an object moving in a circle, this force is directed towards the centre of the circle and is called the centripetal force.
4) For orbiting objects, this force is provided by gravity (gravitational force).
5) This force would cause the object to just fall towards whatever it was orbiting, but as the object is already moving, it just causes it to change its direction.
6) The object keeps accelerating towards whatever it's orbiting but its velocity at any given moment is always at right angles to this acceleration. This keeps it travelling in a circle.
7) For an orbit to be stable the object must be moving at just the right speed — too fast and it'd fly off into space, too slowly and it'd spiral down and crash into whatever it was orbiting.
8) If an object's speed changes, the radius of its orbit must also change for the orbit to remain stable:
   The closer you get to a star or planet, the stronger the gravitational force is.
   The stronger the force, the faster the orbiting object needs to be going to avoid falling in to what it's orbiting. So the closer you get, the faster you need to go to stay in orbit.
   For an object in a stable orbit, if its speed changes, the size (radius) of its orbit must do so too.
   If the object moves faster, the radius must get smaller. If it moves slower, the radius must get larger.

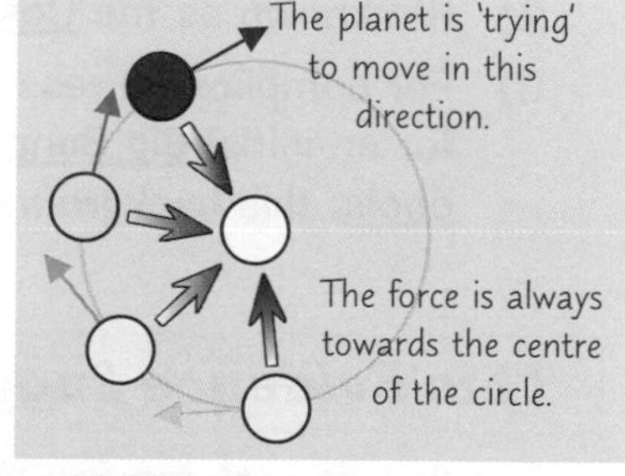

Don't let this stuff get you in a spin...

Remember, for an object in a stable circular orbit, its speed is constant but its velocity is always changing.

Q1 Describe the differences between satellites in geostationary and polar orbits. [3 marks]

The Origin of the Universe

The Big Bang model is the most convincing explanation we've got for how the universe started.

The Universe Seems to be Expanding

As big as the universe already is, it looks like it's getting even bigger.
All its galaxies seem to be moving away from each other. There's good evidence for this:

1) Different chemical elements absorb different frequencies (or wavelengths) of light.
2) Each element produces a specific pattern of dark lines at the frequencies that it absorbs in the visible part of the EM spectrum (see page 66).
3) When we look at light from distant galaxies we see the same patterns but at slightly lower frequencies (longer wavelengths) than they should be.
4) There's an observed increase in the wavelength of light coming from the galaxies — the light is shifted towards the red end of the spectrum. This is called red-shift.
5) Measurements of the red-shift suggest that all the distant galaxies are moving away from us (and each other) very quickly — and it's the same result whichever direction you look in.
6) More distant galaxies have greater red-shifts than nearer ones — they show a bigger observed increase in wavelength.
7) This means that more distant galaxies are moving away faster than nearer ones. This provides evidence that the universe is expanding.

An absorption spectrum showing dark lines measured on Earth.

The same absorption spectrum measured from light from a distant galaxy. The dark lines in this spectrum are red-shifted.

Red-shift is the same effect as the vrrrrrm from a racing car or the sound of an ambulance as they drive past you. The noise sounds lower-pitched when it's travelling away from you because it drops in frequency (the Doppler effect).

There's Microwave Radiation from All Directions

This is another observation that scientists made. It's not interesting in itself, but the model that explains all this evidence definitely is.

1) Scientists can detect low frequency microwave radiation coming from all directions and all parts of the universe.
2) It's known as the Cosmic Microwave Background Radiation (CMBR).
3) For complicated reasons this background radiation is strong evidence for an initial Big Bang (see below). As the universe expands and cools, this background radiation 'cools' and drops in frequency.

This Evidence Suggests the Universe Started with a Bang

The galaxies are moving away from each other at great speed — suggesting something must have got them going from a single starting point. That 'something' was probably a big explosion — the Big Bang:

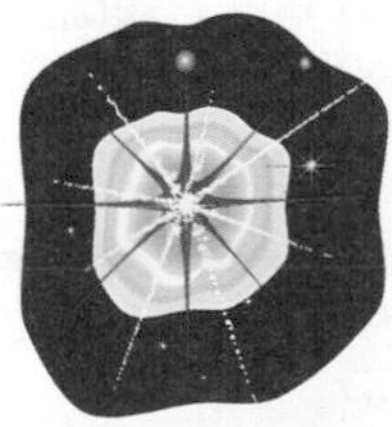

1) Initially, all the matter in the universe occupied a single point.
2) This single point then 'exploded' — the Big Bang.
3) Space started expanding, and the expansion is still going on.

According to the Big Bang model, the CMBR is the leftover energy of this initial explosion. Pretty neat, eh?

My brain's shifted towards the tired end of the spectrum...

The Big Bang model is the best one we've got to explain how the universe began, but it may need some tweaking in the future if we find new evidence it can't explain. Scientists, pfft, don't they ever finish anything?

Q1 a) Describe the Big Bang model. [3 marks]
b) State two pieces of evidence that support the Big Bang model. [2 marks]

The Life Cycle of Stars

Stars go through many traumatic stages in their lives — just like teenagers.

PROTOSTAR

CLOUD OF DUST AND GAS

1) Stars initially form from clouds of dust and gas.

2) The force due to gravity draws together the gas and dust and they spiral together to form a protostar. The temperature rises as the star gets denser and the particles collide with each other more often and with more force. When the temperature gets high enough, hydrogen nuclei undergo nuclear fusion (see page 80) to form helium nuclei. This gives out massive amounts of energy. A star is born.

MAIN SEQUENCE STAR

3) The star immediately enters a period of equilibrium — the energy released by nuclear fusion results in an outward pressure that tries to expand the star, but this is balanced by the force due to gravity pulling everything inwards (gravitational collapse). In this stable period it's called a main sequence star and it typically lasts several billion years. (The Sun is in the middle of this period.)

RED GIANT or RED SUPERGIANT

4) Eventually the hydrogen in the core begins to run out and the fusion of heavier elements occurs. The star swells up and turns red (it becomes red because the surface cools). Small-to-medium-sized stars like our Sun are called red giants at this stage.

5) Bigger stars form red supergiants rather then red giants — they start to glow brightly again as they undergo more fusion and expand and contract several times, forming even heavier elements in various nuclear reactions.

large stars...

small stars...

PLANETARY NEBULA...

... and a WHITE DWARF

6) When a red giant runs out of fuel, it becomes unstable and ejects its outer layer of dust and gas as a planetary nebula.

7) This leaves behind a hot, dense solid core — a white dwarf, which just cools down and eventually fades away.

SUPERNOVA

8) For red supergiants, it's all a bit more dramatic. When they run out of fuel to fuse, they collapse in on themselves in a massive explosion called a SUPERNOVA.

NEUTRON STAR

BLACK HOLE

9) The exploding supernova throws the outer layers of dust and gas into space, leaving a very dense core called a neutron star. If the star is big enough this will become a black hole — a super dense point in space that not even light can escape from.

All a bit of a downer really, isn't it? Poor stars...

Lots of details to learn here, so make sure you've got a handle on them all before you move on.

Q1 Describe the life cycle of a star the size of our Sun, beginning from a cloud of dust and gas. [6 marks]

Emitting and Absorbing Radiation

All objects, including yourself, emit and absorb radiation constantly. No wonder I'm so tired all the time...

All Objects Emit Radiation

See page 66 for more on EM waves.

1) All objects emit electromagnetic (EM) radiation.
2) This radiation covers a range of energy values, wavelengths and frequencies.
3) The intensity and wavelength distribution depends on the object's temperature.
4) Intensity is power per unit area. So the y-axis of the graph on the right shows how much energy each wavelength of the emitted radiation transfers to a given area in a certain amount of time.
5) As the temperature of an object increases, the intensity of every emitted wavelength increases.
6) However, the intensity increases more for shorter wavelengths than longer wavelengths (because shorter wavelengths of EM radiation transfer more energy). This causes the peak wavelength (the most common wavelength) to decrease.
7) So as objects get hotter, the peak wavelength gets shorter and the intensity-wavelength distribution becomes less symmetrical.

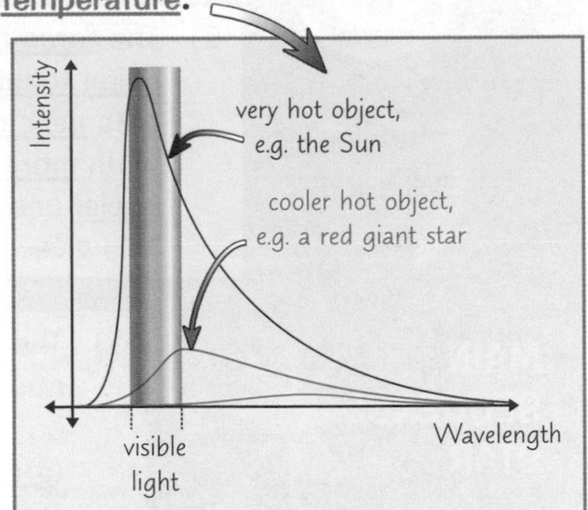

8) At most temperatures you'll encounter in day to day life, the peak wavelength is in the infra-red (IR) region. So most of the objects around you are mostly emitting IR (some hot objects emit a fair bit of visible light too — think of a glowing ring on an electric hob, or a filament bulb).

Every Object Absorbs Radiation Too

As you saw above, all objects are continually emitting radiation, but they also all absorb radiation too. The balance between absorbed and emitted radiation affects an object's temperature:

1) An object that's hotter than its surroundings emits more radiation than it absorbs. So over time, it cools down (like a cup of tea left on your desk).
2) An object that's cooler than its surroundings absorbs more radiation than it emits. Over time, the cool object warms up (e.g. ice cream on a hot day).
3) When an object emits the same amount of radiation as it absorbs, its temperature will stay the same.

Hot objects give out more IR radiation than they absorb, so they cool down.

Radiation Affects the Earth's Temperature

The atmosphere still affects radiation that passes through it though, e.g. visible light gets refracted by water droplets.

1) The Sun emits a spectrum of EM radiation, including UV, IR and visible light.
2) Some reflects off the Earth's atmosphere, some is absorbed by the atmosphere (e.g. UV and IR) and some passes through to reach Earth (e.g. some UV, IR and light).
3) The overall temperature of the Earth depends on the amount of radiation it reflects, absorbs and emits:

> During the day, lots of radiation is being absorbed, causing an increase in local temperature.
> At night, less radiation is absorbed than is emitted, causing a decrease in the local temperature.
> Overall, the Earth's temperature stays fairly constant (one side is absorbing as the other's emitting).

4) Some of the radiation that is absorbed by the Earth is re-emitted from Earth. Some of this re-emitted radiation is absorbed by gases in the atmosphere like carbon dioxide. The gases re-emit this radiation in all directions, including back towards Earth. This 'greenhouse effect' helps keep the Earth warm.
5) Changes to the atmosphere can lead to changes in the Earth's temperature, e.g. increasing CO_2 levels in the atmosphere increase the amount of radiation the atmosphere absorbs, contributing to global warming.

Don't let this get you hot under the collar...

The peak wavelength of radiation you emit is about 10 μm — and you thought this page was dull...

Q1 When pies are taken out of a hot oven they will start to cool down. Explain why. [1 mark]

Sonar and Seismic Waves

Bloop bloop bloop bloop bloop bloop bloopbloopbloop. My REVISION-NAR is working at last...

We Use Waves to Explore Structures that we can't Usually See

When a wave arrives at a boundary, a number of things can happen:

1) It can be reflected — partially or completely if it can't travel through the new material.
2) It can continue travelling, but at a different speed. This change of speed (and so change of wavelength) sometimes causes refraction (see page 61).
3) It may be absorbed.

By studying where waves are detected or not detected (for absorption and reflection) and if their speed or direction has changed you can work out the structure of objects that you can't directly see. You can do this with lots of different waves — sound and seismic waves are just two examples you need to learn:

Sonar uses Sound Waves

1) Sonar is used to measure the depth of the seabed or detect things in the ocean, e.g. a submarine.
2) A transmitter and receiver on a boat send out and detect pulses of sound waves.
3) When the sound waves reach a boundary, e.g. between the sea and the seabed, they are reflected back towards the boat.
4) By timing how long the reflected waves take to return, the distance to the seabed or an object can be calculated (see page 65 for more).

Seismic Waves Tell us About the Earth's Structure

1) Earthquakes produce seismic waves which travel out through the Earth. We detect these waves all over the surface of the planet using seismometers.
2) When these waves reach a boundary between different layers of the Earth, some are reflected.
3) The waves also change speed as the properties (e.g. density) of the Earth change. This change in speed causes the waves to refract.
4) Most of the time the waves change speed gradually, resulting in a curved path. But when the properties change suddenly, the wave speed changes abruptly, and the path has a kink.
5) By observing where and when these waves are detected, scientists can work out how they're reflected and refracted and where the properties of the Earth change dramatically:

There are two main different types of seismic waves — P waves and S waves. They have different properties, so they're transmitted through the Earth differently:

P WAVES are longitudinal waves that travel through solids and liquids. They're faster than S waves.

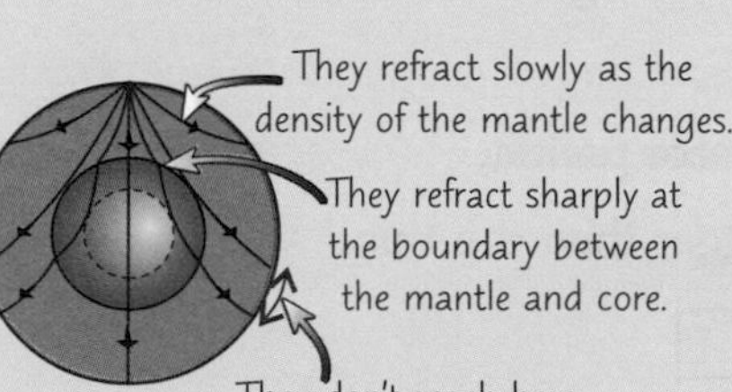

They refract slowly as the density of the mantle changes.
They refract sharply at the boundary between the mantle and core.
They don't reach here.

S WAVES are transverse waves that only travel in solids. They travel more slowly than P waves.

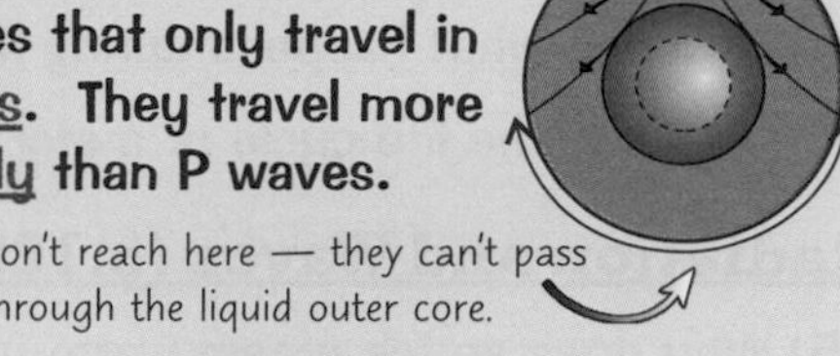

They don't reach here — they can't pass through the liquid outer core.

6) Our current understanding of the internal structure of the Earth is based on these observations — a shallow crust at the surface, the mantle beneath (which has the properties of a solid but flows very slowly), a liquid metal outer core and a solid metal inner core.

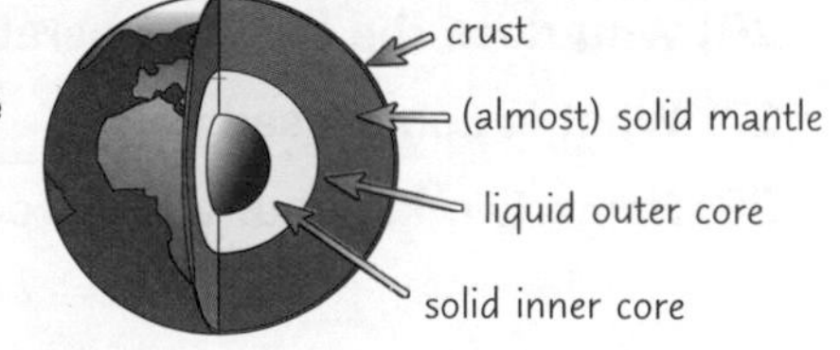

All this talk of waves has got me quaking in my boots...

Waves are really handy — for 'seeing' things we can't actually see. And hands are really wavy — for saying bye.

Q1 Describe how sonar can be used to locate objects in the sea. [3 marks]

Revision Questions for Topic P8

Congratulations! That's it for the theory. There's just the practical stuff to go now. Oh, and these questions...

- Try these questions and tick off each one when you get it right.
- When you've done all the questions under a heading and are completely happy with it, tick it off.

Everyday Transport (p.89-91)

1) Estimate typical speeds for a) walking, b) running, c) sound.
2) Explain how crumple zones reduce the risk of injury in a crash.
3) State two factors which affect braking distance for a stopping car.
4) What is meant by a driver's reaction time?
5) Describe an experiment to measure reaction times.
6) Estimate the stopping distance of a car travelling at 30 mph.
7) Estimate the mass of a typical car.

Generating and Using Electricity (p.92-96)

8) List four non-renewable energy sources.
9) Describe how electricity is generated in a nuclear power station.
10) List three environmental problems associated with non-renewable energy resources.
11) What's the difference between renewable and non-renewable energy sources?
12) Describe how electricity is generated using wind power.
13) Give one disadvantage of generating electricity from the tides.
14) What is the voltage and frequency of the mains electricity supply in the UK?
15) What is the difference between direct voltage and alternating voltage? Sketch a CRO trace for each.
16) Why does the national grid carry electricity at such high voltages?
17) What is used to increase the voltage between a power station and the cables of the national grid?
18) What are the three main wires in a plug?

Space and the Universe (p.97-99)

19) List the planets in the Solar System.
20) What is the difference between a planet and a moon?
21) How does the speed of an orbiting object change if the radius of its orbit increases?
22) What is CMBR?
23) Describe what happens during a star's stable period.
24) Describe the life cycle of a star much bigger than the Sun.

Radiation and Waves (p.100-101)

25) Why does an ice cream warm up on a hot day?
26) Why does the local temperature of the Earth increase during the day but decrease at night?
27) What is sonar used for?
28) Name two kinds of wave produced by an earthquake. Describe them both.

Apparatus and Techniques

- Topic P9 covers practical skills you'll need to know about for your course (including 15% of your exams).
- You'll have to do at least 8 practical activities (experiments). These are covered in Topics P1-P8 earlier in the book and they're highlighted with practical stamps like this one.
- The following pages of this topic cover some extra bits and bobs you need to know about practical work. First up, using apparatus to take measurements...

PRACTICAL

Mass Should Be Measured Using a Balance

1) For a solid, set the balance to zero and then place your object onto the scale and read off the mass.
2) If you're measuring the mass of a liquid, start by putting an empty container onto the balance. Next, reset the balance to zero.
3) Then just pour your liquid into the container and record the mass displayed. Easy.

Measure Most Lengths with a Ruler

1) In most cases a bog-standard centimetre ruler can be used to measure length. It depends on what you're measuring though — metre rulers or long measuring tapes are handy for large distances, while micrometers are used for measuring tiny things like the diameter of a wire.
2) The ruler should always be parallel to what you want to measure.
3) If you're dealing with something where it's tricky to measure just one accurately, e.g. waves in water, you can measure the length of ten of them and then divide to find the length of one.
4) If you're taking multiple measurements of the same object (e.g. to measure changes in length) then make sure you always measure from the same point on the object. It can help to put a marker or pointer onto the object to line up your ruler against.

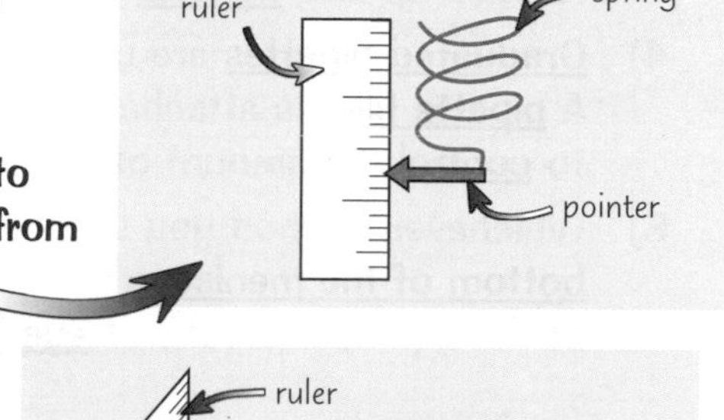

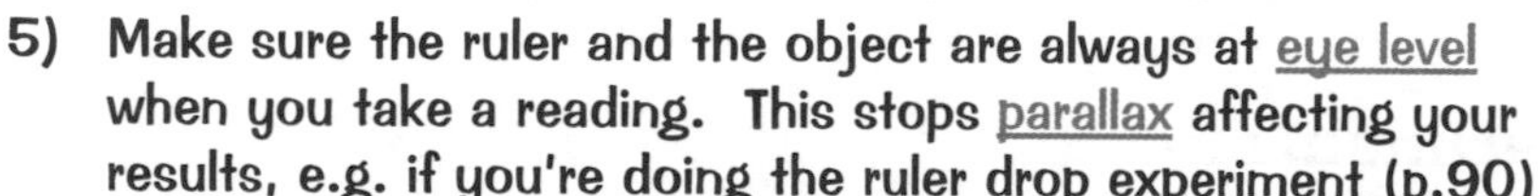

5) Make sure the ruler and the object are always at eye level when you take a reading. This stops parallax affecting your results, e.g. if you're doing the ruler drop experiment (p.90).
6) Parallax is where a measurement appears to change based on where you're looking from. The blue line in the diagram on the right shows the real position of the hand relative to the ruler. If the eye isn't level with this line, it looks like the hand is too low or too high.

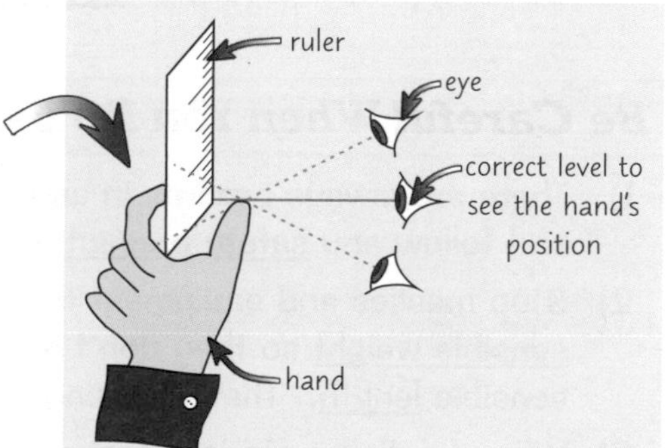

Use a Protractor to Find Angles

1) First align the vertex (point) of the angle with the mark in the centre of the protractor.
2) Line up the base line of the protractor with one line that forms the angle and then measure the angle of the other line using the scale on the protractor.
3) If the lines creating the angle are thick, align the protractor and measure the angle from the centre of the lines. Using a sharp pencil to trace light rays or draw diagrams helps to reduce errors when measuring angles.
4) If the lines are too short to measure easily, you may have to extend them. Again, make sure you use a sharp pencil to do this.

Measure Temperature Accurately with a Thermometer

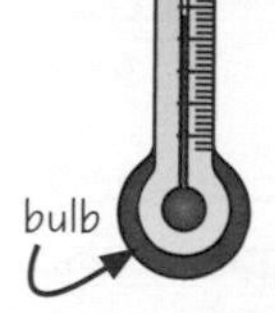

1) Make sure the bulb of your thermometer is completely submerged in any substance you're measuring.
2) Wait for the temperature to stabilise before you take your initial reading.
3) Again, read your measurement off the scale on a thermometer at eye level.

When you're reading off a scale, use the value of the nearest mark on the scale (the nearest graduation).

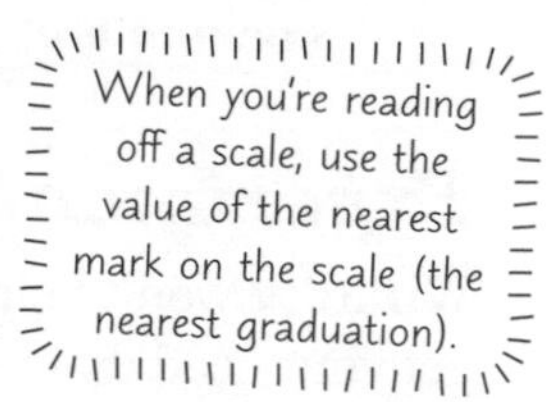

Apparatus and Techniques

You May Have to Measure the Time Taken for a Change

1) You should use a stopwatch to time most experiments — they're more accurate than regular watches.
2) Always make sure you start and stop the stopwatch at exactly the right time. Or alternatively, set an alarm on the stopwatch so you know exactly when to stop an experiment or take a reading.
3) You might be able to use a light gate instead (see page 105). This will reduce the errors in your experiment.

Measuring Cylinders and Pipettes Measure Liquid Volume

1) Measuring cylinders are the most common way to measure a liquid.

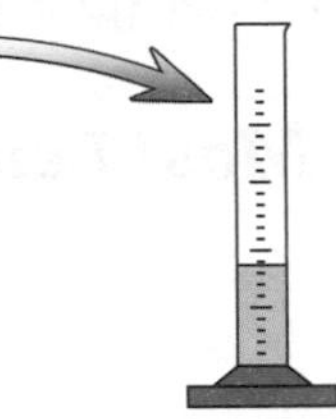

2) They come in all different sizes. Make sure you choose one that's the right size for the measurement you want to make. It's no good using a huge 1 dm^3 cylinder to measure out 2 cm^3 of a liquid — the graduations (markings for scale) will be too big and you'll end up with massive errors. It'd be much better to use one that measures up to 10 cm^3.
3) You can also use a pipette to measure volume. Pipettes are used to suck up and transfer volumes of liquid between containers.
4) Graduated pipettes are used to transfer accurate volumes. A pipette filler is attached to the end of a graduated pipette, to control the amount of liquid being drawn up.

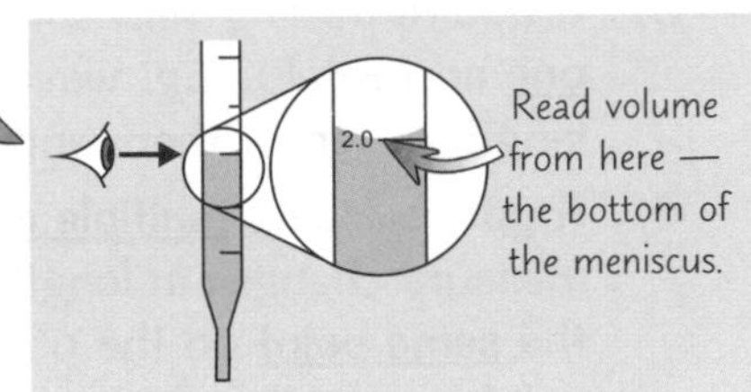

5) Whichever method you use, always read the volume from the bottom of the meniscus (the curved upper surface of the liquid) when it's at eye level.

Be Careful When You Do Experiments

1) There are always hazards in any experiment, so before you start an experiment you should read and follow any safety precautions to do with your method or the apparatus you're using.
2) Stop masses and equipment falling by using clamp stands. Make sure masses are of a sensible weight so they don't break the equipment they're used with, and use pulleys of a sensible length. That way, any hanging masses won't hit the floor during the experiment.
3) When heating materials, make sure to let them cool before moving them, or wear insulated gloves while handling them. If you're using an immersion heater to heat liquids, you should always let it dry out in air, just in case any liquid has leaked inside the heater.
4) If you're using a laser, there are a few safety rules you must follow. Always wear laser safety goggles and never look directly into the laser or shine it towards another person. Make sure you turn the laser off if it's not needed to avoid any accidents.
5) When working with electronics, make sure you use a low enough voltage and current to prevent wires overheating (and potentially melting) and avoid damage to components, like blowing a filament bulb.
6) You also need to be aware of general safety in the lab — handle glassware carefully so it doesn't break, don't stick your fingers in sockets and avoid touching frayed wires. That kind of thing.

Experimentus apparatus...

Wizardry won't help you here, unfortunately. Most of this'll be pretty familiar to you by now, but make sure you get your head down and know these techniques inside out so they're second nature when it comes to any practicals.

Working with Electronics

Electrical devices are used in a bunch of experiments, so make sure you know how to use them.

You Have to Interpret Circuit Diagrams

Before you get cracking on an experiment involving any kind of electrical devices, you have to plan and build your circuit using a circuit diagram. Make sure you know all of the circuit symbols on page 45 so you're not stumped before you've even started.

There Are a Couple of Ways to Measure Potential Difference and Current

Voltmeters Measure Potential Difference

1) If you're using an analogue voltmeter, choose the voltmeter with the most appropriate unit (e.g. V or mV). If you're using a digital voltmeter, you'll most likely be able to switch between them.
2) Connect the voltmeter in parallel across the component you want to test. The wires that come with a voltmeter are usually red (positive) and black (negative). These go into the red and black coloured ports on the voltmeter. Funnily enough.
3) Then simply read the potential difference from the scale (or from the screen if it's digital).

Ammeters Measure Current

1) Just like with voltmeters, choose the ammeter with the most appropriate unit.
2) Connect the ammeter in series with the component you want to test, making sure they're both on the same branch. Again, they usually have red and black ports to show you where to connect your wires.
3) Read off the current shown on the scale or by the screen.

> Turn your circuit off between readings to prevent wires overheating and affecting your results.

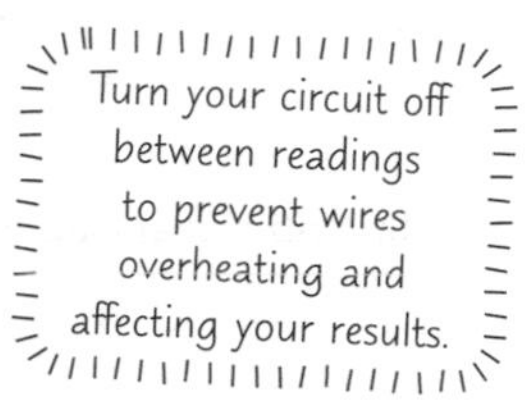

Multimeters Measure Both

1) Instead of having a separate ammeter and voltmeter, many circuits use multimeters. These are devices that measure a range of properties — usually potential difference, current and resistance.
2) If you want to find potential difference, make sure the red wire is plugged into the port that has a 'V' (for volts).
3) To find the current, use the port labelled 'A' or 'mA' (for amps).
4) The dial on the multimeter should then be turned to the relevant section, e.g. to 'A' to measure current in amps. The screen will display the value you're measuring.

Light Gates Measure Time, Speed and Acceleration

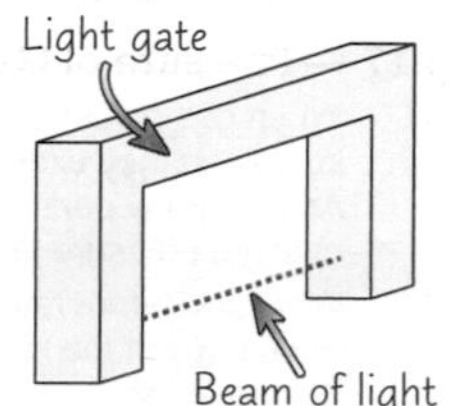

1) A light gate sends a beam of light from one side of the gate to a detector on the other side. When something passes through it, the light beam is interrupted. The gate can measure when the beam was interrupted and how long it was interrupted for.
2) To find the speed of an object, connect the light gate to a computer. Measure the length of the object and input this using the software. It will then automatically calculate the speed of the object as it passes through the beam.
3) To measure acceleration, you can use an object that interrupts the signal twice in a short period of time, e.g. a piece of card with a gap cut into the middle.

Card interrupts the beam

4) The light gate measures the speed for each section of the object and uses this to calculate its acceleration. This can then be read from the computer screen.

Have a look at page 23 and page 28 for some examples of light gates being used.

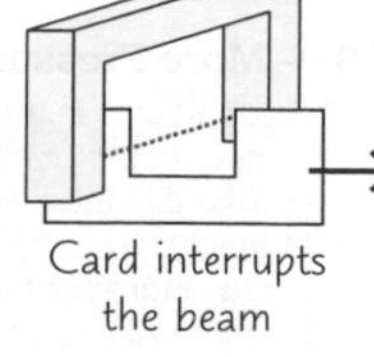

A light gate is better than a heavy one...

After finishing this page, you should be able to take on any electrical experiment that they throw at you... ouch.

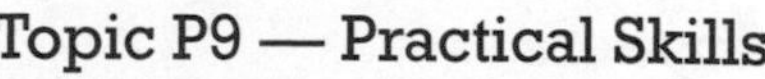

Answers

p.12 — The History of the Atom and Atomic Structure

Q1 In the Thomson model, atoms are made of negatively charged electrons spread through a positively charged 'pudding' ***[1 mark]***.

Q2 An atom is made up of a small central nucleus ***[1 mark]*** containing neutrons and positively charged protons ***[1 mark]*** surrounded by negatively charged electrons orbiting it in shells ***[1 mark]***.

p.13 — Density

Q1 E.g. use a mass balance to find the mass of the object ***[1 mark]***. Fill a eureka can with water to just below the spout, then immerse the object in the can ***[1 mark]***. Collect the water displaced by the object as it flows out of the spout in a measuring cylinder and record its volume ***[1 mark]***. Then calculate the density of the object using density = mass ÷ volume ***[1 mark]***.

Q2 volume in m^3 = 75 ÷ (100^3)
= 7.5 × 10^{-5} m^3 ***[1 mark]***
density = mass ÷ volume ***[1 mark]***
= (4.5 × 10^{-2}) ÷ (7.5 × 10^{-5}) = 600 kg/m^3
[1 mark]

p.14 — Particle Theory and States of Matter

Q1 As a typical substance changes from solid to liquid to gas, its density will decrease ***[1 mark]*** as its mass will stay the same ***[1 mark]*** but its volume will increase ***[1 mark]*** as the particles have more energy to overcome the forces between them ***[1 mark]***.

p.15 — Specific Heat Capacity

Q1 change in thermal energy = mass × specific heat capacity × change in temperature, so:
change in temperature = change in thermal energy ÷ (mass × specific heat capacity)
[1 mark]
= 1680 ÷ (0.20 × 420) = 20 °C ***[1 mark]***

p.16 — Specific Latent Heat

Q1

[1 mark for showing the line as flat at 0 °C, 1 mark for showing the line as flat at 100 °C. 1 mark for drawing a straight line with a positive gradient for temperatures below 0 °C, between 0 and 100 °C, and above 100 °C.]

p.17 — Pressure of Gases

Q1 When gas particles collide with the walls of their container, they exert a force on it ***[1 mark]***. Across many particles, this force causes an outward pressure ***[1 mark]***.

Q2 When the temperature of a gas decreases, the energy in the kinetic store of its particles decreases so their velocities decrease ***[1 mark]***. This means they hit the walls of the container less hard ***[1 mark]*** and less often ***[1 mark]*** which decreases the pressure ***[1 mark]***.

p.18 — More Pressure of Gases

Q1 Gas particles in the tyre exert a force on the plunger of the pump, so work must be done against this force to push down the pump ***[1 mark]***. This transfers energy to the kinetic energy stores of the gas particles, increasing their internal energy ***[1 mark]***. Temperature is a measure of the internal energy of the particles in a system, so this means the temperature of the gas (and therefore the tyre) increases ***[1 mark]***.

p.19 — Atmospheric Pressure and Liquid Pressure

Q1 pressure due to a column of liquid
= height of column × density of liquid × g, so:
difference in pressure =
difference in depth × density × change in depth × g ***[1 mark]***
= 1000 × (320 –120) × 10
= 2 000 000 kg/m^2 (or Pa) ***[1 mark]***

Q2 Pressure in a liquid increases with depth ***[1 mark]***. This pressure acts in all directions ***[1 mark]***. This means the force pushing upwards on the bottom of the object due to the water pressure is greater than the force pushing down on the top of the object, which means the object experiences an upwards force from the water ***[1 mark]***.

p.21 — Speed and Velocity

Q1 First convert minutes into seconds:
2.0 × 60 = 120 s ***[1 mark]***
Then substitute this into the equation for speed:

$$\text{speed} = \frac{\text{distance travelled}}{\text{time}} = \frac{660}{120} = 5.5 \text{ m/s}$$ ***[1 mark]***

Q2 First convert 54 km/hr into m/s:
54 km/hr ÷ (60 × 60) = 0.015 km/s
0.015 km/s × 1000 = 15 m/s ***[1 mark]***
Then substitute into the equation for distance travelled:
distance travelled = speed × time
= 15 × 24
= 360 m ***[1 mark]***

p.22 — Acceleration

Q1 $$\text{acceleration} = \frac{\text{change in velocity}}{\text{time}}$$
So change in velocity
= acceleration × time
= 8.25 × 4.0 ***[1 mark]***
= 33 m/s
As the initial speed is 0 m/s,
the maximum speed is: 33 m/s ***[1 mark]***
To find distance covered, rearrange the equation $v^2 - u^2 = 2 \times a \times d$ for distance:
$d = (v^2 - u^2) \div (2 \times a)$
= (33^2 – 0^2) ÷ (2 × 8.25) ***[1 mark]***
= 66 m ***[1 mark]***

p.23 — Investigating Motion

Q1 Use the light gates to time how long it takes the object to pass between the two light gates ***[1 mark]***. Measure the distance between the two light gates ***[1 mark]***. Divide the distance by the time taken for the object to travel between the two light gates ***[1 mark]***.

Q2 Using a stopwatch introduces human errors like reaction times, which aren't present with light gates ***[1 mark]***. This matters more for short intervals, as the reaction time is a larger proportion of the interval being timed ***[1 mark]***.

p.24 — Distance-Time Graphs

Q1 E.g.

[1 mark for a continuous line that initially curves upwards, and which curves downwards at the end until it becomes horizontal. 1 mark for a straight middle section.]

p.25 — Velocity-Time Graphs

Q1 E.g.

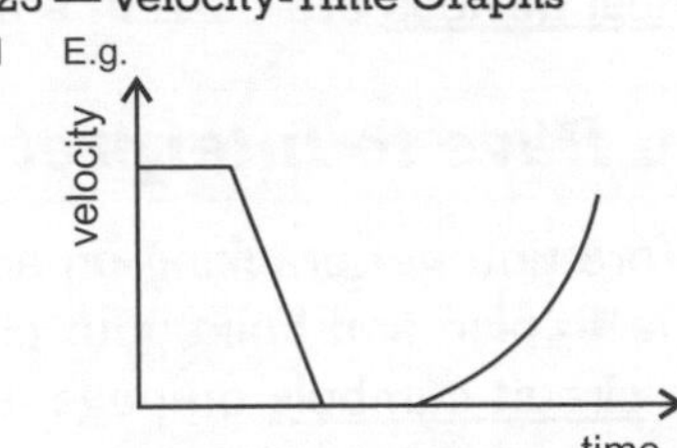

[1 mark for line which is initially horizontal, then bends to give a straight line with a negative gradient, continuing until it meets the time axis. 1 mark for showing the line then continuing horizontally along the time axis, and 1 mark for then showing the line curving upwards.]

p.26 — Forces and Free Body Force Diagrams

Q1 a)

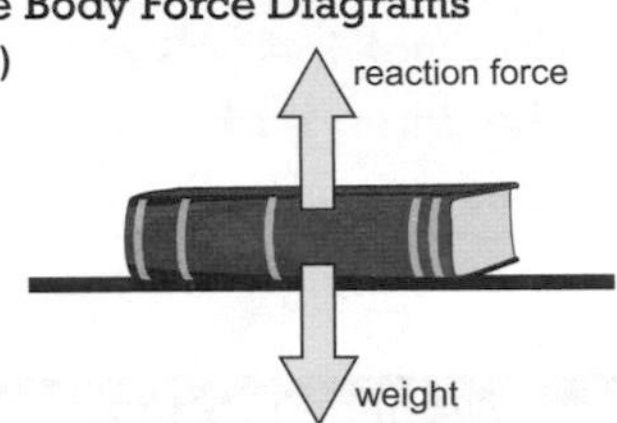

[1 mark for arrows pointing in the right direction and labelled correctly, 1 mark for arrows being the same length]

b)

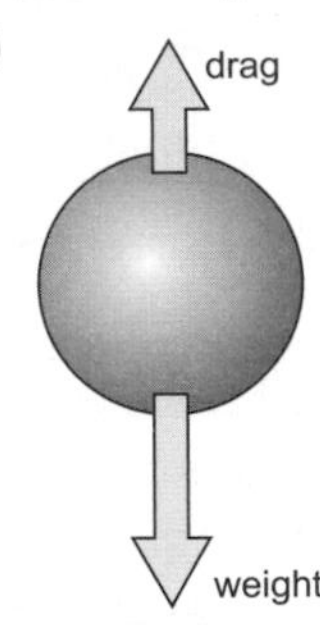

[1 mark for arrows pointing in the right direction and labelled correctly, 1 mark for the weight arrow being longer than the drag arrow]

p.27 — Scale Diagrams and Forces

Q1 E.g.

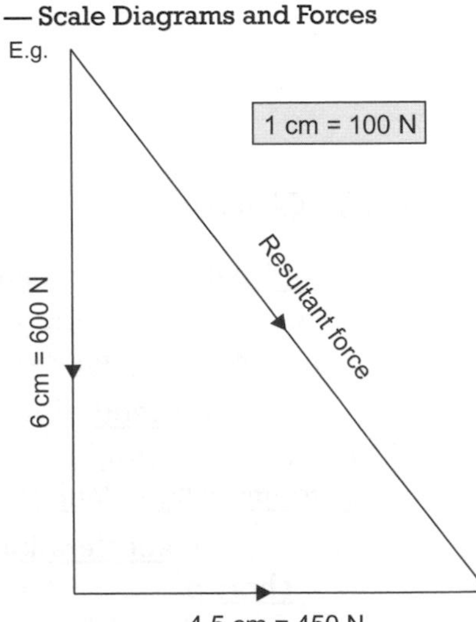

[1 mark for a scale drawing, drawn accurately using any sensible scale.]

In this scale drawing:
length of resultant force vector = 7.5 cm
1 cm = 100 N
Therefore, resultant force = 75 N ***[1 mark]***

p.28 — Newton's First and Second Laws of Motion

Q1 $F = ma = 26\,000 \times 1.5$
$= 39\,000$ N ***[1 mark]***

p.29 — Friction and Terminal Velocity

Q1 Initially, the thrust is much larger than the drag acting on the boat ***[1 mark]***, so the boat accelerates ***[1 mark]***. As the velocity of the boat increases, the drag increases, but the thrust remains the same, reducing the acceleration ***[1 mark]***. Eventually the thrust is balanced out by the drag and the boat travels at a constant (terminal) velocity ***[1 mark]***.

p.30 — Inertia and Newton's Third Law of Motion

Q1 An object with a smaller mass (in this case the empty trolley) will have a smaller inertia, so less force is needed to stop it ***[1 mark]***.

p.31 — Momentum

Q1 momentum = mass × velocity
= 220 000 × 250
= 55 000 000 kg m/s ***[1 mark]***

Q2 First, convert quantities to the correct units:
58 g = 0.058 kg
11.6 ms = 0.0116 s ***[1 mark]***
Then calculate the change in momentum:
change in momentum
= momentum after – momentum before
$= (m \times v) - (m \times u)$
= (0.058 × 34) – (0.058 × 0) ***[1 mark]***
= 1.972 kg m/s ***[1 mark]***
Then substitute this into the equation for force:

$$\text{force} = \frac{\text{change in momentum}}{\text{time}}$$

$$= \frac{1.972}{0.0116} = 170 \text{ N}$$ ***[1 mark]***

(NB: You could also use the alternative method of calculating the acceleration of the ball first (from acceleration = change in velocity ÷ time) and then calculating the force using $F = ma$. If you have got the correct answer using this alternative method, you still get all 4 marks.)

p.32 — Conservation of Momentum

Q1 Total momentum before collision
= (2.0 × 1.5) + (3.0 × 0)
= 3 kg m/s ***[1 mark]***
The total momentum before the collision is equal to the total momentum after the collision.
Total momentum after collision
= total mass of trolleys × final velocity
3 = (2.0 + 3.0) × velocity
velocity = 3 ÷ (2.0 + 3.0) ***[1 mark]***
= 0.6 m/s ***[1 mark]***

p.33 — Mass, Weight and Gravity

Q1 weight $= m \times g$
= 67 × 10
= 670 N ***[1 mark]***

Q2 Rearrange equation for mass:
$\text{mass} = \frac{W}{g} = 820 \div 10$ ***[1 mark]***
= 82 kg ***[1 mark]***

p.34 — Mechanical Energy Stores

Q1 $PE = m \times h \times g$
= 0.80 × 1.5 × 10
= 12 J ***[1 mark]***

Q2 $KE = 0.5 \times m \times v^2$
$= 0.5 \times 4.9 \times (2.0)^2$
= 9.8 J ***[1 mark]***

p.35 — Work Done and Power

Q1 For the book to stop, it will need to do work against friction equal to the energy in its kinetic energy store. Rearrange the work done equation for distance:
distance = work done ÷ force ***[1 mark]***
= 1.25 ÷ 5.0 = 0.25 m ***[1 mark]***

p.36 — Forces and Elasticity

Q1 The extension of the spring
= 0.20 – 0.16 = 0.04 m ***[1 mark]***
Rearrange $F = x \times k$
So $k = \frac{F}{x} = \frac{3.0}{0.04}$
= 75 N/m ***[1 mark]***

p.37 — Investigating Hooke's Law

Q1 First calculate the extension of the spring:
extension = 1.3 – 1.2 = 0.1 m ***[1 mark]***
Then substitute this into:
energy transferred in stretching
= 0.5 × spring constant × (extension)^2
$= 0.5 \times 54 \times 0.1^2$
= 0.27 J ***[1 mark]***

p.38 — Moments

Q1

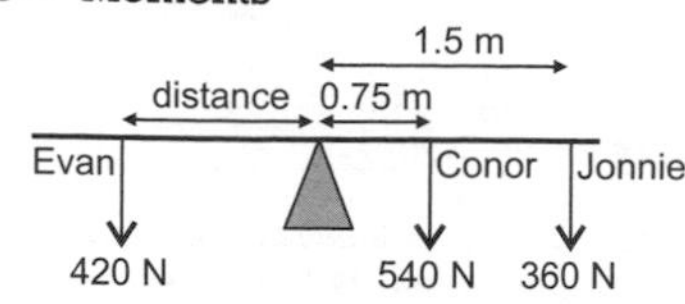

anticlockwise moments = clockwise moments
420 × distance = (540 × 0.75) + (360 × 1.5) ***[1 mark]***
420 × distance = 945
So distance = 945 ÷ 420
= 2.25 m ***[1 mark]***

p.39 — Levers and Gears

Q1 Ratio of teeth = 9 : 6 = 3 : 2
So 3 turns of cog B = 2 turns of cog A.
So for only 1 turn of cog A, there will be 1.5 turns for cog B. ***[1 mark]***

p.40 — Hydraulics

Q1 First calculate the pressure on the liquid:
$P = F \div A$
= 3 ÷ 0.2 = 15 Pa ***[1 mark]***
Then rearrange the pressure equation to find the cross-sectional area of piston 2:
$A = F \div P$
= 90 ÷ 15 = 6 m^2 ***[1 mark]***

p.42 — Static Electricity

Q1 E.g. hold the object near some small scraps of paper ***[1 mark]***. If the object is charged, the scraps of paper will be attracted to it, making them 'jump' towards it ***[1 mark]***. / Touch the object against the plate of a gold leaf electroscope ***[1 mark]***. If the object is carrying a charge, the gold leaf on the electroscope will rise ***[1 mark]***.

p.43 — Electric Fields

Q1 The strength of the electric field increases as you move towards the sphere ***[1 mark]***.

Q2

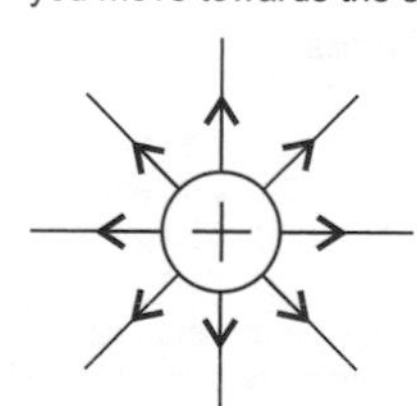

[1 mark for lines at a right angle to the surface, 1 mark for lines pointing away from the sphere]

p.44 — Current and Potential Difference

Q1 charge = current × time, so
time = charge ÷ current
= 120 ÷ 2.5 ***[1 mark]***
= 48 s ***[1 mark]***

Q2 energy transferred = charge × potential difference so:
potential difference = energy transferred ÷ charge
= 360 ÷ 75 ***[1 mark]***
= 4.8 V ***[1 mark]***

p.45 — Circuits — the Basics

Q1

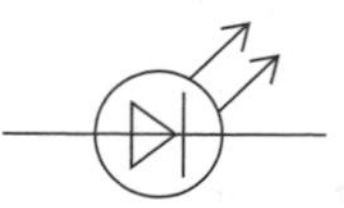

[1 mark]

Q2

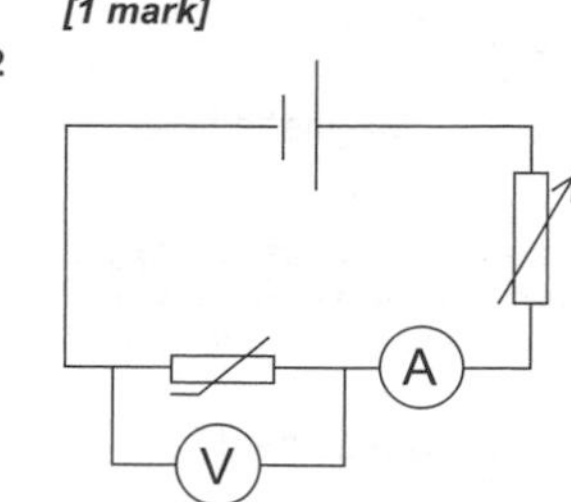

[1 mark for a complete circuit with a power supply showing a thermistor in series with a variable resistor, 1 mark for a voltmeter connected across the thermistor and an ammeter connected in series with the thermistor.]

p.46 — Resistance and $V = I \times R$

Q1 potential difference = current × resistance, so
resistance = potential difference ÷ current
= 4.25 ÷ 0.25
= 17 Ω ***[1 mark]***

p.47 — Circuit Devices

Q1 a) *I*, *V*

[1 mark]

b) As the current through the thermistor increases (in either direction), the thermistor warms up ***[1 mark]***. This decreases the resistance of the thermistor, causing the *I-V* graph to curve ***[1 mark]***.

p.48 — Series and Parallel Circuits

Q1 3.6 ÷ 3 = 1.2 V ***[1 mark]***

p.49 — More on Series and Parallel Circuits

Q1 3.5 V ***[1 mark]***

p.50 — Energy and Power in Circuits

Q1 11 × 60 = 660 seconds ***[1 mark]***
energy transferred = power × time
= 1500 × 660
= 990 000 J ***[1 mark]***

Q2 Power = potential difference × current, so
current = power ÷ potential difference
= 8.5 ÷ 2.5 ***[1 mark]***
= 3.4 A ***[1 mark]***

Q3 power = current^2 × resistance, so
current = $\sqrt{\text{power} \div \text{resistance}}$ ***[1 mark]***
= $\sqrt{375 \div 15}$ ***[1 mark]***
= 5 A ***[1 mark]***

p.52 — Magnets and Magnetic Fields

Q1 Put the magnet on a piece of paper and put a compass next to it, marking on the piece of paper the point at which the compass needle is pointing ***[1 mark]***. Then move the compass so that the tail of the compass needle is where the tip of the needle was previously, and mark again where the needle is pointing ***[1 mark]***. Repeat this several times and then join up the markings for a complete sketch of a field line around the magnet ***[1 mark]***. Do this several times for different points around the magnet to get several field lines ***[1 mark]***.

Q2 Copper is not a magnetic material ***[1 mark]***.

p.53 — Electromagnetism

Q1 a) E.g.

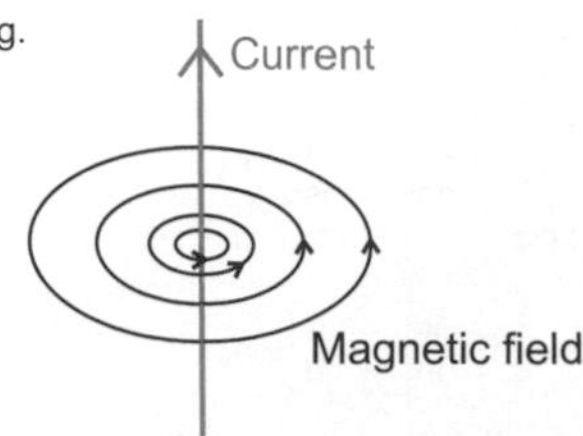

[1 mark for correct shape of field lines, 1 mark for correctly showing the direction of both the current and the magnetic field lines]

b) E.g.

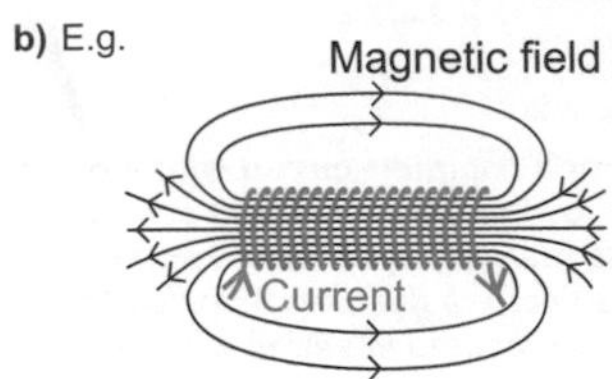

[1 mark for correct shape of field lines, 1 mark for correctly showing the direction of both the current and the magnetic field lines]

p.54 — Magnetic Forces

Q1 Thumb — direction of the force ***[1 mark]***.
First finger — direction of the magnetic field ***[1 mark]***.
Second finger — direction of the current ***[1 mark]***.

Q2 35 cm = 0.35 m
Rearrange $F = B \times I \times l$ for the magnetic flux density, B:
$B = F \div (I \times L)$
$= 9.8 \div (5.0 \times 0.35)$ ***[1 mark]***
$= 5.6$ T ***[1 mark]***

p.55 — Motors and Loudspeakers

Q1 Any two from: decrease the current / decrease the number of turns on the coil / decrease the magnetic flux density.
[1 mark for each correct answer]

p.56 — Electromagnetic Induction

Q1 An alternator produces a.c. and a dynamo produces d.c. ***[1 mark]***

p.57 — Transformers

Q1 You are looking for the number of turns on the secondary coil, so rearrange $\frac{V_P}{V_S} = \frac{N_P}{N_S}$ for N_S:
$N_S = N_P \times \frac{V_S}{V_P}$ ***[1 mark]***
$= 22\,000 \times \frac{0.40}{1.6} = 5500$ turns ***[1 mark]***

p.59 — Wave Basics

Q1 $7.5 \div 100 = 0.075$ m ***[1 mark]***
wave speed = frequency × wavelength, so frequency = wave speed ÷ wavelength
= 0.15 ÷ 0.075 ***[1 mark]***
= 2 Hz ***[1 mark]***

p.60 — Wave Experiments

Q1 E.g. attach a signal generator to a dipper and place it in a ripple tank filled with water to create some waves ***[1 mark]***. Place a cork in the water and count how many times it bobs up in 20 seconds ***[1 mark]***. Divide this number by 20 to give the frequency of the wave ***[1 mark]***.

p.61 — Reflection and Refraction

Q1 The light will bend away from the normal ***[1 mark]***.

p.62 — More on Reflection

Q1 E.g.

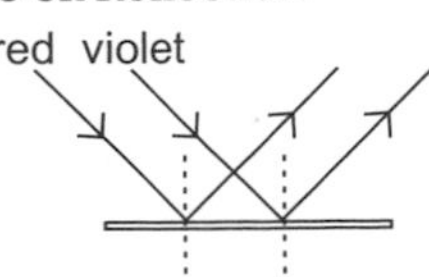

[1 mark for drawing two rays with parallel incident and reflected rays. 1 mark for the angle of reflection being equal to the angle of incidence for each ray and ~45°.]

p.63 — More on Refraction

Q1 E.g.

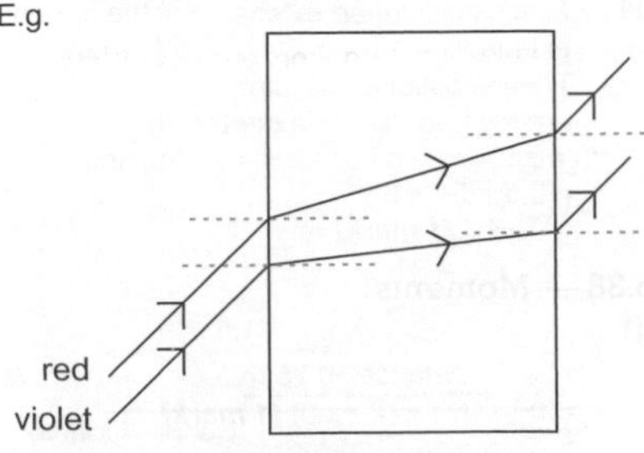

[1 mark for two parallel rays bending towards the normal as they enter the block. 1 mark for the violet ray bending more than the red ray. 1 mark for both rays bending away from the normal as they leave the block, 1 mark for the emerging rays being parallel.]

p.64 — Sound Waves and Hearing

Q1 Because sound travels by causing the vibration of particles ***[1 mark]*** and space is a vacuum, so there are no particles to vibrate ***[1 mark]***.

Q2 Sound waves reach the eardrum causing it to vibrate ***[1 mark]***. These vibrations are passed to the ossicles and through the semi-circular canals on to the cochlea ***[1 mark]***, which converts them into electrical signals that your brain interprets as sound ***[1 mark]***.

p.65 — Sonar and Ultrasound

Q1 distance = speed × time,
so time = distance ÷ speed
= 2500 ÷ 1520 ***[1 mark]***
= 1.64... s ***[1 mark]***
This is the time it takes for the pulse to reach the seabed — to find the time taken for the sound to return to the submarine, double it:
1.64... × 2 = 3.28...
= 3.3 s (to 2 s.f.) ***[1 mark]***

p.66 — Electromagnetic Waves

Q1 E.g. gamma rays are ionising so they can cause tissue damage and cancer, but visible light isn't ionising ***[1 mark]***. Visible light is reflected or absorbed by the skin, but gamma rays can pass through the skin and so can damage deeper tissues ***[1 mark]***.

p.67 — Uses of EM Waves

Q1 An alternating current of a set frequency in an electric conductor causes charges to oscillate ***[1 mark]***, creating an oscillating electric and magnetic field (an EM wave) of the same frequency — a radio wave ***[1 mark]***.

Q2 E.g. infra-red cameras / night-vision cameras / medical imaging / heating / cooking ***[1 mark]***

p.68 — More Uses of EM Waves

Q1 Any two from, e.g: sterilising medical instruments / sterilising food / treating cancer / medical imaging ***[2 marks]***

p.69 — Waves in Medical Imaging

Q1 X-rays can be used to take 'photos' of hard tissues in the body to diagnose conditions like bone fractures or dental problems ***[1 mark]***. X-rays are also used in CT scans to produce high resolution 2D and 3D images of soft and hard tissues ***[1 mark]***.

p.70 — Visible Light and Colour

Q1 a) A cucumber looks green because it reflects green light ***[1 mark]***, but absorbs all other colours of light ***[1 mark]***.

b) black ***[1 mark]***

p.71 — Lenses and Images

Q1

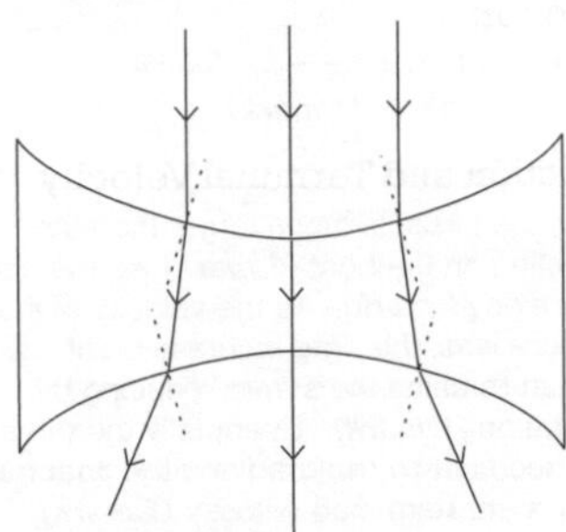

[1 mark for the central ray remaining straight as it passes through the lens. 1 mark for both of the outer rays bending towards the normal as they enter the lens, and 1 mark for both of the outer rays bending away from the normal as they leave the lens].

p.72 — More on Lenses

Q1 Short-sighted people can't focus on distant objects, because light rays are brought into focus in front of the retina ***[1 mark]***. Putting a concave lens in front of the eye fixes this by diverging light rays before they enter the eye ***[1 mark]***, so the eye brings them into focus on the retina, giving a clear image ***[1 mark]***.

p.74 — Isotopes and Radioactive Decay

Q1 Number of protons in isotope B = 7
(the same as isotope A).
So mass number
= number of protons + number of neutrons
= 7 + 7 = 14 ***[1 mark]***

p.75 — Radiation Properties and Decay Equations

Q1 ${}^{238}_{92}\text{U} \longrightarrow {}^{234}_{90}\text{Th} + {}^{4}_{2}\alpha$

[1 mark for the correct mass number of uranium, 1 mark for correct alpha particle symbol and mass and atomic numbers and 1 mark for the correct mass number for thorium]

p.76 — Electron Energy Levels

Q1 A positive ion is an atom that has lost one or more electrons ***[1 mark]***. An ion is formed when an outer electron absorbs enough energy that it leaves the atom ***[1 mark]***.

p.77 — Half-Life

Q1 The number of half-lives in 240 hours is
240 ÷ 60 = 4 half-lives ***[1 mark]***
Initial count = 480
after 1 half-life = 480 ÷ 2 = 240
after 2 half-lives = 240 ÷ 2 = 120
after 3 half-lives = 120 ÷ 2 = 60
after 4 half-lives = 60 ÷ 2 = 30
So the activity after 240 hours
= 30 counts per minute ***[1 mark]***

p.78 — Dangers of Radioactivity

Q1 Radiation can cause minor damage to a cell that causes it to mutate / radiation can cause cells to divide uncontrollably / causes cancer ***[1 mark]***. Radiation can also kill a cell completely ***[1 mark]***.

Q2 The alpha-emitting radioactive source has a lower irradiation risk than the beta-emitting radioactive source ***[1 mark]***, as alpha particles have a lower range in materials compared to beta particles ***[1 mark]***. There is no contamination risk for both sources ***[1 mark]***, as they are both solids and so an object wouldn't become contaminated if it didn't touch the sources ***[1 mark]***.

p.79 — Half-Life and Uses of Radiation

Q1 Alpha radiation is highly ionising so would damage cells in the body ***[1 mark]***.
Alpha radiation can't penetrate through tissue, so it wouldn't be detected outside the body with the radiation detector ***[1 mark]***.

p.80 — Fission and Fusion

Q1 Energy is carried away by gamma radiation ***[1 mark]***.

Q2 The mass of the nuclei before fusion is larger than the mass of the nucleus after. The extra mass is converted into energy. ***[1 mark]***

p.82 — Conservation of Energy

Q1 As the ball falls, energy is transferred mechanically from its gravitational potential energy store to its kinetic energy store ***[1 mark]***. When the ball hits the ground, energy is transferred away by sound waves ***[1 mark]***. The rest of the energy is carried away by heating to the thermal energy stores of the ball, the ground and the surroundings ***[1 mark]***.

Q2 Energy in the chemical energy store of the wood is transferred by heating to the thermal energy stores of the surroundings ***[1 mark]***. The rest of the energy is transferred away by light waves ***[1 mark]***.

p.83 — Efficiency

Q1 Useful output energy transfer
= 500 – 420 = 80 J ***[1 mark]***

$$\text{Efficiency} = \frac{\text{useful output energy transfer}}{\text{input energy transfer}}$$

$= \frac{80}{500} = 0.16$ ***[1 mark]***

0.16 × 100 = 16% ***[1 mark]***

p.84 — Energy Transfer by Heating

Q1 Black surfaces are better emitters of radiation, so a black mug would radiate energy more quickly than a white mug ***[1 mark]***. So energy would be carried away more quickly from the thermal energy store of the water ***[1 mark]***.

p.85 — Reducing Unwanted Energy Transfers

Q1 Any three from: install loft insulation / install a hot water tank jacket / introduce cavity walls and cavity wall insulating foam / install draught-proofing / install double glazing / put up thick curtains / make the walls thicker / replace walls with walls that have a lower thermal conductivity / decrease the length of the hot water pipes / increase the width of the hot water pipes / insulate the hot water pipes / paint the hot water pipes white.
[1 mark for each correct answer]

Q2 Its thickness ***[1 mark]*** and its thermal conductivity ***[1 mark]***.

p.86 — Mechanical Energy Transfers

Q1 energy transferred in stretching
= 0.5 × spring constant × (extension)^2 ***[1 mark]***
= 0.5 × 6.50 × 0.120^2
= 0.0468 J ***[1 mark]***

p.87 — Electrical Energy Transfers

Q1 Energy transferred to bulb
= power × time ***[1 mark]***
= 35 × (2.0 × 60)
= 4200 J ***[1 mark]***
The energy transferred by the bulb as light waves will be less than the energy transferred to the bulb by the battery, as the bulb transfers some energy by heating to the thermal energy stores of its surroundings/energy is transferred to the thermal energy stores of the wires by heating ***[1 mark]***.

p.89 — Everyday Speeds and Accelerations

Q1 70 – 50 = 20 mph
20 × 1.6 = 32 km/hr
32 ÷ 3.6 = 8.88... m/s
[1 mark]
Estimate 4 seconds to accelerate.
[1 mark for any value in the range 2 s to 5 s.]
acceleration = change in velocity ÷ time
= 8.88... ÷ 4 = 2.22...
= 2 m/s^2 (to 1 s.f.)
[1 mark for dividing 8.88... m/s by the time that you estimated.]

p.90 — Stopping Distances and Reaction Times

Q1 If you're tired, e.g. from a long journey, your reaction time is likely to be longer ***[1 mark]***, which would increase thinking distance and so stopping distance ***[1 mark]***. This would make an accident more likely if you were forced to brake ***[1 mark]***.

p.91 — Stopping Safely

Q1 $v^2 - u^2 = 2ad$, so
$a = (v^2 - u^2) \div (2d)$
= (0^2 – 16^2) ÷ (2 × 50) ***[1 mark]***
= –2.56 m/s^2 ***[1 mark]***
$F = ma$
Estimate the mass of the lorry to be 30 000 kg
[1 mark for any value in the range 25 000 kg to 35 000 kg.]
F = 30 000 × (–2.56) = –76 800
= –80 000 N (to 1 s.f.)
[1 mark for multiplying the mass that you estimated by the acceleration. The question only asks for the size of the force (not its direction), so you still get the mark if you didn't include the minus sign in your final answer.]

p.92 — Non-Renewable Energy Sources

Q1 As the coal burns it heats the water in the boiler. The water boils, making steam ***[1 mark]***. The steam drives a turbine, which in turn drives a generator, generating electricity ***[1 mark]***.

p.93 — Renewable Energy Sources

Q1 Any two from: e.g. bio-fuels / wind power / the sun/solar power, hydro-electricty / the tides ***[2 marks]***

Q2 Any two from: e.g. some people think wind turbines spoil the view / wind turbines can be quite noisy / you can only generate electricity when it's windy/the electricity supply is unreliable / you can't generate more electricity in response to high demand. ***[2 marks]***

p.94 — More On Energy Sources

Q1 Advantage, e.g. the electricity supply is reliable / you can generate more electricity in response to high demand / it has minimal running costs. ***[1 mark]***
Disadvantage, e.g. it has a big impact on the environment / the initial cost is high / you need to flood a valley / it can lead to a loss of habitat. ***[1 mark]***.

Q2 Renewable sources won't run out but non-renewable will ***[1 mark]***. Also, renewable energy sources tend to cause less damage to the environment than non-renewables, so it's better to try to use more of these sources ***[1 mark]***.

p.95 — Electricity and the National Grid

Q1 p.d. (primary coil) × current (primary coil) = p.d. (secondary coil) × current (secondary coil)
so current (primary coil) =
(p.d. (secondary coil) × current (secondary coil)) ÷ p.d. (primary coil)) ***[1 mark]***
= (210 × 0.20) ÷ 42
= 1 A ***[1 mark]***

p.96 — Wiring in the Home

Q1 a) The kettle needs an earth wire because the live wire may develop a fault and come into contact with the metal body of the kettle, which could cause electric shocks or fires ***[1 mark]***. If this happened, the earth wire has low resistance, so the resistance of the circuit will fall and the current will increase ***[1 mark]***. The surge in current would melt the fuse, isolating the appliance, preventing shocks and fires ***[1 mark]***.

b) 0 V ***[1 mark]***

p.97 — The Solar System and Orbits

Q1 Any three from: geostationary satellites orbit around the equator, whereas satellites with polar orbits sweep over the poles. / Satellites with polar orbits are closer to the Earth/have lower orbits than geostationary satellites. / Geostationary satellites orbit once every 24 hours, but those in a polar orbit take about 2 hours. / Satellites with polar orbits travel faster than geostationary satellites. / Geostationary satellites stay above the same point on Earth but those in polar orbits move over the Earth's surface. ***[3 marks]***.

p.98 — The Origin of the Universe

Q1 a) The Big Bang model states that all the matter in the universe occupied a single point ***[1 mark]***. This single point exploded (the Big Bang) ***[1 mark]*** causing the universe to start expanding ***[1 mark]***.

b) The red-shift of light from distant galaxies ***[1 mark]***. Cosmic Microwave Background Radiation (CMBR) ***[1 mark]***.

p.99 — The Life Cycle of Stars

Q1 A cloud of dust and gas is attracted together by gravity, forming a protostar ***[1 mark]***. As the star gets denser, it gets hotter and hotter, until nuclear fusion of hydrogen nuclei starts to happen ***[1 mark]***. The star enters a period of equilibrium where the energy released by nuclear fusion results in an outward pressure that is balanced by the force due to gravity / gravitational collapse ***[1 mark]***. When the star runs out of hydrogen to fuse in the core, it will expand and cool, becoming a red giant ***[1 mark]***. A star the size of the Sun will then become unstable, and eject its outer layers of dust and gas to form a planetary nebula ***[1 mark]***. The hot dense core of the star will be left behind as a white dwarf ***[1 mark]***.

p.100 — Emitting and Absorbing Radiation

Q1 The pies are hotter than their surroundings so they emit more radiation than they absorb, cooling them down ***[1 mark]***.

p.101 — Sonar and Seismic Waves

Q1 Transmitters on boats send out pulses of sound waves ***[1 mark]***. When the waves reach an object (boundary) they're reflected back and are detected by receivers on the boat ***[1 mark]***. By measuring how long the reflected pulse takes to return, you can calculate the distance to the object ***[1 mark]***.

Index